D1342088

16

*Major-General Henry Scott, CB*
*Model of the proposed buildings to complete the*
*South Kensington Museum, 1869. Destroyed.*

VICTORIA AND ALBERT MUSEUM

# 'Marble Halls'

## rawings and Models for Victorian Secular Buildings

Exhibition August-October 1973

John Physick and Michael Darby

LONDON 1973

# Contents

reword  7

knowledgments  8

troduction  9

e Architectural Model during the Victorian Period  13

mpetitions  17

ote on the Catalogue and Biographical entries  20

ographies  21

atalogue  31

National Buildings  31
*e Houses of Parliament; the Government Offices and Whitehall; w Scotland Yard; the Law Courts; the Monumental Halls*

Country Houses  53
*ghclere; Osborne; The Grange, Ramsgate; Deysbrook; Bylaugh; ownsea Castle; Bushey Heath; Red House; Elvetham; Sandringham; dge, Kew; Bear Wood; Cardiff Castle; Lodge, Broadlands; ton Hall; Adcote; Loughton Hall; Ken Hill; Broadleys*

Town Houses  79
*ensington Palace Gardens; Bridgwater House; Grosvenor House; d House, Bayswater; Old Swan House, Chelsea; The White House, elsea; Studio, Chelsea; Leighton House; Harrington Gardens; agpie and Stump House, Chelsea*

Commercial Buildings  93
*anch Bank of England, Liverpool; Coal Exchange; Tea Warehouse, ymouth; Billingsgate Market; Caledonian Market; Warehouse, anchester; Osler's Gallery, Oxford Street; Warehouse, Wapping; neral Credit Company, Lothbury; Atherton Colliery; 25 Austin iars; Law Fire Insurance Office, Chancery Lane; Maclean's llery, Haymarket; Royal Exchange Assurance Company Office, ll Mall; 'Glasgow Herald' Building; Queensferry factory*

Schools, Colleges  113
*gent's Park School; Liverpool Pauper's School, York and pon Diocesan Training School; Orphans' School, Brixton; andough School; Gonville and Caius College, Cambridge; Exeter ammar School; Bushey School*

Asylums, Prisons, Hospitals  121
*thlem Hospital; Rainhill Lunatic Asylum; Holloway Prison; uper Lunatic Asylum, Dartford*

7 Civic Buildings  125
*St George's Hall, Liverpool; Assize Courts, Cambridge; Leeds Town Hall; Northampton Town Hall; Congleton Town Hall; Turkish Baths, Leeds; Manchester Town Hall; Baths and Wash-houses, Manchester; Swimming Baths, West Bay; Commissioners of Sewers Offices, London*

8 Town Planning  139
*Thames Embankment; Cannon Street; Bedford Park; Birchington; Saltaire*

9 Theatres, Music Halls, Clubs  145
*Travellers' Club; Gresham Club; Army and Navy Club; Savoy Theatre; Royal Standard Music Hall*

10 Railway, Carriages  151
*Euston Station; York Station; Horley Station; Swindon Station; Scarborough Station; railway carriage; Paddington Station; Ellesmere Port and Whitby Station; Temple Meads Station; Waterloo Station; Victoria Station, Bombay*

11 Exhibition Buildings  165
*Great Exhibition; Crystal Palace; St Cloud, Paris; 1862 Exhibition*

12 Bridges, Lighthouses  173
*Son Bridge, Patna; Tower Bridge; Eddystone Lighthouse*

13 Hotels, Inns, Boarding Houses  179
*Gt Western Hotel, Paddington; Dunraven Arms Hotel, Bridgend; Midland Hotel, St Pancras; Grand Hotel, Scarborough; Tabard Inn, Bedford Park; Central Hotel, Glasgow; 'Last Sailor' Hotel, West Bay*

14 Museums, Libraries, Art Galleries  189
*Taylor and Randolph Building, Oxford; Public Record Office; British Museum Reading Room; Burlington House; National Gallery; Natural History Museum; Imperial Institute; Horticultural Gardens; Royal Albert Hall; South Kensington Museum; Victoria and Albert Museum*

15 Memorials  209
*Scott Monument, Edinburgh; Albert Memorial, Manchester; Albert Memorial, London; Shaftesbury Memorial Fountain, Piccadilly Circus; Fountain at Gloucester*

Index of Lenders  217

Index of People  218

Index of Places  220

# Foreword

e exhibition of Victorian architecture, which this catalogue
companies, ranges as widely as possible within limits determined
its special character: that is, by the fact that the exhibits are,
dominantly, original drawings, and models prepared by or for
ctorian architects themselves. Although the scope of the exhibition
widened by the inclusion of books and engravings from Victorian
hitectural periodicals, it is for the sake of the drawings and models
t the exhibition has been arranged, and it is these alone that are
orded in the catalogue.

The drawings and models comprise designs for as many different
es of building as possible. Many key buildings are included, and
attempt has been made to show something of the work of most of
important Victorian architects. But the exhibition cannot claim to
er a completely rounded or representative survey of Victorian
hitecture. The survival of drawings and models has been largely
ected by chance, and it has been our aim, to call attention to a part
what survives, and to use this material to give a view of Victorian
hitecture. No religious buildings are included in the exhibition,
ce this aspect was covered by the Victorian Church Art Exhibition
d in the Museum in 1971-72. In consequence, the selection here
own preserves a more accurate balance between the Classical and
thic tendencies which were opposed to one another during most of
e period it surveys.

A large number of the drawings shown come from the Department
Prints and Drawings, which has organized the exhibition. The
oks have been selected and arranged by Anthony Burton, Assistant
eeper in the Library. The Museum has acquired architectural
awings since 1857. Those of Victorian buildings were considerably
riched during the early twentieth century by the generous gifts of

the architect friends, and their relations, of the late Richard Phené
Spiers, and many are included in the exhibition.

Other drawings have been borrowed from various sources: the
Royal Institute of British Architects deserves special thanks, and we
are also grateful to the lenders listed on p. 217. Although the Museum
does not usually collect architectural models, some of those shown
belong to the Museum; they are legacies from the Museum of
Construction, and from past building projects with which the Museum
was concerned. Among other lenders of models the Department of the
Environment deserves special thanks.

The interest of architectural drawings lies primarily in the purpose
for which they were conceived. They serve not only as a historical
record (the more valuable when the buildings for which they
were made have been destroyed, as is the case with several items
in the exhibition), but as evidence of an architect's intentions, which
may well be more clearly seen in a design than in a completed building.
In the case of buildings unfinished or not begun they are specially
important evidence. The drawings in this catalogue will help to
reinforce our growing knowledge of the complete professionalism of
the major Victorian architects and the rich inventiveness of their
remarkably diverse styles. Architectural drawings are characterized
by logic and clarity; but occasionally pictorial qualities supervene.
This is the case with the perspectives, which have always enjoyed a
place in the Royal Academy's summer exhibitions. They never,
perhaps, quite cross the border from technical drawings into topographical drawings, but they were wrought to please the eye and some
are certainly fine examples of the art of persuasion.

GRAHAM REYNOLDS
*Keeper, Department of Prints & Drawings and Paintings*

# Acknowledgments

We should like to thank first of all those who have made loans to the exhibition and particularly those for whom the tasks of preparing the exhibits for transportation presented special problems.

In the selection and preparation of exhibits from particular collections we are particularly grateful to Miss Patricia Allderidge, Archivist, Bethlem Royal Hospital and the Maudsley Hospital; Mrs H. Anderson, Public Record Office; Mrs M. Archer, India Office Library and Records; Mr M. F. Bond, OBE, Clerk of the Records, House of Peers; Mr John Charlton, MVO, Principal Inspector of Ancient Monuments, Department of the Environment; Mr W. Drummond, Sabin Galleries Limited; Mr Hugh Hamersley, Elvetham Hall; Mr C. T. Ineson, FRIBA, Deputy City Architect of Cardiff; Mr A. Little, FRIBA, Thomas Worthington and Sons; Miss Bette Masters and her assistants, Corporation of London Records Office; Mrs Margaret Richardson and Miss Jenny Berry, Royal Institute of British Architects; Mr A. Simpson, Royal Scottish Museum; and Mr John Wilton-Ely.

For advice on specific entries we are grateful to Miss Elizabeth Aslin, Messrs Charles Burnett, T. A. Greeves, Peter Howell, John O'Callaghan, Christopher Monkhouse, Andrew Saint, Clive Wainwright, David Walker and David Van Zanten. For help with the preparation of the catalogue indexes, and other tasks, we are grateful to Mr John Compton, and for typing the manuscript we are grateful to Miss E. Turner.

We are particularly indebted to the Right Hon. The Viscount Cowdray, TD for arranging the photography of his model of Dunecht, and to Mr Alasdair A. Auld, Curator of Prints, Drawings and Art Objects, Glasgow Art Gallery and Museum for arranging the photography of the drawings of Thomson's Natural History Museum and Anderson's Central Hotel.

The collection and preparation of the exhibits has involved much hard work on the part of many of our colleagues. We should particularly like to thank Messrs R. Smith, A. E. Maxwell, and the Museum Assistants, Department of Prints and Drawings; Messrs E. R. Gorton, W. Jackson, C. Kennett, H. H. Rogers and other members of the Department of Conservation and Technical Services, and Messrs S. Eost, R. Luke and K. Smith, Photographic Studio.

All the photographs in the catalogue are Crown Copyright Victoria and Albert Museum, with the exception of those listed below; for permission to reproduce them we are grateful to the copyright owners named:

Aerofilms pp. 39, 189; Bearwood College 27; Bradford City Libraries 95; British Railways Western Region 110; Cardiff Corporation 29: Corporation of London Records Office 50, 52, 53, 53a, 70, 77, 78, 90, 92, 120, 122; *Country Life* 16, 21, 27, 28, 32, 34 (2); Viscount Cowdray p. 12; the late Sir Arthur Elton 126; Glasgow Art Gallery and Museum 13, 138; Glasgow University, Mackintosh Collection 65; Hounslow Libraries, Chiswick Library 93; B. Howarth Loomes 128; India Office Library 112, 119; Leeds City Art Galleries 83; Liverpool City Museums 81; London Museum 98; National Monuments Record 31, 49, 50, 80, 83, 110; Perth Museum and Art Gallery 151; Public Record Office 3, 4, 20, 67, 109, 127, 134; Royal Academy of Arts 9, 13, 58, 96, 101; Royal Institute of British Architects 14, 16, 22, 38, 46, 51, 57, 59, 61, 62, 64, 66, 68, 74, 76, 79, 86, 88, 89, 97, 102, 104, 111, 121, 124, 132, 140, 141, p. 9; Royal Library Windsor Castle 17; Royal Scottish Museum 123; Sabin Galleries Limited 21; Scarborough Public Libraries 128; Thomas Worthington and Sons 149.

# Introduction

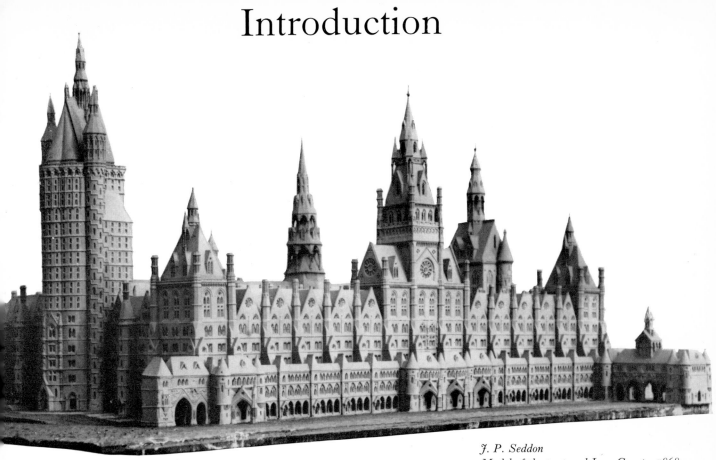

*J. P. Seddon*
*Model of the proposed Law Courts, 1868.*
*Courtesy RIBA. Destroyed.*

e Industrial Revolution ensured that
nitectural practice during the nineteenth
tury differed radically from that of any
vious era. The scope of the architect's
·k extended far beyond that of his eight-
·th century counterpart to embrace the
ole field of building. His involvement with
levels of society placed a growing emphasis
 accurate costing, and other economic
tters, while industrialization introduced
 element of competition with all its ensuing
·blems. Furthermore, the architect was
·ected to contend not only with a growing
nber of technical questions induced both
 the introduction of new materials and by
·reasingly involved legislation, but also with
·eral totally new building types such as
·way stations, exchanges, museums, exhi-
·on buildings and factories.

These factors inevitably led to changes in
 division of labour—the general contractor,
·ntity surveyor and other middlemen grew
 in place of individual master-craftsmen—
·I to the growth of professionalism. Such a
·elopment was predictably accompanied by
 foundation of various societies and
·titutions specifically connected with archi-
·ture. James Elmes had considered the
·ssibility of a Royal Academy of Architecture
·810, and in 1819 was appointed Secretary
 an Institution for the Cultivation and

Encouragement of Architecture, but nothing
came of either of these projects. Similarly an
effort by the Royal Academy students, who
formed themselves into an Architectural
Students Society in 1817, to press for a
School of Architecture, failed. These and
other societies reflected both the need to meet
to exchange ideas and the desire of students
to supplement the education received in their
masters' offices by attending lectures and
classes elsewhere. It was not until the formation of the Institute of British Architects,
later the Royal Institute of British Architects, in 1834 that a move was made towards
the establishment of a code of conduct, the
extension of control over educational institutions, the growth of a system of examin-
ations, and generally towards the other
objects of a professional institution. In fact
architecture differs from almost every other
profession in that the technique contains an
aesthetic element. Indeed that element is
very important, since, whatever improvements
may take place in the types of material available to the architect, his concern must be to
organize them in a way that is not only
structurally rational, but also aesthetically
satisfactory. It was the difficulty of combining
these two problems, as is clearly shown in the
exhibition, that caused so much concern during
the nineteenth century.

It has been remarked that architecture,
during this period underwent a transition
from the status of applied art to that of quasi-
art. That is to say that architects allowed
aesthetic solutions to override problems of
convenience and function. It is possible to see
the growth of such a situation as a result of the
architect being able to delegate many of his
previous tasks, since this meant that he needed
only to concern himself, if he so chose, with
the evolution of the first design, and could
leave the tasks of preparing working drawings
and supervising erection to others. Thus, the
St Pancras Hotel (127) was created in two
weeks while Gilbert Scott was staying in an
inn; and the jibe that the task of providing
Sir Ernest George's 'happily imagined exteriors' with suitable floor plans 'would often
cause a good deal of trouble in the office.' But
the artistic element itself was in turn the
cause of debate and argument since it was
subject to the vagaries of fashion, and fashion
during the nineteenth century was synony-
mous with style.

Interest in the aesthetic possibilities of
various different styles of building had been
realized in the eighteenth century, when
many architects added Gothic, Chinese and
Classic designs to their vocabulary. Such
studies were given added emphasis during
the nineteenth century by the greater ease

9

with which travel became possible. Almost every architect whose work is shown in the exhibition undertook some form of Grand Tour and many extended it to include Egypt and the Near East, and even India. James Fergusson, for example, studied Indian buildings in great detail, publishing in 1876 a *History of Indian and Eastern architecture*. Such volumes not only helped to disseminate knowledge of little known styles, but also helped to establish the reputation of their authors. Thus it was customary for young architects returning from abroad to publish lavish volumes of their drawings. Wilkins published his *Antiquities of Magna Graecia* in 1807, Inwood, *The Erectheion* in 1827, and Owen Jones *Plans, elevations, sections and details of the Alhambra* from 1836.

These volumes inevitably led to a greater academic involvement with style. Very few architects were content to copy exactly from their sources, most attempted to break away from such archaeological restrictions by adapting, combining or improving them. Charles Barry's final design for Highclere (16) was in a style which he called 'Anglo-Italian'. The result of combining Elmes designs for St George's Hall (79) and the Assize Courts at Liverpool was Graeco-Roman, a fact which Cockerell, who took over the work of completing the building after Elmes's death, realized and enhanced with his rich internal polychromy. Philip Hardwick's Great Western Hotel at Paddington (124) was said by the *Illustrated London News* to be 'French of Louis XIV or later' but it contains few elements of that date and appears to modern eyes closer to Visconti's New Louvre of the Second Empire.

Hardwick's ornamentation, like that of Barry, not only disguised the method of construction, but related in little measure to the internal arrangement of the building and in no way to its function. Such designs were not rational and that was what critics of the architect as artist most despised. They advocated buildings such as Pugin's The Grange at Ramsgate (18), where the care and attention lavished on the internal arrangements and planning was clearly reflected in the simple unornamented façades, and where stucco was not allowed to hide the brickwork. The Grange was the product of Pugin's involvement with the principles of Gothic planning and construction. The two great rules of architectural design he laid down in 1841 in his *True principles of Pointed or Christian architecture* were (1) that there should be no features about a building which were not necessary for convenience, construction or propriety; and (2) that all ornament should consist of enrichment of the essential construction of the building. Pugin found in an analysis of past styles that it was in Gothic architecture alone that these

principles were fulfilled. When coupled with his belief that Gothic was the only morally acceptable style for a Christian community, this was a persuasive argument for its revival.

In France a similar plea for rational building had been made at the close of the eighteenth century by the architect J. L. N. Durand. His *Précis des Leçons d'architecture données à l'Ecole Polytechnique* published in 1802-05 attempted to analyse the dreams of Ledoux, Boullée and other late eighteenth century French architects. The application of this teaching was brilliantly carried out by Durand's pupil Henri Labrouste, whose Bibliothèque Sainte Geneviève is the masterpiece of early French functionalism. Without recourse to Gothic Labrouste solved the formal problems of style and ornament by first considering the technical problems of material and space; what decoration is used consequently evolved logically from the construction.

In England in a lecture read before the Architectural Society in 1835 entitled 'On the Influence of Religion on Art', Owen Jones noticed that all great architecture in the past had been the result of purely religious motivations 'But if the Reformation has destroyed religious architecture, and the chain which held society together, there has arisen upon its ruins a religion more powerful, whose works equal, nay, surpass all that the Egyptians, Greeks, or Romans had ever conceived, Mammon is the god; Industry and Commerce the High Priests.' Jones believed, as did Pugin and Durand, in the rational use of materials, but unlike Pugin he did not accept that the Gothic style was the necessary mode of expressing such views. He allied himself more closely to Labrouste, believing that the use of new materials would in itself lead to a new and appropriate style. 'It is quite evident that if we resist the indolent temptation to imitating the genius of others, invention must result. Thus, if we leave the six-inch [iron] column in its place, we cannot consistently give it the base and capital which we had intended for its [Classical] casing of four feet, and must therefore imagine something to supply its place. As in the columns throughout as with cast iron, so it is with every other method of scientific construction, unknown to former ages.'

This philosophy involved Jones during the 1850s and 1860s in the design of a series of buildings, represented in the exhibition by Osler's shop (56), and by a project for an exhibition at St Cloud outside Paris (117), which utilized colour, iron, glass, papier-mâché, fibrous plaster, tiles and other new materials to brilliant effect. Jones was not alone in believing that the achievements of contemporary society could best be reflected in architecture by a new style. John Burley Waring wrote in the introduction to his

*Illustrations of architecture and ornam* published in 1866, 'what pleasure can man with true artistic feelings have in des ing adaptations of Italian, Gothic, or other style, borrowing one bit here another there turning himself into a kin architectural cook, and serving dead m brains to us as nourishing food—we forward then to the time when our grea national works shall be characterized sufficient originality in point of construct and application of ornament to form nucleus of a new style; grouping togethe perfect combination all the highest and n educated art of the period.' Waring's style can be seen in his project for a Natio Institute of Art and Science in Piccad (136), which consisted in just such a grouping of existing elements, and is unsa factory for that reason. His design for a gr of shops (55), however, appears to rely m on structural ironwork, and less on m formal elements, and is consequently m successful.

The desire for a rational approach and a return to the study of the basic principle architectural design saw its finest express during the nineteenth century in the erect of purely utilitarian buildings such as t designed by Paxton for the Great Exhibit (113-114) or by Barlow for the station of Midland Railway at St Pancras. These w essentially engineering rather than arc tectural works, and it was for that reason t many architects felt the need to disguise conceal them. They believed that the Crys Palace could only become architecture wl clothed with masses of masonry articula in the Classic or Gothic vocabularies. Si larly Gilbert Scott and the majority of competitors in the competition for the Pancras Hotel allowed their designs co pletely to obscure the station. In a sense t attitude perpetuated that established Hardwick at Euston, where a colossal Gr Propylaeum (101) was considered to the most appropriate expression of technological achievements manifested in railway works themselves.

While Pugin and others argued for the of Gothic, and the advocates of a 'new st for the acceptance of modern materials a industry in general, interest in the buildi of the Italian Renaissance developed as natural symptom of the desire, felt example by Elmes at St George's Hall, a richer classicism. Charles Barry's expe ments with Anglo-Italian had not prov particularly successful, but at Trentham H and at the Travellers' (96) and Reform C houses, he established the villa and pala styles which were to rival Gothic during next decade. In 1839 in an essay appended Barry's *The Traveller's Club House*, one of series of 'Studies and Examples of ern School of English Architecture', H. Leeds wrote 'Notwithstanding its isite beauties it must be admitted that Grecian style is deficient in variety [but] in architecture comprises so many sities that it is hardly possible to affix to it ning like a precise character—it possesses y excellences and recommendations, and iety of resources, which render it capable eing turned to far greater account than rto has been done.—It does not call for use of columns, in order to give it cient expression and dignity; and further makes provision for all that can be ired with regard to windows.'

us a further possibility was added to the dy large number of styles available to the orian architect, and, for those who were innovators themselves, the dilemma of h to use was further increased. James ning accepted the castellated style at oway (77) because its implied impreg-lity was peculiarly appropriate to prison tecture, but at the Coal Exchange (50) mpressive use of cast iron in the principal ior space bore no relationship to the nate façades which surrounded it. The otomy of Bunning's position as architect e Corporation of London—on the one l he was involved with the essentially tical tasks of planning new streets and on other hand with aesthetic problems of gning façades—and its realization in the Exchange serves to emphasize that of orian architecture in general.

cause, as W. H. Leeds had pointed out, Italianate style 'made provision for all can be required with regard to windows', as readily accepted by the architects of ice houses and shops, who, by simply ying the correct details to the stucco ces they had erected since the beginning he century, were able to make them onable. The same critics that had railed nst Nash's terraces in Regent Street inued to attack such building, pointing that it was monotonous, dull and aeologically implausible. Belcher's de-s of 1855 for new blocks in Bunning's non Street (92) clearly reflected his reness of such criticism. He not only ied more ornament than had been used e earlier blocks in the same street, but, ot using stucco, he allowed the contrast d brick and whitened cement to further ctuate the even rhythm of his design.

f the same date as Belcher's Cannon et shops is Alfred Waterhouse's design a warehouse for Binyon and Fryer in chester (54); George Godwin, the Editor he *Builder* had remarked in 1848 about chester 'there is less bad building in chester than in London. Brick work is lly very well and soundly executed there, would put to shame much of it that has

been and is being, done in and around the Metropolis.' The Renaissance style had been established there by Barry, not long after its advent in London, with his Athenaeum of 1837, and was developed during the 1840s in a series of great warehouses designed by Edward Walters and J. E. Gregan. Water-house's design, however, owes little to these earlier precedents; the polychrome, diapered brickwork is obviously inspired not by the Palazzo paradigm but by earlier Venetian prototypes and particularly that of the Ducal Palace itself. Interest in Venetian building had been stimulated by Ruskin's *Stones of Venice*, which had appeared two years earlier, and Waterhouse's design reflects the natural desire of a young man—he was only twenty-four when he prepared it—to keep pace with modern developments. As Ruskin pointed out, Venetian buildings offered a much more suitable precedent for Victorian commercial architecture than did the palazzi because, of course, the Venetians themselves had been great merchants. G. E. Street, in a lecture entitled 'On the Revival of the Ancient Style in Domestic Architecture' of 1853, noted that the Gothic style had found very little appli-cation to street architecture, and remarked that it was necessary 'to accommodate our architecture to every want of this nineteenth and most exigent of centuries'. Thus the arguments in favour of Venetian Gothic, especially when one also took into account the practical considerations of the greater area of window which continuous arcading provided and the possibility of an infinite number of floors, were very strong. A later example in the exhibition of building in this vein is pro-vided by Somers Clarke's eccentric offices in Lothbury (59), where the details appear to have been taken directly from the types advocated by Ruskin.

While the problems surrounding High Victorian commercial buildings were in large measure solved during the early 1850s, those relating to public buildings were still in their infancy and did not reach a peak until the competition for the Foreign and War Offices provoked the famous Battle of the Styles in 1857. The story is told in that part of the catalogue relating to the Government Offices; how Palmerston persuaded Scott to abandon his Gothic designs in favour of the present Renaissance buildings. As it happened, this proved only a temporary setback to the Gothic cause. The doctrine of Ruskin that Gothic could be used for anything, coupled with two very influential competition designs of the early 1850s, by Deane and Woodward for the Oxford University Museum, begun in 1854, and by George Gilbert Scott for Hamburg Town Hall of the same year, ensured that Gothic would become the dominant style for major secular buildings for the next two decades. As E. A. Freeman

put it in a letter to *The Times* in 1859 'Gothic is national, constructional, real, adaptable to all kinds of buildings, it is convenient, it is cheap because it can be either simple or ornate, whereas Classical must be ornate or else it is not architecture.'

The Oxford Museum and rejected Ham-burg Town Hall designs were both conceived with symmetrical front façades with steeply pitched roofs and dormers, and rows of uniform windows, about a central tower; the same formula in fact that Scott used in 1857 for his first design for the Government Offices. It is possible to detect their influence in numerous later designs, such as Fuller and Jones's Canadian Parliament buildings at Ottawa or Alfred Waterhouse's Manchester Assize Courts, but in the exhibition their influence is most apparent in the designs by Edward Godwin for the town halls of North-ampton (84) and Congleton (85) of 1861 and 1864 respectively.

The rigidity of these designs of the 1850s and early 1860s soon gave way to much freer, asymmetrical compositions, with more varied façades, like that by Scott for the St Pancras Station Hotel or those by Waterhouse for Eaton Hall (31), Gonville and Caius College, Cambridge (72), and Manchester Town Hall (87). These departed radically from the principles laid down by Pugin but contrived to retain some sense of restraint; Waterhouse was, after all, considered to be a master of planning, and Scott had said in his *Remarks on secular and domestic archi-tecture present and future*, published in 1858, that the aesthetic of the 'picturesque' and of the 'sublime' should be rationalized in con-struction. But the competition for the Law Courts in 1874, in which eleven Gothic designs were entered, broke, in the eyes of the general public at least, all rules of propriety and sensi-bility, and may be taken as marking the end of the Gothic revival. The designs ranged from William Burges's fantastic medieval palace, foreshadowing on an enormous scale his later work at Cardiff (28-29), to Seddon's turreted, spired and pinnacled building in the manner of his earlier Aberystwyth hotel.

It is perhaps ironical that Street's design, which was eventually selected for erection, should have contained some of the elements which were to characterize later building. His great hall for example was lit not by small panes of glass sandwiched between heavily mullioned casements, but by plate-glass sash-windows. It was these windows which in the hands of the next generation of architects such as Norman Shaw, William Nesfield, and John Stevenson were to form so important a part of the 'Queen Anne' style. 'The revival of such windows changed the whole character of the domestic architecture in this country, at once becoming extremely popular with those wearied of peering between the mullions of the Gothic revival,' remarked Goodhart Rendel in his *English architecture since the Regency.*

Norman Shaw's work, and even more that of Charles Voysey, represented not only an escape from the constricted atmosphere of stereotyped architecture as represented by the Gothic revival, but also a change in the architect's clientele. The rising middle classes involved him in larger town houses, like those by Stevenson and George in Kensington (42, 47) and Shaw at Bedford Park (93, 130), and in smaller country houses such as Blomfield's Denton Manor, Nesfield's Loughton Hall (33), and Voysey's Broadleys (35). These were built not as the expression of an uncertain vision but for the convenience and comfort of their occupants. Their essentially rational designs relate more closely to the work of the early Victorian period than to the High Victorian Gothic, against which they were a reaction. Thus in one sense at least architecture had made little progress since the 1830s. It had, however, undertaken a radical re-examination of its basic functions and motivations, and it is the embodiment of this searching self-criticism in building that makes the study of Victorian architecture both so stimulating and so rewarding. By 190 process was complete and architecture clined in a state of relief and anticipa feeling perhaps like the artist describe Henry Wilson's account of the receipt o news of Ruskin's death in the same 'There came a sudden clamour outside door burst open and another well-kr artist rushed in dancing and franti waving an evening paper. "Ruskin's c Ruskin's dead!" he cried; then sinking a chair. "Thank God, Ruskin's dead! me a cigarette!".'

*Dunecht, Aberdeenshire*
*Plans for the original house designed by John Smith for Lord Crawford survive in the Estate Office at Dunecht. This model appears to have been made at the time William Smith, John Smith's son, altered and extended the house in 1859. After additions by G. E. Street in 1877 Dunecht was sold in 1900 to A. C. Pirie, who employed G. B. Mitchell to make further alterations. Lord Cowdray purchased the house in 1912 and in the following year employed Aston Webb to make new additions.*

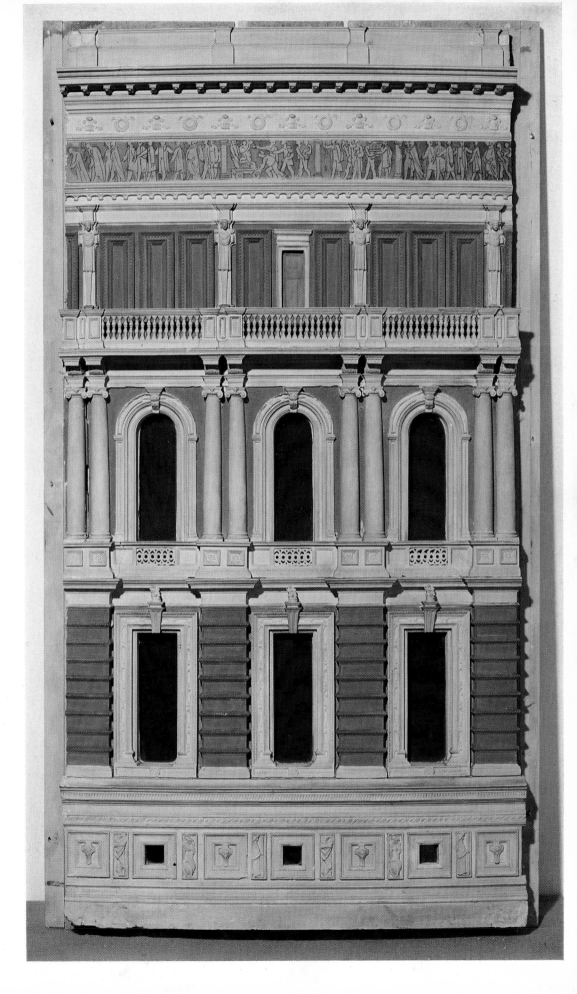

*Catalogue 116*

*Catalogue 117*

# The Architectural Model during the Victorian Period

e organizers of the exhibition of archi-
tural models held at Nottingham Uni-
sity Art Gallery in 1965 found almost no
dels of Victorian date and concluded that
ing that period 'the model appears to have
yed little part in architectural design'. The
lanation, they believed, was that archi-
s 'tended to see their compositions in
ns of pictorial values and as façades,
er than in three-dimensional form.'[1] In
nt of fact there is every reason to believe
t more models were made during the
torian period than during any previous

n 1839 competitors in the first great
npetition of Victoria's reign, for the Nelson
nument in Trafalgar Square, submitted
re than seventy models besides numerous
spective views and elevations. In the same
r the *Civil Engineer and Architects' Journal*
cribed a conversatione held by T. L.
lker, the President of the Institute of Civil
gineers, noting that 'several beautiful plans
models—of railways, bridges, piers and
er public works were visible.'[2] Later in the
r the same Journal reported that Brunel
experimenting with models to test the
ibility of the Atmospheric Railway.[3] In
2 Thomas Sopwith was awarded the
ford Medal of the Institute of Civil
gineers for a paper on the construction and
of geological models, and in 1854 he read
aper before the Royal Society of Arts' On
dels and Diagrams', noting that 'the real
of the model is to carry the mind from the
ual observation of a small object, presented
he eye, to the comprehension of a large
ect not presented to view; and in doing this,
mind is necessarily employed in the study
elative dimensions, and of corresponding
ns.'[4]
onsiderable public attention was drawn
rchitectural model-making when, in 1846,
cas's models of the Parthenon were
uired by the British Museum, and again
851, when the Corporation of London
cted a temporary building to exhibit a
del of the proposed alterations to Smith-
Market. In their desire to appease local
dents the Corporation provided a lecturer
full-time attendance to answer questions.
s drew forth the comment that 'If the
vernment had shown the model of the
ish Museum barracks and stockade, or
of the monstrosities they had perpetuated,
public could have exercised their judge-
t before it was too late. The Government
uld in all cases of public works, be called

on to exhibit a model.'[5] In the same year more
than seventy models were shown in the Great
Exhibition. The majority were of engineering
works and projects, particularly bridges, light-
houses and harbours, but models by Richard
Turner of the Great Palm Stove at Kew, the
Winter Garden in Regent's Park, the roof of
Lime Street Station, Liverpool, and a roof
for a wet dock; by E. Clarke of the Britannia
bridge; by Wyatt and Brandon of the Assize
Courts at Cambridge (82) and the church of
St Mary and St Nicholas, Wilton; and by
G. G. Scott of the church of St Nicholas,
Hanbury, were also included.

Displays of models were held at the
Architectural Exhibitions from 1855, where
a special department for 'Models, Carvings,
Decorations, Specimens of Manufacture and
Inventions connected with Building' was set
aside. The catalogue of the 1855-56 exhibition
lists nine models including an 'accurate model
of Cheshunt Church, Herts. four feet to the
inch, showing its exact appearance at the
present time' by R. Lambert, a model of
Florence Cathedral by R. Hesketh, a model
of a rifle-practice gallery barracks and drill
shed by Lieut.-Col. Waugh; and a model of
the 'proposed new line of street, along the
centre of the Thames, from Westminster to
London Bridge, showing construction of the
sewers for effectually relieving the Thames'
by G. Parminter. Such displays were common at these annual exhibitions and later
included models of the Assize Courts at
Manchester by Alfred Waterhouse, exhibited
in 1861, and of 'a cathedral suitable for the
nineteenth century' by G. H. Birch in the
following year.

At the International Exhibition held in
Paris in 1855 the *Civil Engineer and Architects'
Journal* noted that 'the architectural models
were almost entirely from England and
France.'[6] Amongst the English exhibits they
recorded examples of the Metropolitan Cattle
Market by Bunning, the Victoria Bridge over
the Clyde at Glasgow by Walker and Burges,
a bridge at Leeds by Messrs Leather, and an
iron revolving observatory dome at Brad-
stones, near Liverpool, by Mr Lassell. The
catalogue also records that Decimus Burton
showed models of the entrance to Hyde Park
from Piccadilly and of his London Coliseum,
and N. Humphreys of two projected buildings
in the city. At the next great International
Exhibition held in London in 1862 the display
of more than twenty-six English models,
which included examples of Brunel's Saltash
and Chepstow bridges forwarded by his son,

a spectacular model of the Bilbao railway in
Spain, of Saltaire by H. F. Lockwood, the
arcades and terraces in the Horticultural
Society's Gardens designed by S. Smirke and
made by H. Harrison, and the west façade of
the Royal Exchange by William Tite, was
eclipsed by the French display, for which a
separate catalogue was issued.

Apart from the displays at these periodical
exhibitions and at those of the Architectural
Exhibition, models were also occasionally
shown at the Royal Academy. In 1838 a model
of the pauper lunatic asylum at Hanwell was
shown by W. Moseley and another of Christ
Church, Alstone, by R. W. and C. Jerraud,
and in 1839 H. E. Kendall and Thomas
Allom exhibited a model of their design for
the West of London and Westminster
cemetery, which had gained second premium.
Among more interesting later examples were
two by H. Grissell of E. M. Barry's iron and
glass International Exhibition building designed for the Emperor of Russia, and two of
the apse of St Paul's Cathedral by William
Burges showing his proposed embellishments.
The latter were made by Robert P. Whellock,
a pupil of F. C. Penrose. Between 1874 and
1896 only one model, also of part of St Paul's,
was exhibited by E. J. Poynter, which caused
the *Building News* to remark 'The most
noticeable feature of the gallery is one we
gladly welcome viz. the introduction of
models.' They referred to examples in wax of
a small country house by E. S. Prior and of
Tyntesfield Chapel by Blomfield.[7]

The catalogues of many later International
and other exhibitions record that numerous
models continued to be made throughout the
Victorian period. Several which had not been
shown in exhibitions, and others which had
been entered for competitions, or made for
other purposes, found their way into the
collections of the Museum of Construction.
The catalogue of the Museum published in
1876 lists many models, some of which entered
the collections of the Victoria and Albert
Museum after the Museum of Construction
was disbanded, and have been included in
the present exhibition. Among those which
have not been traced were sectional models of
King's Cross Station by Lewis Cubitt made
in 1858; of Leeds Town Hall made in 1862 by
G. Elsley; of Preston Hall, Aylesford, Kent,
made by A. White in 1874; of a poultry house
designed for Queen Victoria by John Taylor;
of the Thames Embankment by Sir Joseph
Bazalgette made in 1873; and of the terrace
pier at Gravesend by J. B. Redman in 1873.

*Owen Jones*
*Photographs of two models of proposed exhibition buildings at St Cloud, outside Paris, c. 1860. That at the top is based on his earlier design for a crystal palace on Muswell Hill,* *which was not carried out. That at the bottom appears to be the inspiration for a later proposal by Joseph Paxton for a building on the same site. (117).*

Similarly J. P. Seddon's spectacular model of his competition entry for the Royal Courts of Justice has since disappeared although fortunately a number of photographs have survived.

Wilton-Ely's study of seventeenth, eighteenth and twentieth century models enabled him to distinguish five separate types: 'the conceptual or visionary model independent of practical considerations, the experimental model, chiefly concerned with such problems as structure and lighting, the display model, produced for the benefit of a client, a committee or a competition jury; the working model, produced either to guide the builder on specific aspects of the structure, or for the guidance of the designer's successors; and finally the site model, in which the arrangement of a group of buildings is demonstrated.' These types hold true for nineteenth century models except that one could perhaps extend the purposes of the display model to include exhibition and public criticism, and that of

the experimental and working models to include their use in the solution of the architect's practical and aesthetic problems. It is tempting to speculate on the wider use of photography and models. Charles Garnier used photographs of a model composed of interchangeable parts to study his design for the Paris Opera in 1861[8] and five years later Owen Jones superimposed a photograph of a model of his competition design for the National Gallery over photographs of the site. Similarly the water-colour of Jones's final design for an exhibition building at St Cloud, outside Paris, of 1860, appears to have been based on photographs of a model. These models depict few details of the structure and seem to have been made solely to study the effects of mass and light. In one sense the subject of photography and models was anticipated in the first volume of the *Builder*, published in 1843, which noted 'modelling should be an excellent handmaid to the philosophy of architecture; but it has a wider

range, or at any rate, has a range that ＿ beyond mere structural representations. V＿ the aid of optical ingenuity, various eff＿ may be portrayed to the life, indeed ther＿ no saying to what end a facility in model＿ such as this supplies will tend.'[9]

Owen Jones's model of his projected de＿ for a Crystal Palace on Muswell Hill, w＿ was exhibited at Colnaghi's in 1859, was m＿ of plaster, as were the earlier models of ＿ Victoria Tower and central octagon at ＿ Houses of Parliament made for Sir Cha＿ Barry, which are shown in the exhibi＿ (1, 2). The use of plaster in this connec＿ appears to have been a nineteenth cent＿ development. Henry Liddell wrote to ＿ editor of the *Builder* in 1843 'I have l＿ been of the opinion that too little attentio＿ paid to architectural modelling, and also of＿ mode of exhibiting them, for the purpose＿ studying the effect when placed un＿ different points of view. Although in no ＿ connected with building matters, I have t＿ on several occasions experiments, for ＿ purpose of making a composition that wo＿ supersede the use of plaster of Paris, wh＿ is of too friable nature to bear much handl＿ in the delicately ornamented parts of a sm＿ model.'[10] Liddell's composition, which

d papyrus powder, was essentially a form
ery fine papier-mâché and may have
ed part of the base of later materials. The
der was enthusiastic about the invention
stated 'We will have this powder worked
nd are ready to carry out his [Liddell's]
lent intentions, by doling out portions to
friends who may apply.' Besides plaster
papier-mâché, and wood which had been
ly used for earlier models, cardboard was
nsively employed, and occasionally other
rials such as Portland Stone, slate,
ite, wax, cork and Elder pith. The
lity of many of these materials, as evinced
he model of the Victoria Tower in the
bition, undoubtedly explains why so few
els appear to have survived.
y the twentieth century many architects,
Mies van der Rohe, set aside rooms in
offices for model storage and making,
during the nineteenth century it appears
ave been customary to employ the services
n outside professional. Directories record
names of some, but they are often included
modellers, who carried out the carving
casting of full-size architectural enrich-
ts, and the makers of mechanical and
r models, and it is consequently difficult
now how many were engaged specifically
he manufacture of architectural models.
e large firms such as Jackson's, advertised
they would make all types of model,
ch undoubtedly included work for archi-
. The name of one individual, however,
. Thwaite, does occur frequently enough
ndicate that he was extensively employed
different architects. He exhibited models
different designers of the Crossley Orphan
ols, Halifax, and Bowden Church,
chester, at the London Exhibition of
; the church of St James the Less,
tminster,[11] a dairy at Appleton Hall,
shire, a house 'The Woodlands', Over
win, Lancashire; the Priory, Windermere,
a church at Kettering at the Architectural
ibition, 1865; the east and west windows
he church of St Paul, Charlton, Kent, and
south front of Shepalbury House at the
hitectural Exhibition, 1866; and a door-
, Hyde Road Schools, Manchester, and
proposed Architectural Museum, London,
he Architectural Exhibition, 1868.[12] The
il Engineer and Architects' Journal noted
the models, already mentioned, of
nel's Chepstow and Saltash bridges and
of the Bilbao railway were 'from the
erienced hands of Mr. Stephen Salter';
le those made by the Mabeys of the
ses of Parliament and the Government
ces would appear to indicate that they ran
established model-making firm for the
iod between those works at least. Salter,
won a medal for his models, Thwaite,
the Mabeys appear to be the only three
itectural model-makers whose work, in

this brief survey at least, render them worthy
of particular notice.

Apart from the importance of working and
other models in assisting the architect in the
preparation of his design, many critics noted
that a model was more useful than a perspective drawing in giving an accurate picture
of a proposed building. Indeed, many
reviewers of exhibitions of architectural
drawings noted that some artists distorted
their perspectives to enhance the appearance
of their design, while others allowed artistic
effects to obscure the architecture. 'There are
many drawings which although exceedingly
showy and captivating for their colouring and
execution—for their brilliant skies, their gay
and sunny landscapes, and the effect given
them by figures and other accessories, prove
on inspection to have very little architectural
interest, and do not display anything like
equal taste and ability in architectural
composition. Indeed there are one or two
things of this kind that might be still further
improved by painting out the architecture
altogether.'[13] The ideal was to have, as did
Sir W. E. and Lady Welby-Gregory in
Dicksee's painting, both drawings and a
model. The plan as well as the elevations
could then be more easily understood. The

Building News remarked that Burges's models
of his proposed decoration of the apse of
St Paul's were excellent, but should have been
accompanied by drawings. At the same time,
however, it was in no doubt about 'the
superiority of the model as the means of
exhibiting the effect of a building—and as
enabling the architect to study what he is
doing "in the round".' An opinion which was
supported by a writer in the Quarterly Review
who had remarked in 1839 'the lines and
colouring of a geometrical elevation—can be
made to look just as the artist pleases. If
solid models were more in use, the effect of
our buildings would be better understood
both by the architect and by his employer.'

It is perhaps not surprising that models
should have been extensively used during the
nineteenth century. The re-examination of
the fundamental motivations and principles
of architecture which took place during that
period involved a searching use of every
facility by which such a study could be more
easily achieved. As the painter was able to
sketch out his first designs so the model provided the only method by which the architect,
whose creative desire lay naturally in three
rather than two dimensions, could realize his
designs without the expense of building.

*Captain Francis Fowke, RE*
*Model for the proposed Albert Hall, 1864.*
*(142).*

[1] J. Wilton-Ely, *The architect's vision*, 1965.

[2] *Civil Engineer and Architects' Journal*, 1839, p. 268.

[3] *Ibid.*, p. 233.

[4] *Ibid.*, 1854, p. 327. Reprinted.

[5] *Ibid.*, 1851, p. 120.

[6] *Ibid.*, 1855, p. 21.

[7] Photographs of what may be this model are preserved amongst the Prior material in the Royal Institute of British Architects.

[8] Archives Nationales, Paris. F 21/830.

[9] p. 189.

[10] *Builder*, 1843, p. 198.

[11] This model was shown in the Victorian Church Art exhibition, Victoria and Albert Museum, 1971-72, no. E.4.

[12] There is a model made by Thwaite in 1874 of the Strand façade of Northumberland House, at Syon House.

[13] *Civil Engineer and Architects' Journal*, 1838, p. 224.

# Competitions

result of the incredible growth of ...ing in nineteenth century England ... the development of the competition. ...e were arranged for not only the great ...nal buildings, but for the town-halls, ...ols, libraries, hospitals, swimming-baths, ...ches, cathedrals, cemeteries, memorials ...much else. At the beginning of Victoria's ..., architects were not sufficiently organ... to take united action, and consequently ...competitive system was often abused by ...promoters; during the nineteenth century, ...efore, a large part of the architectural ...s was taken up by complaints, and by the ...s for a code of conduct to be drawn up. ...re one might have expected competitions ... non-controversial—those organized by ...Government—one finds the greatest ...usion, almost invariably indecision, and ...oudest complaints.

...he competition was not a nineteenth ...ury innovation, for there had been ...ral during the previous hundred years; ...the Mansion House, for example, and ... for its sculptured decoration. The ...ruction of the Houses of Parliament in ...4, and the resulting search for a great and ...ressive Gothic palace led to a contest ...veen nearly a hundred architects, who ... in almost a thousand drawings. The ...sequent choice of Charles Barry as the ...itect of the most important building in ...don of that time, was viewed with ...icion and with rumours of a 'fiddle,' and ... set the pattern for almost every other ...petition for a large number of years. ...ny of these criticisms were, in fact, ...rely justified.

...ard on the heels of the Houses of ...liament competitors came those hoping ...be chosen for the Nelson memorial ...posed for Trafalgar Square in 1839. Even ...early the *Art-Union* wondered 'that so ...ny men of talent, notwithstanding the ...sent defective management of public ...petition, and the *entire want of confidence ...ein which prevails*, should have given up ...r time and attention to the preparation of ...igns.'[1] The answer, no doubt, was pride, ... the hope of a chance of winning the ...stige of a major national commission. The ...ice of Railton's Corinthian column was ...eived with hilarity, and the competition ...abandoned, and a second one organized. ...some this was 'mortifying and dis...rtening'.[2] There were, even so, no fewer ...n 167 designs submitted to this second ...petition. Again the *Art-Union* forcefully ...ed that the 'time is fast approaching when ...lic competitions of this nature will be

conducted in such a manner as to ensure to every candidate fair play, and a careful examination of his design placed on an equal footing with the designs of his rival. Through the exertions of the periodical press . . . the Committee appointed to carry the Nelson Testimonial into effect have been led to state they should admit the public to an examination of the designs *previous to the declaration of their decision*, a departure from the method heretofore pursued in these matters, as unexpected as it is important.'[3] This was obviously a step in the right direction, but in the event, it did not work too well, as only a few people were able to acquire tickets of admission. Another defect of the competition was that the organizers had not set any standard to be maintained for the scale of the exhibits. This meant that some of the models shown were vast, while others were minute. The result of the second contest was a compromise; Railton's column was united with the crowning statue of Nelson by E. H. Baily, with which the latter had gained the Second Premium in the original competition.

Almost immediately afterwards attention was focused on the competition for the Royal Exchange, to replace the building destroyed by fire in 1838. This proved controversial, and it was one of the first in which the competing designs were set aside, and an architect appointed who had not even bothered to enter in the first place. Such an action was repeated in 1850. The search for a suitable building to house the Great Exhibition in Hyde Park proved unfruitful; the Committee produced its own design, and then suddenly everything was hurriedly abandoned when a late entry was allowed from Joseph Paxton (114). The matter was urgent, but the Committee could not make up its mind, so Paxton forced its hand by publishing his design in the *Illustrated London News*, 'thus becoming the first man to realize such possibilities in the recently established picture press.'[4]

The Government Offices competition of 1857 caused uproar, as all the main premium winners were ignored, and Gilbert Scott was asked to be the architect of the Foreign Office. His Gothic design was, as is well known, given a classical appearance at the whim of one man, the Prime Minister, Palmerston (8, 9). In less than a year, there was further disillusionment over the Wellington monument. Before the competition, Baron Marochetti let it be known that, though he was not competing, he was hard at work on the monument, confident that the Government would be forced to turn to him in the

end. Public concern forced his elimination altogether. Unlike many competitions, models which were larger than the size stipulated in the conditions were excluded; but after a year of wrangling the artist at last selected was the winner of a premium no higher than sixth[5]—but in this case, at least, the right choice was made.

The competition for the National Gallery (137) produced no winner, and that for the Law Courts was, to a large extent, inconclusive (114). Herbert Gribble won the Brompton Oratory commission with designs which had been published two years earlier. The award in 1864 of the Natural History Museum to a Royal Engineer, and not to an architect, was received with fury by the profession, and with suggestions that impartiality had not been observed by the authorities.

This was a constant criticism of competitions organized throughout the country when opinion in a town often favoured the local boy. The premiums in the Bristol Lunatic Asylum competition, 1857, were all awarded to architects from Bristol or Gloucester, which looked 'very like a job'.[6] At first, the design selected for the First Premium for Wolverhampton Town Hall was that of a local man, but, after Alfred Waterhouse—almost a professional adjudicator—had been appealed to, he awarded the premium to a London man,[7] whereupon it seems that the Town Council declared 'no competition', refusing to pay anything to anybody.[8]

By a very strange coincidence, Lewis Angell, Surveyor to the Board of West Ham, won the competition organized for a design for West Ham Town Hall in 1867. Although members of the Board denied that they had any idea which of the drawings submitted had come from Angell, the *Builder* revealed that it had certainly been known before the competition that the designs entered by 'Civis' were by him.

Perhaps the most blatant example of civic manipulation was displayed by Bradford, in Yorkshire. The town council there had not been caught by the town hall fever until 1869. In May of that year the competition was announced, and Bradford received about 400 applications for the conditions. These conditions were then found to be somewhat unsatisfactory, and led to a good deal of correspondence, until competitors were 'virtually told that they might do just as they liked.' This was enough to raise suspicions in the minds of many, and it was further increased by a letter asking architects to state what space they would require their drawings to be given for display, accompanied by a form which effectively destroyed any secrecy.[9] Only thirty designs were entered, most of them being from outside the area, and nearly half from London. The reason that many northern architects did not enter the competition, suggested the *Builder*, was that they, unlike the Londoners, suspected the intense 'family feeling' prevailing within Bradford. On the last day for entries to be received, one very surprised competitor witnessed a procession of large drawings by a local architect, completely uncovered for all to see, carried through the streets of the town. Consequently, no one should have been at all surprised when all Premiums were awarded to local men, the First being won by Lockwood & Mawson, although 'there was a very pretty bit of innocent by-play at the opening of the sealed envelopes . . . calculated, however, to deceive few . . .'[10] It was later considered that William Burges had had a hand in Lockwood & Mawson's design, which Burges was forced publicly to deny.[11] Lockwood & Mawson confessed that their tower was a copy of that of the Palazzo Vecchio, in Florence, and that other prominent details were taken from Amiens Cathedral. They were prepared 'to apologize in the most frank manner if these tolerably well-known examples should prove to be the exclusive copyright of Mr. Burges'.[12]

In 1869 the drawings entered in the competition for a new church at Bridlington Quay were said to have been judged by the family of one of the competing architects; and in the same year Woolwich asked a local firm of auctioneers to design a workhouse for the district.

At the same time as the Bradford argument, William Burges was drawn into another at Bexley Heath, in Kent. There a new church was required, and Burges had been asked to assess the various entries. He had selected a design by William Knight, of Nottingham, and two others. All three were rejected by the Building Fund Committee by a majority of only one vote; this majority 'included two individuals, non-residents in the parish and non-attendants at the Parish Church, who would appear to have been imported into the committee at the last moment, with a view to carrying the adverse vote, and who can hardly be said to represent the feelings in this matter of the large body of subscribers or of the parish generally.' As a protest the chairman of the committee resigned, stating the reason for his action in the *Architect*.[13] The rejected winner, 'Veritas Vincit', asked for an explanation from the committee.[14] A long argument developed; it was agreed that Burges had been right architecturally, but in the matter of detail he was not. The parish had asked for seating for 900 adults, and White had provided for only 600 with

additionally some 300 children. Therefore he had not fulfilled one of the conditions; moreover, as the site was only 150 feet in length, why had White produced, and Burges selected, a church 152 feet long? Although a body of opinion supported the Committee's rejection of White's plans, they were eventually, well into 1870, persuaded to accept them.

Slightly earlier, the design by Alfred Waterhouse for Manchester Town Hall had not been given a smooth ride. The committee in Manchester had asked for designs in 1867; these formed a basis for a second competition between up to twelve selected architects. Among them were Thomas Worthington, Cuthbert Brodrick, J. Oldrid Scott, and Waterhouse, who had been chosen from the 123 original entrants. Their second group of drawings were looked over by T. L. Donaldson and G. E. Street, who gave Waterhouse first place for plan, economy, light and ventilation, but the last place for 'architectural excellence'. However, they awarded Waterhouse the First Premium; their report pleased no one but Waterhouse, and there was quite a wrangle with the other disappointed architects before he was allowed to get on with the work.[15]

Burges and Street respectively were awarded the First and Second Premiums in the Lille Cathedral competition. French pride, however, refusing to believe that anyone other than a Frenchman could design a cathedral, reversed the decision, and gave the commission to Lassus.[16] The same two English architects had found themselves placed in similar positions in the Crimea Memorial Church competition for Constantinople. Burges began work, but proved so intransigent when modifications were suggested, that he was removed, and Street was asked to build his own church, though not to the designs entered for the competition.[17]

During 1884 the Whitehall offices were again the subject of controversy when designs were invited for a new Admiralty and War Office, which were judged by Ewan Christian. He selected those submitted by two unknown young men from Halifax, John and Joseph Leeming (11, 12). When the drawings were made public, criticism was so virulent that a Select Committee eventually recommended that the building should be abandoned, although the Leeming brothers were given £8,000 for their trouble and disappointment.

They were luckier than many architects competing for work in other parts of the country, where it was fairly generally held that local committees were out to get something for nothing or on the cheap.

At the beginning of 1866 Bristol Corporation invited plans for rebuilding the Guildhall, and for erecting new Assize Courts. For these there was no guarantee

that any design would be accepted, nor there any offer of payment in the form premiums. A group of Bristol archit protested that designs could not be produ for nothing, and asked the Corporation offer premiums high enough to att reputable architects to compete.[18] Corporation took no notice, with the re that only one architect sent in any drawi These were returned to him, and the C poration, brought to its senses, held a sec competition, with premiums, judged Alfred Waterhouse. When the result announced, three unsuccessful archit immediately challenged whether the des could be built within the amount of mo allowed, and stipulated in the competi conditions. The situation deteriorated to extent that the President of the RI Beresford Hope, together with Gilbert Sc Ewan Christian, J. P. Seddon, Owen Jo F. C. Penrose and others, wrote to the Ma asking him to 'avert, if possible, the g injustice threatened'.

The *Architect* printed the statement Plymouth, when inviting designs for Guildhall, that 'the competitors must solely to the premiums for their remunerat as the Town Council will not employ any the architects whose plans may be accept The First Premium was £100 for a buildi estimated to cost £25,000, so that less t $\frac{1}{2}\%$ was offered, but, as the *Architect* sa noted, 'twenty-six designs were submit even on those conditions'.[19] In 1878 the sa journal reported the case of the Liverp architect whose design for a church rejected by a local committee, only to later that the church had actually been b to it. Another man, also from Liverp similarly had his drawings for a church tur down, and then found that the succes architect had used all his 'special and pecu features'. When he protested, he was told the local committee that they had 'been l to incorporate these details by further st of the problems of the site.

It is, consequently, hardly surprising t determined efforts were made during second half of the century to lay dow standard set of conditions, which could communicated to the organizers of arc tectural competitions. 'Pretty' water-col perspectives would not be allowed; all dra ings should be in pen and ink, and to same scale; and adequate financial rewa should be offered.

By 1880, as nothing had been settled, m than three hundred members of the RII including M. B. Adams, Ingress Bell, A. Blomfield, James Brooks, H. A. Darbish T. L. Donaldson, Benjamin Ferrey, Err George, F. C. Penrose, H. Saxon Snell, J. Seddon, R. Phené Spiers, Thomas Worthi ton, as well as a thousand other archite were not members of the Institute, tioned the President and Council to ize a scheme whereby all members of the fession can agree not to take part in any lic competition unless a professional dicator of established reputation ointed . . .'

he RIBA set up a Competitions Com- tee to investigate; in 1883 a set of gestions' had been drawn up,[20] and in following year a standard letter was sent committees organizing competitions when essary.[21] J. M. Brydon read a paper to the titute in 1888 on 'Architectural Com- tions and the methods of their decision'.[22] hat there had not been an overall rovement was demonstrated by an adver- ment recorded in 1894 for a new school the Hartlepool School Board. The Board not bind itself to accept any plan sent in, did it offer any premium, nor did it ee to return any drawing, nor to appoint assessor, qualified or otherwise. In fact, Board 'undertakes to do absolutely hing in exchange for the designs which y invite',[23] was the comment of the 3A, which felt that Hartlepool would be eedingly fortunate if any architect was lish enough to enter for its competition.

he end of Queen Victoria's reign came in uary 1901, by which time we might expect competition controversies to have been ned out somewhat—but not a bit of it. that month the Chairman of the Glasgow titute of Architects wrote to the Chairman he Glasgow Royal Infirmary:

Recognizing it to be your earnest desire t the Infirmary when reconstructed, uld conform to the most modern standards design in this class of building, and that subscribers and the general public have ight to expect this, we, the Glasgow titute of Architects, as a body of technical erts in such matters, feel it to be our y to state that, in our opinion, this result l not be achieved if the reconstruction is ceeded with according to the plans cted by your sub-committee in the recent npetiton.

We attribute this failure not to any lack of l on the part of your committee, or of any lity on the part of the competing architects, mainly to the manner in which the npetition was initiated and carried ough . . .

Apart from the all-important question of erection with the public funds of an rely adequate and modern hospital, we, Institute of Architects, feel it necessary to ge a protest against the setting aside by sub-committee, without any reason given, the award of the professional Assessor, Rowand Anderson—the more so that a ple majority of one was considered ficient to overturn his judgment—as liable

to prejudice the success, alike of promoters and architects, of future competitions in Glasgow. And we have further to state that the erection of a Jubilee block, such as is proposed, seven stories high, and in the position selected, will, if proceeded with, dwarf and irretrievably injure for all time the external appearance of the Cathedral.'

The rest of the story does not belong to Victoria's reign. . .

*The Lay of the Last Competitor*[24]

Ye great and mighty architects, who sit at
    home at ease,
Accustom'd long to calculate at five per cent
    your fees;
(Now feasible no more, alas! unless we one
    and all
Unite like bricks to save ourselves from going
    to the wall).

Let sleep and health and happiness, await a
    future day,
And let your midnight lamps be trimmed, to
    lengthen out the ray;
For a prize is in the market, a fat prize to be
    won!
So says the *Builder's* title-page, and all can
    read who run.

The burial board of Sunderland require of
    plans the best,
For chapels, lodges, cemetery-grounds, walls,
    fences, and the rest;
And that liberal and fair may be the order of
    the day,
Full twenty pounds they offer for the best
    designs to pay.

No fame nor fortune to the wight who wins
    the bulky prize,
His services the burial board will never
    recognize;
Wry-hopes, indeed! these Ryehope-men hold
    out unto the craft,
They look upon the draughtsman as an
    animal of draught.

Almost two thousand pounds they'll spend,
    whilst twenty is the prize
As architects have sinecure appointments in
    their eyes;
Their labour is diversion, or they work per-
    haps for fame,
Content to leave posterity a tombstone, and
    a name.

The architects who notice such advertisements
    as these
Shall die the death of those who feed their
    own disease;
And burial board, while wandering the
    cemetery round.
May see the ghosts of those who paid a visit
    to the ground.

Why, England, merry England, 'where
    health and plenty cheer
The lab'ring swain', are architects denied
    their beef and beer?
Have cultivated intellects no claim upon your
    soil?
Or is the labour lighten'd when the mind
    bears all the toil?

The competition still goes on, as it is wont to
    go,
The day will come when burial boards may
    yet, for aught we know,
Have competitions for their graves, nor ever
    die until
Each member finds the cheapest man his
    vacancy to fill!

[1] March 1839, p. 18.
[2] J. Physick, *Designs for English sculpture 1680-1860*, Victoria and Albert Museum, 1969, p. 181.
[3] June 1839, p. 82.
[4] C. H. Gibbs-Smith, *The Great Exhibition of 1851*, Victoria and Albert Museum, 1951, p. 9; *Builder*, 20 July 1850, p. 337.
[5] J. Physick, *The Wellington Monument*, Victoria and Albert Museum, 1970.
[6] *Builder*, 21 March 1857, p. 165.
[7] *Ibid.*, 31 March 1866, p. 237.
[8] *Ibid.*, 16 June 1866, p. 454.
[9] *Ibid.*, 23 October 1869, p. 840.
[10] *Ibid.*
[11] *Architect*, 4 December 1869, p. 279.
[12] *Architect*, 11 December 1869, p. 290. In the Department of Prints and Drawings are several designs for a building which, from the heraldry depicted, appear to be for Bradford Town Hall. They are unsigned, but stylistically are probably by E. W. Goodwin.
[13] *Architect*, 11 December 1869, p. 290.
[14] *Loc. cit.*, 18 December 1869, p. 302.
[15] *Builder*, 11 April 1858, p. 259; A. Water-house, 'Description of the new Town Hall at Manchester,' RIBA *Papers*, 19 February 1877, pp. 117-36.
[16] Victorian Church Art Exhibition, 1971-72, Catalogue no. D11.
[17] *Ibid.*, no. D12.
[18] *Builder*, 27 January 1866, p. 70.
[19] *Architect*, 8 January 1870, p. 15.
[20] RIBA, *Journal*, January 1883, p. 51.
[21] *Loc. cit.*, October 1884, p. 2.
[22] *Loc. cit.*, n.s., vol. iv, 9 February 1888, pp. 157-64.
[23] *Loc. cit.*, 3 s., vol. i, 1894, pp. 623-24.
[24] *Builder*, 3 January 1857, p. 15, by C. G. of Dublin.

# Note on the Catalogue and Biographical entries

The drawings and models are arranged in chronological order within each section.

The following symbols are used in the entries

Exhib.   Exhibitions in which the object has been previously shown

Illus.   Published works in which the object has been previously illustrated

Lit.   Literature in which the object or building has been mentioned

Books and periodicals have been abbreviated as follows:

| | |
|---|---|
| A | *Architect* |
| AR | *Architectural Review* |
| BA | *British Architect* |
| BN | *Building News* |
| Br | *Builder* |
| CE&AJ | *Civil Engineer and Architects' Journal* |
| CL | *Country Life* |
| ILN | *Illustrated London News* |

Institutions have been abbreviated as follows:

| | |
|---|---|
| AA | The Architectural Association |
| RA | The Royal Academy of Arts |
| RIBA | The Royal Institute of British Architects |

# Biographies

...AMS, Maurice Bingham (1849-1933)
...ned by H. N. Goulty. At one time he was assistant to Sir William ...rson and architect to the Brighton Borough Council. In 1872 he ...ed to London and joined the staff of the *Building News*, of which ...ter became architectural editor. He designed several buildings for ...more Edwards, the proprietor of the *Building News*, including ...ries at Acton (1899), Camberwell (1902), Shepherds Bush and ...am; houses at Chalfont (1895-1911) and the Passmore Edwards ...h London Art Gallery at Camberwell (1896-98). His other works ...ded additions to Norman Shaw's church at Bedford Park and to ...eter, London Docks; houses at Port Sunlight and almshouses for ...Chiswick Charity Trustees. It was, however, as a draughtsman ...he was best known. He retired from practice in 1923. He was the ...or of several publications on architectural subjects. ARIBA 1876, ...A 1886.

...CHISON, George (1825-1910)
...of an architect of the same name, to whom he was articled after ...ng Merchant Taylors' School. Studied at the Royal Academy ...ools and at London University. After travelling with William ...res on the Continent, where he met F. Leighton and A. Water-...e, he became his father's partner in 1859. When the latter died ...861 he succeeded him as architect to the St Katherine's Dock ...pany. His work included warehouses and wharves on the Thames; ...es at 59-61 Mark Lane; Leighton House, Holland Park Road, ...don; and numerous interior decorative schemes including the ...lsmiths' Hall and the Founders' Hall. Drawings for many of ...e works were presented to the Royal Institute of British Architects ...is Executors in 1910. He was President of the Architects' Benev-...t Society 1897-98; Professor of Architecture at the RA 1887-1905; ...A 1862; Vice-President (1889-93) and President (1896-99) of the ...A and received its Gold Medal 1898. He was also a member of ...ral foreign architectural bodies and won a number of medals for ...seas architectural exhibitions.

...LOM, Thomas (1804-1872)
...n in London. Articled to Francis Goodwin for at least seven years. ...velled extensively in Europe and Asia. He was as much an artist ...n architect and, besides illustrating many topographical books for ...ue & Co. and Heath & Co., he made drawings for other architects. ...ongst these were views of the Houses of Parliament which Barry ...ented to the Czar of Russia in 1843. His main architectural works ...e the Church of St Peter, Kensington Park Road, Paddington, ...don (1852); The Town Hall, Harwich, Essex, built as the Great ...ern Hotel (1864); and the hotel at Lord's Cricket Ground, ...ohn's Wood, London. He also designed the Dodd mausoleum in ...wood Cemetery, and several of the interiors at Highclere Castle, ...s.

...DERSON, Sir Robert Rowand (1834-1921)
...almost no professional training but studied the medieval ...itecture of England and the Continent, and construction and ...gn while serving with the Royal Engineers. His first important ...k was the new Medical School of Edinburgh University, won in ...petition in 1876. In the following year he designed Mount Stuart ...the Marquess of Bute. Later work in Edinburgh included the ...servative Club (1883); the National Portrait Gallery (1886-88); ...the National Museum of Antiquities of Scotland. In Glasgow he ...gned the Station Hotel, originally the Caledonia Railway Offices

(1881-84); and the Pearce Institute (1903-05). He restored many Scottish churches including Dunblane Cathedral and the Abbeys of Paisley, Culross and Dunfermline, and carried out extensive alterations at Balmoral. He also designed many Scottish country houses. He entered several competitions without success including those for the Imperial Institute (1887) and the extensions to the British Museum (1902). Knighted 1902. FRIBA 1903 and received the Gold Medal 1916. He was the first President of the Scottish Institute of Architects, founded in 1916. LLD.

ANDREWS, George Townsend (1805-1855 or 56)
Awarded a premium by the Society of Arts 1824. Trained at the Royal Academy Schools from 1825 and then became assistant to P. F. Robinson 1826-36. Most of his work was done in the neighbourhood of York, where he lived, and includes the railway station and hotel, York (1841); railway station and hotel, Hull (1847); railway station (1848) and school (1849) at Richmond, Yorkshire; and the churches of the Holy Evangelists, Skipton (1848-49); St Lawrence, Flaxton-on-the-Moor (1853-54); and All Saints Newton-upon-Ouse (1849).

ASHBEE, Charles Robert (1863-1942)
Studied history at Cambridge. Decided to become an architect and went into office of G. F. Bodley. In 1891, under the influence of Morris and Ruskin he set up in Essex House the Guild of Handicrafts (founded 1888), specializing in furniture, metalwork, etc. Founded Essex House Press 1876. Elected a member of the Art Workers Guild 1897. Founded London Survey Committee and wrote first volume on the parish of Bromley-by-Bow 1900. Moved his Guild to Chipping Campden, Glos., in 1902, but his group of craftsmen split up in 1907. Went on a lecture tour in the United States, where he met Frank Lloyd Wright. In 1917 he went to Egypt, where he took up town planning work and later became civic adviser to the City of Jerusalem. Returned to England in 1924 and lived at Kemsing, near Sevenoaks. His best known architectural works included the rebuilding he did at Chipping Campden, and several houses in Cheyne Walk, including his own house, the Magpie and Stump. His publications included *Where the Great City stands*, 1917.

BARRY, Sir Charles (1795-1860)
Born in Westminster. Articled in 1810 to Middleton and Barley, surveyors of Lambeth, where he remained for six years. Made an extensive tour of Europe and the Near East between 1817 and 1820 and set up in practice on his return. His first works were churches at Brighton, London and in the north, and were all Gothic in style. These were followed by others works in Brighton and in 1824 by the Manchester Royal Institution of Fine Arts, now the City Art Gallery, in the Classical style. His first major building was the Travellers' Club won in competition in 1829; it was also his first major building in the Italian style. In 1832 he won the competition for the King Edward VI Grammar School in Birmingham, which was his first major Gothic building. Pugin and J. Thomas, who assisted him there, also collaborated with him on the Houses of Parliament, begun in 1837 and opened in 1852. Later buildings in London included the Reform Club (1837-41); the layout of Trafalgar Square (1840); and the Board of Trade building in Whitehall (1844). He designed numerous domestic buildings including Bowood (1834); Highclere (1837); Trentham (1838); Harewood (1843-50); Dunrobin Castle (1844-48); Bridgwater House (1847-49); and Cliveden (1851). Knighted 1852. Elected RA 1844. Received the Gold Medal of the RIBA 1850. FRS.

**BELCHER, John (1841-1913)**

Born in Southwark the son of an architect. Educated privately and in Luxemburg and after a few months in Paris joined his father's practice in 1865. After his father's retirement in 1875 he took over the practice until 1905, when he went into partnership with J. J. Joass. His work included various business premises in the city; the Hall of the Curriers' Company; a warehouse for Messrs Rylands, Wood Street, London; the Institute of Chartered Accountants, Moorgate, London (1889); the Convent of the Good Shepherd, near Wargrave, Berks (1894); Pangbourne Tower, Berks (1897-98); Town Hall, Colchester (1898-1902); Electra House, Finsbury (1902); Mappin and Webb's Shop, Oxford Street, London (1907); Whiteley's Store, Bayswater (1912); and the Royal Society of Medicine, Henrietta Place, Marylebone (1910-12). He prepared a design in 1891 for the Victoria and Albert Museum which was not accepted. He received the Gold Medal of the RIBA and was President 1904-06. ARA 1900. RA 1909. FRIBA. His publications included *Essentials in architecture*, 1893, and with Sir Mervyn Macartney, *Later Renaissance architecture in England*, 1897-99.

**BELLAMY, Thomas (1798-1876)**

Worked in the office of David Laing, and after marrying made a tour of the Continent. His practice was limited, and most of his buildings were of little importance. He devoted particular attention to detail, T. L. Donaldson describing him as 'a purist to excess'. His best known works, King's College Hospital and the Law Fire Insurance Office, were won in competitions in 1851 and 1858 respectively. His other works included Hensham Chapel (1839); Hitchin Town Hall (1839); Corsham Court, Wilts (1848); Boys' Home, Camden Town (1870); Sutton House, near Heston, and churches at Malvern, Heston and in the Camberwell Road. He was unsuccessful in the competition for the Fitzwilliam Museum (1835) and gained third prize in that for the Foreign Office. His publications included a pamphlet on fire-proof construction.

**BRANDON, David (1813-1897)**

Articled to George Smith of Mercers' Hall, 1828. Student at the RA 1830. Awarded Silver Medal for the best drawing of the Bank of England 1832. From 1838 to 1851 he was in partnership with T. H. Wyatt and did numerous works in Wiltshire and elsewhere including Wilton Church (1841-45); Dilton Marsh, Wilts (1844); Crockerton, Wilts (1843); St Andrew, Bethnal Green (1847); and St Matthias, Bethnal Green (1847). His major works after 1851 were the Bucks County Lunatic Asylum; Falconhurst Lodge, Cowden, near Edenbridge, Kent; Sidbury Manor, Devon (1853); Junior Carlton Club, Pall Mall (1866); Eagle Life Office, Pall Mall; and Marlborough Club, Pall Mall.

**BRODRICK, Cuthbert (1822-1905)**

Born in Hull, the son of a shipowner. Educated at Kingston College, Hull. Apprenticed to Henry Lockwood and later his assistant 1837-44. Travelled on the Continent 1844-45. Set up in practice in Hull 1845. After retiring early from architectural practice in 1869 he lived in France. Died in Jersey. His work included the Royal Institution, Hull (1852-54); Town Hall, Leeds (1853-58); Corn Exchange, Leeds (1860-63); Grand Hotel, Scarborough (1863-67); Congregational Church, Headingly Lane, Leeds (1864-66); Institute of Science, Art and Literature, Leeds (1860-67), and the city baths (1866). He submitted designs for several competitions unsuccessfully, including Lille Cathedral (1856); Government Offices (1857); Manchester Assize Courts (1859); Bolton Town Hall (1865); National Gallery (1866); and Manchester Town Hall (1866). FRIBA.

**BUNNING, James Bunstone (1802-1863)**

Born in London, the son of a surveyor. Articled to George Smith, set up in practice in the early 1820s. After marrying in 1826 he obtained the District Surveyorship of Bethnal Green and later that of Foundling Hospital Estates. In 1839 he was appointed Surveyor to London Cemetery Company, and later to the Thames Tunnel, Victoria Life Office, Haberdashers' Company, and London & County Bank. In 1843 he became Clerk of the City's Works, a position which he held until his death. His works included the City of London School (1835-37); alterations to Highgate Cemetery and the planning of Nunhead Cemetery; several streets and inns at New Cross; Bethnal Green Union Workhouse (1840-41); a mansion at Lellingstone Dayrell, Bucks; and numerous works for the Corporation of London including several new streets; the Coal Exchange (1847-49); Holloway Prison (1849-51); the Caledonian Market (1855); and the decoration of many streets and buildings on special occasions. He submitted entries in competition for the Houses of Parliament, the Royal Exchange, and the Great Exhibition. FRIBA, FSA.

**BURGES, William (1827-1881)**

Son of a prosperous civil engineer. Educated King's College School. Articled to Edward Blore in 1844. Entered the office of Sir Matthew Digby Wyatt, 1849, and in the same year travelled extensively on the Continent, undertaking a further trip in 1854. Entered the competition for Lille Cathedral in 1855, and for the Crimea Memorial Church, Constantinople, but, although he won both, his designs were not carried out. He was unsuccessful with his competition design for the Law Courts, but did win that for St Fin Barre's Cathedral, Cork (1865-76). His first important secular commission was alterations and additions to Gayhurst, Bucks, for Lord Carrington (1859). This was followed by restorations at Waltham Abbey (from 1860); redecoration at Worcester College, Chapel (1863-64) and Hall (1877); Cardiff Castle (1865-81); Knightshayes, Devon (1869); churches at Studley Royal and Skelton, Yorks (from 1871); Speech Room, Harrow School (from 1872); Trinity College, Hertford, Conn. (from 1873); Castell Coch (begun 1875); and his own Tower House, Melbury Road, London (1875). FRIBA 1860, ARA 1881.

**BUTTERFIELD, William (1814-1900)**

Born in London. Apprenticed 1831 to Thomas Arber, a builder and decorator, and at the same time was a student member of the Architectural Society. After Arber went bankrupt Butterfield went to another builder in Worcester. At the close of his articles, he travelled through England and on the Continent, studying medieval buildings. By 1843-44 had set up in business at 4 Adam Street, Adelphi. His early works include St Andrew's Church, Wilmcote (1841); non-conformist chapels at Bristol (1842-43); and Coalpit Heath, Bristol (1844-45). Through Beresford Hope he received the commission to convert the remains of St Augustine's, Canterbury, into a Missionary College, and to build All Saints, Margaret Street, London, his most famous work. These were followed by St Matthias, Stoke Newington (1850-53); the college and church on the Isle of Cumbrae (1851-59); St Alban's, Holborn (1859-63); and All Saints, Babbacombe (1868-74). Among his best known secular works are Keble College (c. 1870) and various buildings at Rugby School (after 1872). Butterfield never exhibited any of his drawings and shunned publicity to such a degree that, when given the RIBA Gold Medal in 1881, he refused to receive it in public.

**CLARKE, Lieutenant-General Sir Andrew (1824-1902)**

Born in Southsea, son of Lieut.-Col. Andrew Clarke, KH. Educated at the King's School, Canterbury, Portora School, Enniskillen, and Royal Military Academy, Woolwich. Commissioned in the Royal Engineers, 19 June 1844. At own wish sent to Tasmania, 1846,

Zealand, 1848. Returned to Tasmania becoming Private Secretary
he Governor. Clarke became Surveyor-General to the State of
oria, 1853, and drafted a new constitution. Helped to organize the
bourne Exhibition, 1854. Granted annual pension of £800 in event
turning to England. Remained in Melbourne, became member of
Cabinet, and inaugurated the railway system. Promoted First
tain, Clarke returned to England, 1857, and commanded Royal
ineers at Colchester, 1859. With rank of major sent to the Gold
st, 1863. Became Director of Engineering Works at the Admiralty,
don, 1864. Appointed Governor of the Straits Settlements, 1873.
India, 1875, as head of the Public Works Department. Com-
dant, School of Military Engineering at Chatham, 1880, and
inted Inspector-General of Fortifications, with rank of Major-
eral, 1882. Agent-General for Victoria, 1886. Retired from army,
, to stand, unsuccessfully for parliament. Appointed Colonel-
mandant of the Royal Engineers, 1902. CB 1869, KCMG 1873,
1877, GCMG 1885.

ARKE, George Somers (1825-1882)
upil of Sir Charles Barry. Travelled widely in England and on the
tinent. He established a considerable practice designing country
ses, and warehouses and office buildings in London. His work
udes the Turkish Baths, Jermyn Street; Cowley Manor, Oxford
4-62); The Merchant Seamen's Orphan Asylum, Wanstead,
ex (1861); the Auction Mart Company, Lothbury (1866); and the
eral Credit Company, Lothbury (1866). FRIBA.

CKERELL, Charles Robert (1788-1863)
n in London, the second son of S. P. Cockerell. Educated at
stminster School. Entered his father's office, and that of Sir Robert
rke as an articled assistant, 1804. Between 1810-16 he visited
ece, Asia Minor and Italy, and after his return devoted much of
time to the preparation of drawings of Greek antiquities; he also
e lectures on Greek and Roman architecture. In 1819 he succeeded
father as Surveyor of St Paul's Cathedral. His major executed
ks were National Monument, Calton Hill, Edinburgh (1822-30
W. H. Playfair); Hanover Chapel, Regent Street (1823-25);
stminster Fire Office (1829-30); Westminster Insurance Co.
2); Cambridge University Library (1837-40); London & West-
ster Bank, Lothbury (1837-39 with Tite); Sun Fire Office,
eadneedle Street (1841-42); Ashmolean Museum and Taylorian
itute, Oxford (1841-45); completion of H. L. Elmes's St George's
, Liverpool (1851-54); St Bartholomew, Moor Lane (1848-50);
erpool, London & Globe Insurance Co., Liverpool (1855-57); his
xecuted design submitted in competition for the Royal Exchange
840 is generally considered his finest. He used Gothic at Harrow
ool (1818-20) and St David's College, Lampeter (1822-27); and
man at Killerton Park Chapel, Devon. In 1833 he became architect
he Bank of England, and designed the bank's branches at Plymouth
5); Bristol (1844); Liverpool (1845-46); and Manchester (1845-46)
vell as additions to the Bank of England itself (1834-35 and 1848).
cted ARA 1829, RA 1836, and Professor of Architecture 1840. He
red from the professorship in 1857 and from practice in 1859. He
the first architect to be President of the RIBA, 1860-61, and the
recipient of the Gold Medal of the RIBA, 1848. His publications
uded The iconography of the West Front of Wells Cathedral, 1851
vell as papers on several of the Greek temples.

LLCUTT, Thomas Edward (1840-1924)
ined in G. E. Street's office. Developed a large and successful
ctice. His major works include the Imperial Institute (1887-93);
yd's Register of Shipping (1900); Savoy Hotel (1887 & 1903-04);
lland Bank, Ludgate Hill (1890); Royal English Opera House (now
ice Theatre) (1890); Wigmore Hall (1890); The Croft, Totteridge

(1895); Boarding Houses at Eton College (1899-1906). Added attic
storey to the Athenaeum Club house 1899. Other work included the
interior of P & O liners. Awarded prize for architecture at Paris
Exhibition 1899. Received Gold Medal of the RIBA 1902. President
RIBA 1906-08. Was in partnership with Stanley Hamp, President of
the AA, 1922-23.

COLLMANN, Leonard W. (1816-1881)
He exhibited designs at the RA for decorations at Ossington (1842)
and the Oriental Club House (1849). A large collection of his drawings
is preserved in the Victoria and Albert Museum and includes designs
for decorations at Bowood, the Athenaeum Club house, Melchet
Park, Wilts, the Gas Light Company's Hall, Sheffield, and the Town
Hall, Bolton. Hugh Stannus was at one time employed in his office
and Alfred Stevens was a friend. Stannus records that it was through
Collmann that Stevens received the commission to decorate Deysbrook
at Liverpool. Portraits of Collmann and his wife were painted by
Stevens and are illustrated in Stannus, Alfred Stevens and his work,
1891.

CRACE, John Diblee (1838-1919)
Son of John Gregory Crace. Educated at private schools. Travelled in
Italy, Germany, France and later in Egypt, Palestine and Syria.
Articled to his grandfather Frederick Crace, but in 1855 joined his
father's business. He designed the decorative colouring of the National
Gallery; the Victoria Hall in Leeds Town Hall; state rooms at
Longleat; and re-decorations at Brighton Pavilion. His work in
London included the Indian Room at the Imperial Institute;
decorations in several private houses, including Montagu House,
Devonshire House and Grosvenor House; and in several Company
Halls including the Fishmongers' Hall and the Skinners' Hall. In
1884 he was appointed Master of the Painter-Stainers' Company, and
in 1908 he received the Gold Medal of the Institute of British
Decorators, of which he had been the founder and first President. His
publications include Gleanings in the field of ancient art, 1907; The
art of colour decoration, 1913; and a paper on Arabic architecture.

CRACE, John Gregory (1809-1889)
Son of Frederick Crace. Joined his father's decorating business at
14 Wigmore Street, London, in 1826, as his assistant. In 1843 he
made a tour of France, Germany and Northern Italy, and in 1846
made another trip to France visiting the châteaux of the Loire Valley.
In the previous year he had begun working on the painted decoration
of the House of Lords, and in 1847 the firm of Frederick Crace & Son
received the contract for the further coloured decoration of the New
Houses of Parliament. Appointed a Special Commissioner for the
1851 Exhibition, and was one of the Jurors for works of decoration,
furniture and paper hangings; also responsible for the management of
Pugin's Mediaeval Court. Designed and carried out the decoration of
the Manchester Art Treasures Exhibition Building in 1857. In 1860
he undertook the decoration of the Waterloo Chamber at Windsor
Castle, and in 1862 he designed and carried out the decoration of the
International Exhibition Building, London.

CRESWELL, Harry Bulkeley (1869-1960)
Educated at Bedford Grammar School and at Trinity College, Dublin.
Articled in 1890 to Sir Aston Webb and studied also at the RA
schools. Began private practice on his own account in 1900. In 1901
he designed the Queensferry factory, his best known work, and later
Cawston House, Warwickshire (1907); the church of St Philip, Rugby
(1911-13); Stone Edge, Leek Wootton, Warwickshire (1915-16); and
St Alban, Stoke, Coventry (1929). As consulting architect to the Crown
Agents for the Colonies, he designed the Law Courts and Offices for
Sierra Leone and the College of Agriculture for Mauritius. In associ-

ation with Egerton Swarthout and John Russell Pope of New York, he designed the American Memorial Chapel at Brookwood, and the new Parthenon Room at the British Museum. At intervals he worked in association with H. P. G. Maule and W. A. Forsyth. He acquired a considerable reputation as a writer with several works of semi-technical fiction including *The Honeywood File*, 1929; *The Honeywood Settlement*, 1930; *Jago versus Swillerton and Toomer*, 1931; *Diary from a Dustbin*, 1935; *Grig*, 1942; and *Grig in Retirement*, 1943.

## CUBITT, Thomas (1788-1855)

Trained as a carpenter and early went to India. Set up business in London on his return c. 1809. In 1815 he built the London Institution at Finsbury Circus to the design of W. Brooks. He set up a workshop in Gray's Inn Road which he later relinquished to his brother William. In order to keep a large staff Cubitt engaged in speculative building on a large scale. His schemes included villas and houses at Highbury and Newington Green; estates in St Pancras (from 1824), Belgravia and South Belgravia (from 1825); parts of Camden Town, Clapham Park, and Pimlico; houses in Kemp Town, Brighton, etc. He also built the east façade of Buckingham Palace (1846-47) to Blore's design, and Osborne, Isle of Wight. In 1855 he took a leading part in the preparation of the Building Act. His youngest brother, Lewis, was the architect of King's Cross and other stations and probably designed many of Thomas's building schemes.

## DOUGLASS, Sir James Nicholas (1826-1881)

Born in Bow, London, the son of Nicholas Douglass, superintending engineer to Trinity House. Apprenticed to Hunter and English, engineers at Bow. Assisted his father 1847. Manager of Messrs Laycock on the Tyne until 1854. Resident engineer of Gun Fleet pile lighthouse 1854; Smalls Rock lighthouse until 1861 and of Wolfe Rock lighthouse 1861-70. Chief engineer to Trinity House from October 1862 until about October 1892. Douglass designed and erected many lighthouses including the Eddystone, opened 1882. MICE 1861. Knighted 1882. FRS 1887.

## ELMES, Harvey Lonsdale (1814-1847)

Born at Oving, Chichester. Son of the architect James Elmes. Studied in his father's office, at the RA schools, and was assistant to H. E. Goodridge of Bath 1835-38. His major work was St George's Hall, Liverpool. The preparation of the working drawings for this vast building weakened his already poor health and after travelling to Jamaica in an attempt to regain his strength he died there in 1847, aged only 34. Elmes designed several private houses in Liverpool; The Collegiate Institution, Shaw Street (1840-43); the Lancashire County Lunatic Asylum (1847); several houses in Hanover Square, London; and the façade of a terrace opposite Albert Gate, Hyde Park, London.

## FERGUSSON, James (1808-1886)

Born in Ayr, son of the eminent physician Dr William Fergusson (1773-1846). Educated Edinburgh High School and at a private school in Hounslow. Went to Calcutta intending to enter a firm of Indian merchants. Developed a strong interest in Indian architecture and made two lengthy tours of the country between 1835 and 1842. Settled in London in a house which he built at 20 Langham Place. Active member of the Royal Asiatic Society and served for a short time as architectural adviser to the Office of Works. Amongst his architectural work was a picture gallery for Miss North at Kew; a design for a new National Gallery (1850); and for new Government Offices (1857); and a design for the Albert Memorial (1864). The editor of the *Builder* remarked after his death 'He is as important a writer on architecture in the modern world as Vitruvius was in the ancient world.' Awarded gold medal of the RIBA 1871. His publications include *An historical inquiry into the true principles of beauty in art*, 1849; *Illustrated handbook of architecture in all countries of the world from the earliest times to the present day*, 1855; and numer papers on architecture and archaeology. FRS.

## FOWKE, Francis (1823-1865)

Born at Ballysillan, Belfast. Educated at Dungannon College and Woolwich, receiving a commission as a second lieutenant in Royal Engineers in 1842. Served in Bermuda and at Devonport, in 1854 was sent to Paris in charge of machinery for the Paris e bition. He became Inspector for Science and Art at South Kensing in 1857, and Architect and Engineeer to the Department of Scie and Art. His architectural works include the Raglan Barracks Devonport; the South Kensington Museum; Museum of Science Art (now the Royal Scottish Museum), Edinburgh (1860); impro ments and enlargements of the Dublin National Gallery; buildi for the Royal Horticultural Society (1861); the Internatio Exhibition Building (1862); and the Royal Albert Hall. In 1864 produced the winning design for the Natural History Museum, died before it could be executed. As an inventor he designed a m tary fire engine, the 'bellows' camera, collapsible pontoons, a fold india-rubber bath, a vacuum cleaner, and a travelling scaffold. publications include *A description of the buildings at South Kensing for the reception of the Sheepshanks Pictures*, 1858; and *Some acc of the buildings designed for the International Exhibition of 1862.*

## GEORGE, Sir Ernest (1839-1922)

Born in Southwark, London. Educated at a small school at Clapl Common, and at Brighton and Reading. Articled to Samuel He and attended classes at the Royal Academy, where he won the G Medal in 1859. He set up in practice in partnership with Tho Vaughan, and later with Harold Peto (1828-97), and then with Alf Yeates. He had a large and successful practice which included cc missions in India, and was a water-colour artist of great ability. work included St Pancras, Rousdon, Devonshire (c. 1870 v Vaughan); 6-7 St Mary-at-Hill, London (1873 with Vaugha Rousdon House, Devonshire (c. 1880 with Vaughan); houses Harrington Gardens and Collingham Gardens, Kensington, Lon (1881 with Peto); St Andrew, Guildersfield Road, Wandswo London (1886 with Peto); Claridge's Hotel, Brook Street, Lon (1894-97 with Yeates); the Crematorium, Golders Green, Lon (1905 with Yeates); Busbridge Hall, Surrey (1906 with Yeat Royal Academy of Music, Marylebone Road, London (1910-11 v Yeates); and the design of Southwark Bridge, London (1915-19). received the Gold Medal of the RIBA 1896 and was President 1908 Knighted 1907. RA, FRIBA.

## GODWIN, Edward William (1833-1886)

Born in Bristol, the son of a decorator. Apprenticed to W. Armstr and entered into partnership with Henry Crisp. Moved to Londor 1862. His architectural works include the town halls at Northamp (1861-64) and Congleton (1864); the restoration of Dromore Cas Ireland; and many churches, schools and houses near Bristol. His w in London included the Fine Art Society, New Bond Street; a stu for Princess Louise at Kensington Palace; houses in Bedford Park the White House, Tite Street. He contributed regularly to the *Bri Architect* and published *Temple Bar illustrated*, 1877, and *Arti conservatories and other horticultural buildings*, 1880.

## HARDWICK, Philip (1792-1870)

The son of Thomas Hardwick. Educated at Dr Barrow's School Soho. Attended the Royal Academy Schools from 1808 and stud architecture in his father's office. Visited France and Italy 1815-19 then started independent practice in London. He was appoin Architect to the Bridewell and Bethlehem Hospitals 1816, a positi he held for 20 years; to the St Katherine's Dock Company 1825 St Bartholomew's Hospital 1827; and to the Goldsmiths' Comp

. He was also architect to the Duke of Wellington, and Surveyor
e Portman Estate. In 1847 his health failed, and from then till his
ement in 1861 his son, Philip Charles, took over much of his
tice. His work included Christ Church, Lisson Grove, London
2-25); Babraham Hall, Cambs (1832); the Free Grammar School,
kport, Cheshire (1829-32); Goldsmiths' Hall, Foster Lane,
don (1829-35); 19 Old Broad Street, London (1833-34); the
, Portico, Lodges, and Hotel at Euston Station, London (1836-
Curzon Street Goods Station, Birmingham (1838); the New Hall
Library, Lincoln's Inn, London (1843, built by P. C. Hardwick);
artholomew's Hospital, London (1851—recased original building).
was a member of the Institute of Civil Engineers; an original
ber and Vice-President of the RIBA, and received Gold Medal
. He was treasurer of the RA 1850-61. RA, FRS, FSA.

## RDWICK, Philip Charles (1822-1892)

son of Philip Hardwick. Trained under Edward Blore. Joined his
r's practice in 1842 and virtually took it over in 1847, when the
Hardwick's health declined. He was Architect to the Bank of
and; St Bartholomew's Hospital; the Goldsmiths' Company; the
chant Taylors' Company; Greenwich Hospital; Charterhouse;
Surveyor to the Portman Estate. His work included the Great
at Euston Station, London (1846-49); Aldermaston Court,
s (1848-51); the GWR Hotel, Paddington Station, London
0-52); The Ship Hotel, Greenwich; the Australia and New
and Bank, Threadneedle Street, London (1854); the church of
ohn, Lewisham Way, Deptford, London (1855); the Bank of
and, South Parade, Leeds, Yorks (1862-64); Hassobury House,
ham, Essex (1868); and Charterhouse School, Surrey (1869-72).
ntered unsuccessfully for several competitions including that for
Albert Memorial. FSA, FRIBA.

## MBERT, Albert Jenkins (1822-1878)

up in partnership with Reeks and with him laid out Carlisle
de and Robertson Terrace at Hastings on land belonging to the
vn. They also rebuilt Bodiam Church, Sussex (1853) and sub-
ed designs in the competition for the Government Offices. Humbert
ilt the chancel of the church at Whippingham, used by the Royal
ly when visiting Osborne (1854) and, when the church was
olished, rebuilt it (1860). Subsequently he designed for the Royal
ly the Mausoleum of the Duchess of Kent at Frogmore and that of
Prince Consort, and rebuilt Sandringham. FRIBA.

## ES, Sir Horace (1819-1887)

in Bucklersbury, London, the son of a solicitor. Articled to
Wallen, travelled in Italy and Greece and set up in independent
tice in London 1846. He was Surveyor to the Tufnell Park Estate:
Architect and Surveyor to the Corporation of London 1864-87.
ad a very large and prosperous practice, mostly devoted to public
dings, large markets, offices and shops, and is best known for his
in London, which included Smithfield Market (1866); Marshall
elgrove, Oxford Street (1870, completed by Octavius Hansard);
dhall Free Library and Museum, Basinghall Street (1873);
gsgate Market, Lower Thames Street (1875); Temple Bar
norial (1880); Leadenhall Market (1881); Guildhall School of
ic, John Carpenter Street (1885-87); and Tower Bridge (1886-94
J. Wolfe Barry). FRIBA. President of the RIBA 1881-84. Knighted
.

## ES, Owen (1809-1876)

in Thames Street, London, the son of a Welsh furrier. Educated
harterhouse School. Pupil of Lewis Vulliamy. Travelled on the
inent and in the Near East, where he studied Islamic architecture
rticular, 1830-33. His works included two houses in Kensington

Palace Gardens (1843-47); decoration of the Crystal Palace (1851);
St James' Concert Hall (1856); the crystal palace Bazaar (1857);
Osler's Gallery, Oxford Street, London (1858); and numerous
decorative works. He prepared designs for Crystal Palaces at Muswell
Hill and St Cloud, Paris, which were not carried out, and entered
several competitions unsuccessfully, including Birmingham Town
Hall (1830); Army and Navy Club (1847); Manchester Art Treasures
Exhibition (1856); the National Gallery (1866); and the Midland
Hotel, St Pancras Station (1868). Awarded the Gold Medal of the
RIBA 1856; the Order of King Leopold of the Belgians and the Order
of SS. Maurice and Lazaras. His publications include *Plans, elevations,
sections and details of the Alhambra*, 1836-45, and *The Grammar of
Ornament*, 1856.

## KEMP, George Meikle (1795-1844)

Born at Moorfoot, Midlothian, the son of a shepherd. Attended school
at Penicuik and worked at the farm where his father was employed.
Apprenticed to a master carpenter near Peebles 1809-13. From then
until c. 1830 he worked as a carpenter in Scotland, London and
France, at the same time studying architecture, much of it self-taught
from books. On his return to Edinburgh, became assistant to William
Burn, and in 1838, under an assumed name, won the competition for
the Scott Memorial. He died accidentally by drowning.

## KERR, Robert (1823-1904)

Born and educated in Aberdeen. District Surveyor of St James',
Westminster 1862-1902. His works include Dunsdale, Kent (1858);
Great Blake Hall, Essex (1860); National Provident Institution,
Gracechurch Street, London (1863); Bear Wood, Berks (1868); Ford
Manor, Surrey (1868); and Ascot Heath House (1868). His publications
which were more influential than his works, included the *Newleafe
discourses on the fine art architecture*, 1846; *The English Gentleman's
country house*, 1864; and *The consulting architect*, 1894. He was one of
the founders and the first President of the AA 1847-48; served on the
Council of the RIBA; Fellow of King's College, London, and then
Professor of the Art of Construction there. FRIBA.

## LEEMING, John (c. 1849-1931) and Joseph

Both articled to C. F. Luke Horsfall. Commenced practice in Halifax
together in 1872. Won First Premium in Edinburgh Municipal
Buildings competition, and Second in Lisbon Post and Telegraph
Offices. In 1881 won a premium in the Glasgow Municipal Offices
competition. Winners of the Admiralty and War Offices competition,
1884, although the project, highly criticized, was abandoned a year
later. Employed to design the extension to the Admiralty in Whitehall,
1891. Among their works are Kinloch Castle, for Sir George Bullough;
Market Halls at Leeds, Halifax and Oldham; the Queen Elizabeth
Grammar School, Halifax; and other schools and buildings in Yorkshire and Lancashire.

## LOCKWOOD, Henry Francis (1811-1878)

Born at Doncaster. Articled to P. Robinson of London and set up in
practice at Kingston-upon-Hull 1834. Moved to Bradford 1849, where
he joined William and Richard Mawson, with whom he remained in
partnership for many years. Lockwood was arbitrator to Bradford
Corporation for their street improvement programme, and he and
William Mawson were architects to Sir Titus Salt. Lockwood moved
to London in 1874. His work included Dent Cottage, Winterton,
Lincs (1830); Barclays Bank, Market Place, Boston, Lincs (1835); and
the City Temple, Holborn Viaduct, London (1873-74). His work in
Bradford, with Mawson, included St George's Hall (1851-53); The
Exchange, Market Street (1864-67); the Victoria Hotel (1867); the
Town Hall (1873); Manningham Mills, Lister Park (1873); Airedale
College (1874-77); the Bradford Club, Bank Street (1877); Kirkgate,
Darley Street and Godwin Markets (1877); they also designed Victoria

Chambers, Leeds; much of Saltaire (1850-76); the Mechanics Institute, Keighley, Yorks (1868); the Civil Service Stores, Strand, London (1876-77); and several churches including the Methodist Church, Harrogate, Yorks (1862) and St Stephen, Twickenham (1874).

## MACKINTOSH, Charles Rennie (1869-1928)

Son of a Police Superintendent. Educated Allan Glen's School, and at the Glasgow School of Art. Articled to John Honeyman and John Keppie in 1889. He won the Thomson Travelling Scholarship 1890 and was a member of the Glasgow Institute of Architects. His work in Glasgow included assistance to Keppie on the extension to the Glasgow Herald buildings in Mitchell Street (1893-95); St Cuthbert and Queen's Cross Church (1897-99); Glasgow School of Art (1897-99 and 1907-09, with his partners); Hill House, Helensburgh (1902); Willow Tea Room, Sauchiehall Street (1903); and tea rooms in Ingram Street (1900-11), and elsewhere; Scotland Street School (1904); 78 Derngate, Northampton (1916); and Squire Studio, Glebe Place, Chelsea (1920). FRIBA.

## NESFIELD, William Eden (1835-1888)

Son of William Nesfield the artist and landscape gardener. Educated at Eton. Became a pupil of William Burn 1851-53; of Anthony Salvin, his uncle, 1853-56; and for a short time of Viollet-le-Duc in Paris. After travelling in France and Italy with Norman Shaw, a fellow pupil of Burn, and later again by himself, he set up in practice in 1858 and from 1863 to 1876 shared office premises with Shaw. His work included Cloverley Hall, Salop (1862-70); Lodges in Regent's Park (1864) and Kew Gardens (1866); Kinmel Park (1866-68); Farnham Royal House and Church (1867-69 with Shaw); various works at Radwinter, Essex (1869-87); Lea Wood, Dethick (1870-76); and Loughton Hall, Essex (1878). In 1862 he published *Specimens of mediaeval architecture*.

## PAXTON, Sir Joseph (1801-1865)

Born at Milton Bryant, Beds, and educated at Woburn Free School. Appointed head gardener to the 6th Duke of Devonshire in 1826, and carried his activities far beyond the ordinary duties of such a position, importing many exotic plants, arranging entertainments, building conservatories, rock gardens, the Grand Canal and Emperor Fountain, and above all the Great Conservatory (1836-40) with Decimus Burton. The experience gained with this building prompted him to submit his famous design for the Crystal Palace in 1850. When the building was moved from Hyde Park to Sydenham it was re-erected under his supervision. He laid out the village of Edensor at Chatsworth, several parks including Birkenhead, and cemeteries including Cheylesmore, Coventry. He also designed several large houses including Mentmore, Bucks (1852-54) and Ferrières, outside Paris (1856). He prepared a project for an Exhibition Building at St Cloud, Paris (c. 1862 based on an earlier design of Owen Jones) and an arcade of glass and iron to encircle London called the 'Great Victorian Way', but nothing came of either of these schemes. Paxton was a director of several railway companies and Fellow of the Horticultural and Linnean Societies. Knighted 1851.

## PENNETHORNE, Sir James (1801-1871)

Born at Worcester. In 1820 entered the office of John Nash, who in 1822 placed him under Augustus Pugin to study Gothic architecture. Travelled on the Continent 1824-26 and then returned to Nash. In 1838 he joined Thomas Chawner as one of the architects to the Commissioners for Woods and Forests, and in 1845, when Chawner retired, became the sole holder of that position. In 1840 he was appointed Surveyor to the Land Revenue Department. He designed many large schemes for the Government, few of which were carried to completion; they included the layout of New Oxford Street, Endell

Street, Cranbourn Street, Commercial Street, Garrick St[...] Southwark Street and many others. He designed the Bazaar, St Jam[...] Street (1832); Southland Hall, Leicestershire; Dillington Ho[...] Ilminster; St Julian's, Sevenoaks; the Public Record Office, Chan[...] Lane; the Museum of Economic Geology (1851); the Library of Patent Office; and the University of London, Burlington Gard[...] (1866-69). He also laid out several parks including Kennington P[...] Lambeth (1841-51); and Victoria Park, Hackney (1842-45). FR[...] Received the Gold Medal of the RIBA 1865. Knighted 1870.

## PETO, Sir Samuel Morton (1809-1889)

Born at Cookham, Berkshire. Apprenticed to his uncle Henry P[...] a builder, and received lessons in draughtsmanship from Ge[...] Maddox, and Beazley. Spent three years in a carpenter's shop [...] later learned to lay bricks. In 1830 succeeded to his uncle's busi[...] with Thomas Grissell (1801-74), thus forming the firm of Grisse[...] Peto. They constructed many buildings of great importance, inclu[...] the Hungerford Market (1832-33); the Reform (1836), Conserva[...] (1840), and Oxford and Cambridge (1830) Clubs; sev[...] theatres; the Nelson Column; all the Great Western Railway w[...] between Hanwell and Langley (1840); and the Woolwich Gra[...] Dock. After Grissell & Peto's partnership dissolved in 1846[...] entered into a new partnership with Edgar Ladd Betts, which la[...] until 1872. They built numerous railways all over the world. Pet[...] in Parliament as a Liberal member for various constituencies 1847[...] Associate of the Institution of Civil Engineers 1839. Knighted 1[...]

## PHIPPS, Charles John (1835-1897)

Born in Bath. Articled to the local architects, Wilson and Fowler[...] up his own practice in 1857 and specialized in designing theat[...] These included the rebuilding of the Theatre at Bath (1863); The [...] Royal, Nottingham (1865); Repertory Theatre, Northampton (18[...] and in London, the Savoy Theatre (1881); Vaudeville Theatre (18[...] Lyric Theatre (1888); and Her Majesty's Theatre, Haymarket (18[...] Amongst his other work was the Passmore Edwards Libr[...] Southwark (1898). FSA, FRIBA.

## PLUMBE, Rowland (1838-1919)

Son of Samuel Plumbe. Educated privately and at University Coll[...] Articled to N. J. Cottingham, then to Cooper and Beck. Went to [...] United States in 1858 for two years. Had a large practice and ma[...] special study of Polytechnic Institutions, on which he prepare[...] report. His other work included, in London, the Bank of Cey[...] Ludgate Hill; the Royal National Orthopaedic Hospital, G[...] Portland Street; the YMCA building, Great Russell Street (19[...] the layout of Noel Park Estate, Wood Green; and some early Cou[...] flats in Nile Street, Shoreditch. He designed the churches of [...] Nicholas, Remenham, Berkshire (1870); St Mark's, Wood Gr[...] London (1889); and St John the Baptist, Loxwood, Sussex (1898); [...] several houses including Kneesworth Hall, Bassingham, Can[...] Joined the AA 1862 and was President 1871-72. FRIBA. Membe[...] the Council of the RIBA 1876. At one time was Master of the Pain[...] Stainers' Company.

## PRIOR, Edward Schroeder (1852-1932)

Son of a barrister. Educated Harrow, and Caius College, Cambri[...] Articled to Norman Shaw. His architectural work included the He[...] Martyn Memorial Hall, Cambridge (1887): the New Music Sch[...] Harrow School, Middx (1891); Pembroke College Mission Chu[...] Southwark, London (1892); The Barn, Exmouth, Devonshire (18[...] Zoology Laboratory, Cambridge (1901-04: later the School [...] Medicine); Voewood, Norfolk (1903-05); The Small House, [...] Lavant, Sussex (1912). His most famous work is probably the chu[...]

Andrew, Roker, Co. Durham (1906-07). Prior was a founder of
[Ar]t Workers' Guild, and Master in 1906: Secretary of the Arts
[C]rafts Exhibition Society 1902-17, and Vice-President in 1918.
[auth]or of several standard works on medieval architecture and a
[write]r of repute. He was made Slade Professor of Fine Art at
[Camb]ridge University 1912-32. FSA. Among his published works were
[His]*tory of Gothic art in England; The cathedral builders in England;*
*The mediaeval figure sculpture of England* (with Arthur Gardner).

**[PUG]IN, Augustus Welby Northmore (1812-1852)**
[Train]ed by his father Auguste-Charles Pugin, the architectural
[drau]ghtsman. In 1827 he worked with Wyatville at Windsor and
[desig]ned silver for Rundell. In 1830 he worked as a stage carpenter at
[Cove]nt Garden and then opened a joinery business of his own. This
[faile]d and he returned to stage work. After the death of his father and
[his] wife in 1832 he travelled in England and abroad, eventually
[settli]ng in 1835 in Salisbury, where he began his architectural practice
[at] St Marie's Grange, his own house. Almost immediately he was
[empl]oyed by Barry to prepare detailed drawings for King Edward VI
[Gram]mar School and later the Houses of Parliament. He became a
[Rom]an Catholic in 1835 and much of his subsequent work was for the
[chu]rch. Among his more important secular commissions were Alton
[Tow]ers, Staff (1837-52); Scarisbrook Hall (1837-45); completion of
[Osco]tt College (from 1837); The Grange, Ramsgate, his own house
[(from] 1843); Ratcliffe College, Leics (1834-44); St Patrick's College,
[May]nooth, Eire (1845-52); Lismore, Eire (1849-50). His publications
[inclu]de *Contrasts; or, a parallel between the noble edifices of the 14th and
[15th] centuries, 1836; The true principles of Pointed or Christian
[arch]itecture, 1841; An apology for the Revival of Christian architec-
[ture] in England, 1843;* and other books, articles and pamphlets.

**[PU]GIN, Edward Welby (1834-1875)**
[Elde]st son of A. W. N. Pugin. Trained under his father and after his
[deat]h found himself at the age of seventeen in control of a large
[prac]tice and the completion of many of his father's works. For some
[time] he was in partnership with Ashlin, a former pupil, and with
[Jame]s Murray. During his fourteen years of practice he carried out
[man]y works, chiefly Roman Catholic churches. His secular works
[inclu]de the completion of Scarisbrick Hall and Chirk Castle for his
[fathe]r: the Château of the Bishop of Bruges (1861); the restoration of
[the] Palace at Mayfield, Sussex; Harrington House, Leamington;
[Grant]on Manor; Croston Hall, Leeds; and Carlton Towers, Yorks.

**[REN]DEL, James Meadows (1802-1856)**
[Wor]ked in the west country, where he was noticed by Telford, who
[emp]loyed him to lay out and construct several major roads in Devon
[and] Cornwall. Later he built a cast-iron bridge near Plymouth for the
[Earl] of Morley (completed 1827), and a floating steam-bridge over the
[estu]ary of the River Dart. He subsequently used similar floating bridges
[at D]evonport, Saltash and elsewhere. In 1838 he moved to London,
[and] became involved in numerous works including the construction
[of th]e Birkenhead and Great Grimsby Docks, and of the Birkenhead,
[Lan]cashire and Cheshire Junction Railway Line. He also built several
[railw]ay lines in India. President of the Institution of Civil Engineers
[1852]-53. Prepared many reports for the Government on various
[engi]neering topics including drainage and other public works in
[Engla]nd. FRS.

**[RU]MIEU, Robert Lewis (1814-1877)**
[Pu]pil of Benjamin Wyatt. In partnership with A. D. Gough 1836-48.
[He w]as surveyor to the Gas Light & Coke Company's estate at Beckton,
[the] French Hospital Estate and to several other estates in and near
[Lon]don. His works were numerous and include St Mark's Church and
[pars]onage, Tunbridge Wells; Victoria Ironworks, Isle of Dogs;

St Michael's Church, Islington; the Prudential Assurance Office,
Ludgate Hill; Woodall's carriage manufactory, Orchard Street;
33-35 Eastcheap; 'The Lymes', Stanmore; 'The Cedars', Harrow
Weald; 'The Priory', Roehampton; and 'The Priory', Wimbledon.
He also did much work for Crosse & Blackwell, and with Gough laid
out Milner Square, Islington.

**SCOTT, Sir George Gilbert (1811-1878)**
Born at Gawcott, Bucks, the son of the Rev. Thomas Scott. Articled
to James Edmeston 1827 and studied drawing under George Maddox.
Worked for a short time with the builders, Peto & Grissell, and with
Henry Roberts and Sampson Kempthorne, before setting up in practice
with W. B. Moffatt, a partnership which ended in 1845. During this
period he became interested in Gothic and was later asked to restore
several cathedrals. His practice was enormous and has been said to
have involved more than 750 commissions. The best known are
probably Reading Gaol, Berks (1842-44); Chapel and Library of
Exeter College, Oxford (1856-59); Kelham Hall, Northants (1858-62);
the Albert Memorial, Kensington, London (1863-72); the Home and
Foreign Offices, London (1868-72 with Matthew Digby Wyatt); and
the Midland Hotel, St Pancras Station, London (1868-73). He prepared designs for several competitions, of which those for Hamburg
Town Hall were particularly influential. His publications include
*Remarks on secular and domestic architecture, present and future* and
*Personal and professional recollections.* Knighted 1872. President of the
RIBA 1873. RA, FRIBA.

**SCOTT, Major-General Henry Young Darracott (c. 1822-1883)**
Educated Royal Military Academy, Woolwich, and commissioned into
the Royal Engineers, 1840. Instructor in surveying and practical
astronomy at Chatham, and examiner in military topography for the
Military Education Department at the War Office. Worked at South
Kensington, and, on death of Captain Francis Fowke in 1865, took
over as architect to the Department of Science and Art, completing
Fowke's work on the South Kensington Museum. His own buildings
include the Science Schools (1872), the Cast Courts, and the Art
Library (1882) of the Victoria and Albert Museum. Architect of the
Royal Albert Hall, opened 1871, and is said to have refused a knight-
hood. Retired from the army, 1871, with rank of Major-General.
In 1874 he was one of the seven originators of the International
Exhibition Co-operative Wine Society (which still flourishes). Dismissed from South Kensington by the Office of Works after completing
the Art Library. 'General Scott, like other of his professional brethren,
did not escape official opposition, and so wearing did this become at
last, that his family know that it prematurely killed him' (*Br*, 5 May
1883, p. 618). CB, FRS.

**SEDDON, John Pollard (1827-1860)**
Born in London, the son of Thomas Seddon, the cabinet-maker
Educated at Bedford Grammar School. Articled to T. L. Donaldson
1848-51. Went on a continental tour and on his return set up in
practice in London. In 1852 he entered into partnership at Llandaff
with John Prichard, the Cathedral and Diocesan architect of Llandaff,
and after Prichard's death succeeded to his position. In 1862 he
married, and set up an office at 12 Park Street, Westminster. Between
1885 and 1904 he was in partnership with John Coates Carter of
Cardiff. Seddon's work with Prichard included designing and restoring
numerous churches, schools and parsonages and other buildings in
Wales, and designing Ettington Park, Warwickshire (1858-62). They
also submitted designs in competition for the War and Foreign
Offices. With E. W. Godwin he designed a People's Palace on the
Embankment (1887); with H. R. Gough, St Paul's Church, Hammer-
smith (1882-89); with L. Harvey, the Monumental Halls; and with
J. C. Carter further works in Wales and an entry in competition for

the Birmingham Assize Courts. Seddon also designed numerous houses and other buildings himself, including the University College of Wales, Aberystwyth, begun originally as a hotel in 1864; and submitted a much publicized design in competition for the Law Courts. ARIBA 1852. FRIBA 1860. Hon. Secretary RIBA (with C. F. Hayward) for ten years. Founder member of the AA 1847. His publications included *Progress in art and architecture*, 1852, and a biography of his father.

## SHAW, Richard Norman (1831-1912)

Born in Edinburgh. Educated there and in Newcastle. Articled to William Burn c. 1846. Studied at the Royal Academy Schools, where he was awarded the Gold Medal and the Travelling Scholarship 1854. Travelled on the Continent and on return worked for a short time in Salvin's office before in 1858 becoming a draughtsman with G. E. Street. In 1862 set up in practice in London at 30 Argyll Street sharing an office with W. E. Nesfield. They collaborated very closely till 1868, when Shaw began to work independently, and established a very big and flourishing private practice, specializing in large town and country houses. His work included Leys Wood, Groombridge, Kent (1868); Grimsdyke, Harrow Weald, Middx (1872); Albert Hall Mansions, Kensington, London (1873); the layout and planning of Bedford Park, London (1875-78); Wispers, Midhurst, Sussex (1876); Swan House, Chelsea (1876); Merrist Wood, Worplesdon, Surrey (1877); Lowther Lodge, Kensington, London (1879); Adcote, Salop (1879); New Scotland Yard, London (1888); 170 (1888) and 185 (1890) Queen's Gate, London; Bryanston, near Blandford, Dorset (1890); Alliance Assurance premises, St James's Street, London (1903 with Ernest Newton); and the Piccadilly Hotel, London (1905-08). Shaw was a member of the RIBA for a time, but did not become a Fellow, and resigned in 1872. He was not in sympathy with the policies of the Institute and twice refused the offer of the Royal Gold Medal. His publications included *Architectural sketches from the Continent*, 1858. RA.

## SMIRKE, Sir Robert (1781-1867)

Born in London, educated Apsley School, Beds. A pupil of Sir John Soane for a few months, and of Bush, a surveyor. Entered the Royal Academy Schools 1796, and was awarded the Gold Medal 1799. Travelled on the Continent 1801-05. His architectural career began in 1806, and developed into an extensive public and private practice before his retirement in 1845. He was Architect to the Board of Trade 1807; one of the three Board of Works Architects 1813; Surveyor to the Inner Temple 1814; and Treasurer of the Royal Academy 1820-50. His immense output of work included Walberton House, Sussex (1803); Lowther Castle, Westmorland (1806-11); Eastnor Castle, Herefs (1812); St Philip, Salford, Lancs (1822-25); St Mary, Wyndham Place, London (1823); the British Museum, London (1823-47; the Reading Room by Sydney Smirke); St Anne, Wandsworth, London (1824); the Royal College of Physicians, Trafalgar Square, London (1824-27; additions since; now Canada House); rebuilding of central part of the Custom House, Lower Thames Street, London (1825); the east wing of Somerset House, London (1830-31); the Oxford and Cambridge Club, Pall Mall, London (1835-38 with Sydney Smirke): and Paper Buildings, King's Bench Walk, London (1838 and 1848 with Sydney Smirke). Knighted 1832. A member of the London Improvements Commission 1845-c. 1848: Received RIBA Gold Medal 1853. He published *Specimens of Continental architecture*, 1806, and *A review of a battalion of infantry*, 1809. RA, FSA, FRS, HON. FRIBA.

## SMIRKE, Sydney (1798-1877)

Brother of Sir Robert Smirke, in whose office he trained and with whom he worked in close collaboration. Succeeded his brother as Surveyor

of the Inner Temple 1828; was Clerk of the Works at St J Palace 1828-32, and later Surveyor to the Duchy of Lancaste work included the Town Hall, Shoreham, Sussex (1830; built Custom House); additions to Bethlem Hospital (1838-40); the near Uckfield, Sussex (1838); the Conservative Club, 74 St J Street, London (1843-45 with George Basevi); the T Mausoleum, St Mary, Northiam, Sussex (1846); St John the B Loughton, Essex (1846); the Reading Room, British Mu London (1852-57); Brookwood Cemetery, Surrey (1854 wit William Tite); Dr Johnson's Buildings, Inner Temple, L (1857-58); additions to Burlington House, Piccadilly, London ( and King Edward's School, Wormley, Surrey (1867). He receiv Gold Medal of the RIBA 1860. Professor of Architecture at th 1861-65, and Treasurer 1871. He established the Architects' evolent Society in 1852 and was its President until 1877. His cations included *Suggestions for the architectural improvement Western Park of London*, 1834; *A mode of assisting the eye in the perception of colour in pictures*, 1856; and *The professional life of Cockerell*, 1863. RA, FSA, FRIBA.

## SPIERS, Richard Phené (1838-1916)

Born at Oxford. Educated at King's College School. From 18 1861 he was a student in the atelier Questel of the École des Arts, Paris. Returning to England he became assistant to Sir Ma Digby Wyatt. Attended classes at the Royal Academy, where h the silver and gold medals 1863. Travelled again on the Continer in the Near East. In 1866 he assisted William Burges with the aration of his design for the Law Courts. His executed works in Umberslade Hall, Warwicks; the restoration of churches at Han Poyle and Weston-on-the-Green, Oxon; a house on Chelsea emi ment for Lord Monkswell; two board-schools in London; alterations and additions to Beckett Hospital, Barnsley. In conjun with M. Tronquois of Paris he designed Impney Court, Droitwich. His publications included *Architectural drawing*, and *Architecture East and West*, 1905. President AA 1867-68. S on the Council RIBA 1888-1903; Master of the RA archite school 1870-1906.

## STEVENS, Alfred George (1818-1875)

Born at Blandford, Dorset, the son of a house painter. Studied Naples, Rome, Florence, Milan and Venice 1833-42, at one working under Thorwaldsen. Taught architectural drawing, spective and modelling at the School of Design, London 184 Principal artist to the iron founders H. E. Hoole. His work incl besides many grates and stoves for that firm, the decoration on t the railings in front of the British Museum; the Wellington Monur and mosaics, St Paul's Cathedral; and the decoration of se houses including Dorchester House, Park Lane, London; Deysbrook, West Derby, Liverpool. Among designs which wer carried out were schemes for decorating the British Museum Rea Room; for frescoes in the Houses of Parliament; and for a waiting room at Paddington Station.

## STEVENSON, John James (1832-1908)

Born in Glasgow and educated at the High School and Unive there. Trained for the Ministry in Edinburgh but after a visit to decided to become an architect and in 1856 entered the offic David Bryce and in 1858 that of Sir G. G. Scott. After a further on the Continent became a partner of Campbell Douglas in Glas In 1870 he set up in partnership with E. R. Robson. Stevenson desi many houses in the 'Queen Anne' style in Kensington and elsew including 'The Red House', 140 Bayswater Road (1871) and n schools for the London School Board. He also designed church Monzie (1868); Crieff (1881); Perth (1883); Stirling (1900);

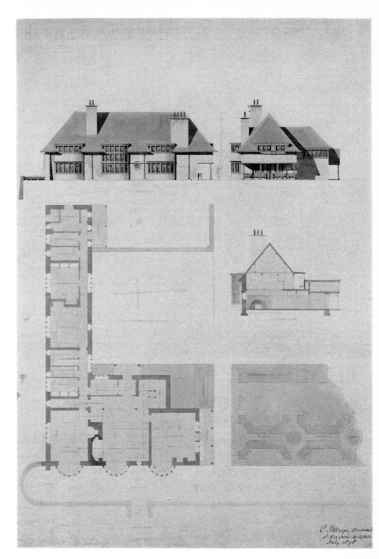

CENTRAL LIBRARY – FINE ART LIBRARY

ow (1900); and several country houses including Westoe, South
ds (1868 and 1874); Ken Hill, Norfolk (1888); and Oatlands
, Weybridge (1893). He also designed the interior fittings of
al steam ships including the SS Orient. His publications included
e architecture, 1879. FSA, FRIBA.

## EET, George Edmund (1824-1881)

at Woodford, Essex, the son of a solicitor. Pupil of O. B. Carter
inchester and in 1844 of G. G. Scott, with whom he worked for
years. Travelled on the Continent in 1850 and 1851. Settled in
at Oxford. In 1853 visited N. Italy and 1854 N. Germany. Set
n office in London at 33 Montague Place in 1855, eventually
ng to 14 Cavendish Place by 1870. Made a tour of Spain 1861-63.
t's works include numerous churches, particularly the Crimean
orial Church at Constantinople (1864-69): All Saints, Boyne
Maidenhead (1854-57); St James the Less, Victoria, London
-61); and St Mary at Holmbury St Mary (1873). His secular
ns included a design for the National Gallery (1866); additions
unecht, Aberdeen; and his most famous work the Law Courts
1866), for which he is recorded to have made 3,000 drawings.
ublications include *Brick and marble architecture in Italy*, 1855,
*Some account of Gothic architecture in Spain*, 1865. FRIBA. Vice-
dent RIBA and received Gold Medal 1874. RA. Professor of
recture at the RA and Treasurer 1879. FSA.

## TERSALL, George (1817-1849)

in London, the son of Richard Tattersall. Showed an early
est in painting and when only 18 years old published an illustrated
book to the Lake District. Apprenticed to an architect and
ually set up by himself at 52 Pall Mall. Exhibited and wrote
works on sporting subjects using the pseudonym 'Wildrake'
many of his buildings were connected with that topic. They
ded stables for several famous sportsmen. His project for the
and Navy Club (1848) appears to have been the only major
n he prepared. His publications included *Sporting architecture*,

## LON, Samuel Sanders (1812-1873)

rench descent, born at Greenwich, London. Articled to George
. Worked in the office of George Porter in Bermondsey. Set up
ivate practice c. 1840. He had a large and successful practice,
included much church building and restoration in the High
rian Gothic style. He designed, laid out, and built the village of
tanworth, Co. Durham (1863) including the Church of St James,
icarage and Schools. His other work included Tortworth Court,
(1850-52); Christ Church, Croydon, Surrey (1851-52); St James,
aston, Birmingham (1852); Almshouses (1858) and School (1860)
uth Weald, Essex; St Mark, Silvertown, London (1861-62);
ham Hall, Hants (1860); Bestwood Lodge, Notts (1862); St Mary,
g, London (1866-73); and St Stephen, Rosslyn Hill, Hampstead,
on (1876). He was an early member of the RIBA, and served on
ouncil. FRIBA.

## MSON, Alexander (1817-1875)

n as 'Greek' Thomson. Born at Balfour in Stirlingshire, one of
y children. Went to Glasgow c. 1824, and there worked in the
s of Robert Foote, and John Baird the elder. Between 1849 and
he was in partnership with John Baird the younger, and from 1857
71 with his own brother George. His practice, which was almost
ly in Glasgow, included 3-4 Dunlop Street (1849); Holmwood,
art (1856); Walmer Crescent and Queen's Park Terrace (1857);
d Presbyterian Church (1858); Grecian Building, Sauchiehall
(1865); Northpark Terrace (1866); Great Western Terrace
); and the Egyptian Halls, Union Street (1871). He was elected
ent of the Glasgow Institute of Architects 1871.

## VOYSEY, Charles Francis Annesley (1857-1941)

Born at Hessle, near Kingston-upon-Hull, the son of a clergyman.
His grandfather, Annesley Voysey, had built lighthouses and bridges.
Moved to London in 1871 and educated at Dulwich College. Articled
to J. P. Seddon for one year and then joined Saxon Snell and later
George Devey. Set up in independent practice in London in 1882. He
produced numerous designs for the applied arts besides his archi-
tectural work. This included The Cottage, Bishops Itchington,
Warwickshire (1888); 14 South Parade, Bedford Park, London (1891);
14-16 Hans Road, Kensington, London (1891); Annesley Lodge,
Hampstead, London (1895); several houses in the Lake District,
including Broadleys, Windermere (1898); The Orchard, Chorleywood,
Hertfordshire, his own house (1900); The Homestead, Frinton
(1905); and Holly Mount, Knotty Green, Bucks (1906-07). He was
Master of the Art Workers' Guild 1924, one of the first Designers for
Industry of the Royal Society of Arts. FRIBA, and received the Gold
Medal of the RIBA 1940. His publications included *'Ideas in things',
the arts connected with building;* 1909, and *Individuality,* 1915; and many
articles and lectures.

## WARING, John Burley (1823-1875)

Born in Dorset. Apprenticed to H. E. Kendall 1840 and later worked
in the offices of A. Poynter, Laing of Birkenhead, Sir Robert Smirke
and David Mocatta. Studied under T. Couture in Paris 1850 and 1852.
Appointed Superintendent of ornamental art and sculpture in
Manchester Art Treasures Exhibition of 1857. Superintendent of
architectural gallery in International Exhibition London 1862. Chief
Commissioner of Exhibition of Works of Art at Leeds in 1868. He
produced several designs for buildings, none of which is known to
have been built; they included various shops, a club house, a tower to
commemorate the 1851 Exhibition, a design for a National Institute
of Art and Science and several houses. Waring is best known for his
publications which included *The arts connected with architecture*,
1858; *Masterpieces of industrial art and sculpture at the International
Exhibition 1862*, 1863; and *Illustrations of architecture and ornament*,
1865.

## WATERHOUSE, Alfred (1830-1905)

Born in Liverpool, educated at Tottenham. Articled to Richard Lane
of Manchester. Travelled in France, Germany and Italy. He first
practised in Manchester, then moved to London, where he established
an enormous practice, in which he was joined in partnership by his
son, Paul, in 1891. Waterhouse was Architect to the Prudential
Assurance Company for many years, and built offices for them in most
large provincial towns. His work included the Assize Courts,
Manchester (1859-64); the Town Hall, Manchester (1868); Tree
Court, Caius College, Cambridge (1870); Municipal Buildings,
Reading, Berks (1872-75); Natural History Museum, London (1873-
81); the Seamen's Orphanage, Liverpool (1874); Prudential Assurance
Company's head office, Holborn, London (1879 and 1899-1906);
St Paul's School, Hammersmith, London (1881-85); The Town Hall,
Hove, Sussex (1882); Buckhold House, Berks (1884-85); the National
Liberal Club, Whitehall Place, London (1885-07); Royal Infirmary,
Liverpool (1887); Metropole Hotel, Brighton, Sussex (1888); Royal
Institution of Chartered Surveyors, Great George Street, London
(1896-98, additions by Paul Waterhouse); and University College
Hospital, London (1897-1906, completed by Paul Waterhouse). He
won the Paris Exhibition Grand Prix for Architecture 1867. FRIBA.
Received the Gold Medal of the RIBA 1878, and was President 1888-
91. RA.

## WEBB, Philip Speakman (1831-1915)

Son of an Oxford doctor. Apprenticed to John Billing of Reading.
Worked with Bidlake and Lovatt in Wolverhampton, before returning
to Oxford to work with G. E. Street, where he first met William

Morris. Travelled with him on the Continent. Both he and Morris moved with Street to London in 1856. Webb was naturally retiring and refused to allow his name to be put forward for the RA and never became a member of a professional institution. Furthermore, with one exception, he did not allow his works to be published. They included Red House, Bexley Heath, Kent (1859); Shops, Worship Street, London (1862); house at Arisaig, Scotland (begun 1863); a house at East Barnet (1868, now demolished); Solicitors' Offices, Lincoln's Inn Fields (1868); 1 Palace Green, London (1868); Joldwynds, Surrey; Church at Brampton; Rounton Grange, Yorks (all early 1870s); Smeaton Manor (1877); New Place, Welwyn (1878); Clouds, East Knoyle (from 1877); and Standen, East Grinstead (1891-94).

## WIGHTWICK, George (1802-1872)

Born at Alyn Bank, Mold, Flint. Educated at Wolverhampton Grammar School and Lord's School, Tooting. Articled to Edward Lapidge and visited Italy 1825-26: then worked for Sir John Soane as a kind of secretary-companion. Went into partnership with John Foulston at Plymouth in 1829 and independently, after Foulston's retirement, until 1851. His work included the Guildhall and the Grammar School, Helston, Cornwall (1834); the Devon & Cornwall Female Orphanage, Plymouth (1834); St Michael, Bude, Cornwall (1835); the Esplanade, Plymouth (1836); the South Devon and East Cornwall Hospital (1836); Plymouth Town Hall (1839-40); St John's Chapel, Pendarves House, Treslothan, Cornwall (1841); St Mary, Portreath, Cornwall (1841); St Luke, Tideford, Cornwall (1845); Holy Trinity, Plymouth (1845); and several buildings in which he co-operated with Foulston. He was the author of many books, including *Select views of Roman antiquities*, 1827; *Remarks on theatres*, 1832; *The Palace of architecture*, 1840; and *Hints to young architects*, 1846.

## WYATT, Sir Matthew Digby (1820-1877)

Born at Rowde, near Devizes, the younger brother of T. H. Wyatt, to whom he was articled. Travelled on the Continent 1844-46. In 1849 he reported to the Society of Arts on an industrial exhibition held in Paris and in 1851 was appointed Secretary to the Executive Committee for the Great Exhibition. In 1855 he became Surveyor to the East India Company. Wyatt's work included the Byzantine, English Gothic, Italian, Pompeian and Renaissance Courts at the Crystal Palace, re-erected at Sydenham, London (1854); Paddington Station, London (1854-55, in association with I. K. Brunel); Chapel at Warley Barracks, Little Warley, Essex (1857); Royal Engineers' Crimean War Memorial, Chatham, Kent (1861); Fernery in the gardens of Ashridge House, Herts (1864); Addenbroke's Hospital, Cambridge (1864-65); Possingworth Manor, Sussex (1866); the Rothschild Mausoleum, Jewish Cemetery, West Ham, London (1867); the courtyard of the former India Office, Government Offices, Whitehall, London (1867); Oldlands, Herron's Ghyll, Sussex (1869). His many published works included *Specimens of the geometrical mosaics of the Middle Ages*, 1848; *The industrial arts of the nineteenth century*, 1851-53; *Metalwork and its artistic design*, 1852; *Illuminated manuscripts as illustrative of the arts of design*, 1860; *The history of the manufacture of clocks*, 1868; and *An architect's notebook in Spain*, 1972. He was Hon. Secretary to the RIBA 1855-59; Vice-President, and received the Gold Medal 1866. Awarded the Telford Medal of the Institute of Civil Engineers, and foreign honours. First Slade Professor of Fine Arts at Cambridge. President of the Graphic Society.

## WYATT, Thomas Henry (1807-1880)

Born in Ireland, the son of a Police Magistrate. Educated privately and in Brussels. Articled to Philip Hardwick. In 1838 he set up in practice and was for a time in partnership with David Brandon. Wyatt was Honorary Architect to the Institution of Civil Engineers, the Athenaeum Club, the Middlesex Hospital, and the Governess Benevolent Society: Consulting Architect to the Commissioners Lunacy; the Incorporated Church Building Society; the Salisbury Diocesan Church Building Society. His practice was very large included much church building and restoration, particularly Wiltshire. His other works included the Assize Court (1835) Roundway Hospital (1851), both at Devizes, Wilts; St Andrew Bethnal Green, London (1841 with Brandon); SS. Mary and Nicholas Wilton, Wilts (1843 with Brandon); Orchardleigh Park, Som (1858); Garrison Church of St George, Woolwich, London (1863) Exchange Buildings, Liverpool (1865); Holy Trinity, Fonthill Gifford Wilts (1866); St Peter, Wimblington, Cambs (1874); the Manor House, North Perrott, Som (1878); Knightsbridge Barracks, London (1878-79); and the southern part of Brompton Hospital, Fulham Road, London (1879-82). President of the Architects' Benevolent Society: Vice-President of the Architectural Society. FRIBA. President of the RIBA 1870, and received Gold Medal 1873.

# Catalogue

## 1 National Buildings

# The Houses of Parliament

The Palace of Westminster, by the 1830s, was a haphazard collection of buildings of all dates, the largest of which was the great medieval Hall with, to the east, St Stephen's Chapel, in which the Commons met. During the 18th century William Kent produced plans for a Palladian building (a number of his drawings are in the Museum's collection), and in the early 19th century Sir John Soane made additions around the House of Lords. Almost everything, except the Hall and parts of St Stephen's Chapel and Cloister, was destroyed by fire during the night of 16 October 1834.

Parliament became homeless, and immediate surveys were made to see if anything could be rebuilt; in fact, certain portions including the Painted Chamber, were fitted out as temporary accommodation. This was not satisfactory, and, although Robert Smirke prepared plans for rebuilding, in June 1835 a Committee decided 'That it is expedient that the design for the rebuilding of the Houses of Parliament be left open to general competition, and that the style of the building be either Gothic or Elizabethan.' The selection of these architectural styles was no doubt influenced by the neighbouring Abbey, the rescued Hall, and perhaps because at that time Gothic was thought to be a peculiarly English form.

At first it was announced that the various competition designs were to be submitted by 1 November 1835, but after complaints from architects about the lack of time given to them, this date was changed to 1 December. From the entries expected the judges were charged to select no fewer than three nor more than five, and to be prepared to state 'the grounds upon which the propriety of such selection and classification is founded'. Conditions were laid down also as to the accommodation which had to be provided.

In spite of having only a few weeks in which to prepare the designs for what was obviously to be the most important architectural commission in this country for the century, 97 sets of designs, amounting to well over 1,000 different drawings, were received. From the first Charles Barry was tipped as the favourite. 'After much consultation' Barry was chosen as architect, a choice which was not received without anger, suspicion, rancour and argument. Barry had asked a young man, Augustus Pugin to draw in the Gothic detailing and ornamentation on the designs he submitted, and their collaboration has ever since been a subject of argument.

Before any building began, Barry made certain alterations to his plans, and according to his critics added elements which had appeared in those of rival architects. As the work on the embankment along the river was

not commenced until 1837, nor the first stones laid before 1840, the Houses of Parliament must be considered Victorian, and also the greatest and most splendid building of the Queen's reign. The House of Lords was ready for occupation by 1847, and the House of Commons by 1852.

As architect Barry did not have a straightforward commission. For one thing he had to contend with the ever-watchful Commons, as well as with a Committee set up under Prince Albert, which had decided that 'so important and national a work as the erection of the Houses of Parliament, affords an opportunity which ought not to be neglected of encouraging, not only the higher, but every subordinate branch of Art in this country'. This Committee chose particularly to experiment in fresco, a form of painting which had never proved popular or successful in England, and which turned out to be singularly unfortunate and a source of trouble, since, almost as soon as these frescoes were painted, they began to deteriorate. Barry was also plagued by a Dr Reid, who managed to gain the support of Parliament for a patent and untried system of ventilation, which soon threatened to swamp the entire building. By the beginning of 1860 the building had cost £2,198,099, a sum which did not include the frescoes and sculpture, for which a further £41,838 had been paid.

Apart from Pugin, who designed many of the interior fittings such as the throne, the wall-papers, furniture, candelabra, and even such minor pieces as coat-hooks, many of the best-known mid-Victorian artists provided other decoration. These include paintings by Maclise, Dyce, Cope, Horsley, and Herbert, and sculpture by Gibson, Philip, John Thomas, J. E. Thomas, Macdowell, Bell, Baily, Foley, Marshall, Theed, Carew, Woodington, J. S. Westmacott and others.

After the death of Sir Charles Barry the work was carried on by his son Edward M. Barry. The younger Barry had the misfortune to be subjected to the activities of the philistine First Commissioner of Works, Acton Smee Ayrton, in 1870; activities which brought the whole architectural profession firmly on to Barry's side.

The Commissioner had decided that the Office of Works should take a more direct part in the various building works undertaken by the Government and, as a result, Barry was told, as far as the Houses of Parliament were concerned, to hand over the contract drawings and plans 'and all other papers necessary for affording a complete knowledge of the building, and of the works carried on in connection therewith'. To Barry, the First Commissioner's letter appeared to dismiss him from the appointment as architect to the Palace, and he protested. The reply from the Office of

Works did no more than coldly to state the First Commissioner had 'not though necessary to enter into any discussion of topics raised in your letter . . . based u assumptions which he does not recogn and repeated the demand for all the drawi

Barry wrote back that he considered letter to Ayrton at least 'worthy of a re and in the absence of one, he asked the Commissioner for further information resp ing his intentions. With respect to drawings and papers, he continued, these into two categories. 'The first comprises drawings &c., prepared by myself and in office during the last ten years. The sec class contains the drawings &c., made du the lifetime of my father. Many of these invaluable to me, being by his own hand, they constitute his only bequest to me at death; I therefore value them accordir and regard them as a sacred deposit cannot believe that the First Commissio will seek to deprive me of this much-pr inheritance . . .'

Ayrton was not going to put up with sort of nonsense, and told Barry that i felt that some of the drawings could considered a 'sacred deposit', then he better make out a list of them, which l Ayrton—would consider. Until Barry i cated that he was prepared to hand over drawings Ayrton declined to enter into negotiations 'relating to your future emp ment'. Barry was not to be intimida however, especially as Ayrton's high-han action was being greatly condemned in architectural press, which displayed absolu no fondness for the First Commissio Barry asked the RIBA for advice, and rece the support of the Council, which decla he hastened to tell Ayrton, 'that by use custom, all the drawings and papers o architect remain his sole property.' Ba therefore, offered to make tracings for Office of Works, if he were allowed to re the originals. The immediate result was Barry found that Ayrton 'abruptly termina his official connection with the Houses Parliament, and he was also told that the Officers of the Crown had advised Ay that the contract plans and elevations other papers did not belong to the archi but were the property of the Crown, so h them over, please. Moreover, consultat then being conducted between the Offic Works and a Committee concerning Central Hall of the Palace were of 'no conc to Barry, and Ayrton 'declined to enter any discussion' with him concerning matter. Barry continued to fight against First Commissioner's demand for the dr ings, but in the end was forced to give in, during November 1870 Ayrton learned 'w satisfaction' that Barry had decided to h over the documents requested.

Sir Charles Barry

Model of the central octagon tower of the Palace of Westminster. c. 1857
*Plaster* 26 × 9¾ × 9¾ (66 × 24.7 × 24.7)
Lent from the Palace of Westminster


Model of the Victoria Tower of the Palace of Westminster. 1857
*Plaster* 30 × 7 × 7 (76 × 17.7 × 17.7)
Lent from the Palace of Westminster

Barry's son Edward, lecturing to the RIBA in February 1858 on the Palace of Westminster, exhibited 'carefully executed' models by Mabey, which are probably these. In a report concerning the model of the Admiralty in 1885, the *Building News* reminded its readers that Barry 'when building the Houses of Parliament, had almost every part made out in model previous to its execution'.

These models of the two towers (there was also a third, of the Clock Tower) were given to the Board of Works in 1916 by a grandson of Sir Charles Barry, provided they were placed in the Houses of Parliament, 'where they can at times be seen by the public' (P.R.O. Works 11/224, information supplied by Mr M. H. Port).

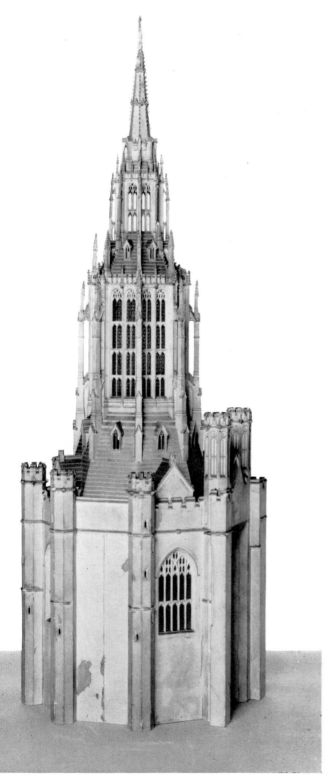

**3** Sir Charles Barry
Elevation of the Palace of Westminster to Old Palace Yard,
with plans of the ground and first floors. On paper water-
marked 1850
*Pencil, pen and ink and wash* $21\frac{1}{4} \times 28\frac{1}{2}$ (54 × 72.3)
Works 29/297
Lent from the Public Record Office

**4** Sir Charles Barry
Contract drawing for the central tower of the Palac[e]
Westminster, elevation and section
*Dated* Westminster Ap. 19. 1850 Ap. 2nd 1851. Insc[ribed]
*with scale*
*Pen and ink wash* 29 × 21 (73 × 53.4)
Works 29/1623
Lent from the Public Record Office

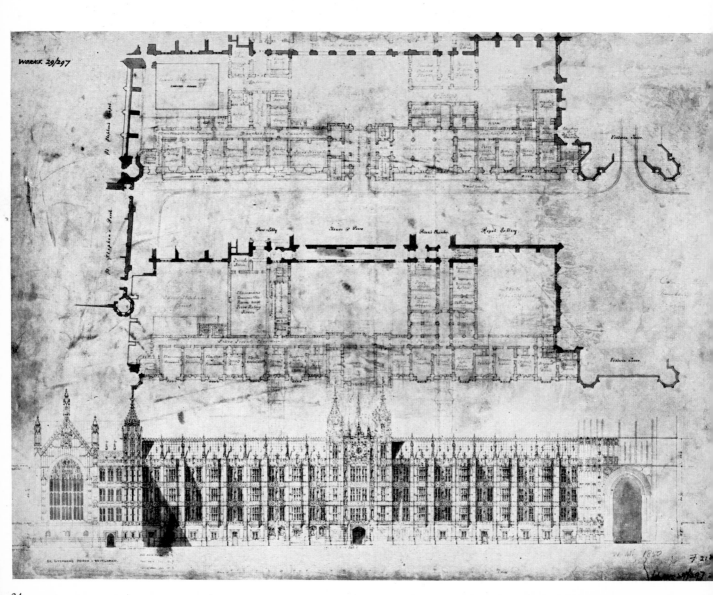

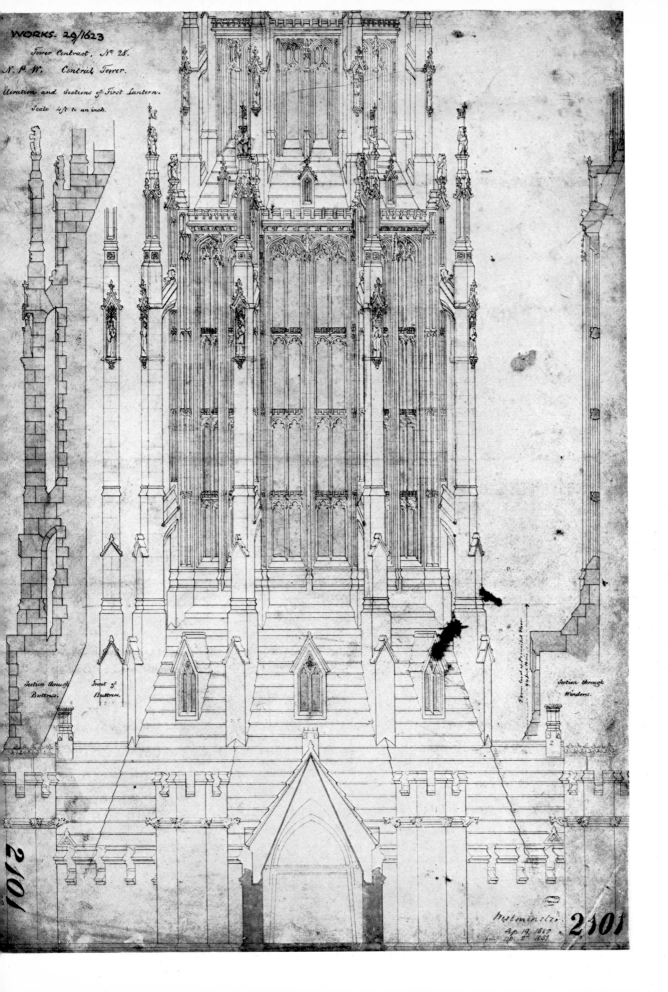

WORKS. 29/1623

Tower Contract, Nº 28.

N. P. W.   Central Tower.

Elevation and Sections of First Lantern.

Scale 4 ft to an inch.

Section through
Buttress.

Front of
Buttress.

Section through
Window.

2101

2101

Westminster
Ap. 19. 1852
Ap. 2ª. 1853

35

**5** Sir Charles Barry
Interior of the House of Lords.
c. 1836-37
*Pen and ink* $16\frac{1}{4} \times 16\frac{7}{8}$ (41.3 × 42.9)
E.67-1912, given by Sir Albert
Richardson, PRA
Victoria and Albert Museum

**5A** Interior of the House of Commons.
c. 1836-37
*Pen and ink* $15\frac{1}{2} \times 21\frac{3}{8}$ (39.3 × 54.3)
E.68-1912, given by Sir Albert
Richardson, PRA
Victoria and Albert Museum

These two drawings are tracings by
John Gibson from designs by Sir
Charles Barry. Gibson (1817-1892) became Barry's pupil in 1835 and spent
much of his time thereafter working on
the Houses of Parliament. He stayed in
Barry's office until about 1844.

The designs must date from an early
stage in Barry's evolution of the Palace
of Westminster, and might possibly be
only slightly later than the competition
of 1835, one of the requirements of which
had been that the Commons chamber
should be square, as is shown in this
drawing for it.

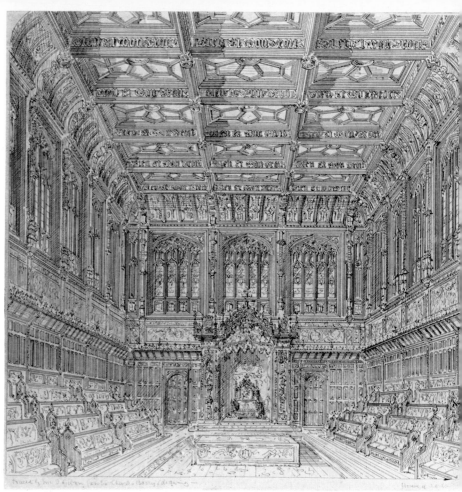

rly as 1839 a Select Committee reported the Foreign and Colonial Offices were quately accommodated in dilapidated s in the Downing Street area. As it was ght uneconomical to spend money on rs, Decimus Burton prepared plans for lding the Foreign Office. Nothing further lone.

teen years later the then First Com-oner of Works, Sir William Molesworth, ed that Burton's plan was out of date nadequate, and asked James Pennethorne oduce another. This, ready by July 1855, osed a large quadrangular building h could be erected in stages) 250 feet by feet. The building would house the sury, Colonial, Foreign and War Offices, he Board of Trade, and provided for a ence for the Chancellor of the Exchequer. he same time Pennethorne prepared ates for the acquisition of all the land een the Treasury, St James's Park, t George Street and Parliament Square, n, it was thought, would cost about ,000. Another Select Committee rec-ended that, should Parliament sanction urchase of the land, there ought to be lic competition for the buildings to be ed on it. So Pennethorne's plan, like that rton, was abandoned.

e *Builder* reported, on 23 August 1856, there were to be new Offices for the gn Secretary and the War Secretary, hat they would go up between Charles t and Downing Street. Later the same h, Sir Benjamin Hall, First Commissioner, number of architects — among them Sir es Barry, Hardwick, T. H. Wyatt, M. y Wyatt, Ferrey, Godwin, Gilbert Scott, on, Pennethorne, and also Edward Poyn-William Railton and William Tite—to their views on the proposed competition. was announced shortly afterwards that were to be three competitions. The Premium for the War Office would be , with six others ranging from £500 to ; for the Foreign Office £700 with s from £400 to £100. The third com-on was for a plan to show how the whole might be laid out, so that the two osed buildings could form part of a rehensive scheme, with suggested road ovements which would take into account roposed Thames Embankment. For this would be Premiums of £500, £200, and

ring the summer of 1857, 218 different ns, comprising nearly 2,000 drawings, exhibited in Westminster Hall, arousing nse public interest. After several weeks, idges, among them Brunel, announced verdicts, thereby giving, said the *Art al*, 'universal dissatisfaction', a not

uncommon result of Government com-petitions.

The First Premium for the Foreign Office was awarded to Coe and Hofland, with Banks and Barry coming second. Gilbert Scott received the Third Premium, and the runners-up were Deane and Woodward; Bellamy, Buxton and Habershon, with G. E. Street at the bottom of the list. H. B. Garling gained First Premium for the War Office, and a Frenchman, named Cressinet, was awarded the top premium for his Site Plan.

None of the winning designs was in a Gothic style, though some of those in sec-ondary places were. This led the *Art Journal* to enquire, 'Are we wrong in surmizing that, being Gothic, the judges were determined not to admit the absolute superiority of these . . . designs over all their fellow-competitors? . . . The opponents of the Gothic have put forth their strength, and in so doing they have both unmasked their resources, and declared their standards of excellence; as the contest proceeds they will learn the nature and the capacity of the Gothic reserve, which has not yet been brought into action.'

However, Lord Palmerston professed not to like any of the winning designs and asked Pennethorne, of the Office of Works to do better. The angry competitors, not un-naturally, banded together, and, led by Gilbert Scott, protested. At this moment, the Government changed, and the triumphant Conservatives 'discovered' that Gilbert Scott had (as they said) at one point during the judges' deliberations been selected for the Second Premium for both the Foreign Office and the War Office. It was therefore proposed that a choice should be made between Scott and Charles Barry. Scott was the lucky one, and at this Palmerston is supposed to have commented on the horse that, though being placed second in two races, had won the stakes. While the argument had been in pro-gress, the War Department had withdrawn from the project, and had been replaced by the India Office. The latter's architect, Mat-thew Digby Wyatt, agreed to work jointly with Gilbert Scott on the new building.

It seemed at this point as if the *Art Journal's* support for a Gothic building had paid off, but no one had reckoned on Palmerston. He was emphatic, while in Opposition, in his condemnation of such a style for a Whitehall building, and, when he returned to power in 1859, told Scott to produce a Classical office. Scott compromised by coming up instead, with a Byzantine one, which, supported by James Fergusson, was approved by Parliament in 1860. Palmerston was not going to allow this, and sending for Scott, told him that there was to be another design—Classical or nothing. Not willing to lose the commission, Scott swallowed his pride, and did as he was told.

The Goths still would not admit defeat. During 1861 Lord Elcho moved in the Commons that it was 'not desirable that the new Foreign Office should be erected accord-ing to the Palladian design now exhibited', and felt that Scott was at fault in allowing himself to act merely as Palmerston's draughtsman. The First Commissioner, William Cowper, replied that Scott's design did him great credit, and Palmerston told the House that the design was the most desirable for a secular building intended for a Govern-ment Office. Lord Elcho's motion was decisively defeated, and work went ahead with the preparation of the site. By July 1866 the construction was, according to the *Builder*, 'considerably advanced', and the periodical illustrated Scott's final Italian design of 1861.

The hotly disputed 'Battle of the Styles' has been summarized by Christopher Hussey in 'Foreign Office's threatened glory' (*Country Life*, 6 April 1964, pp. 272-75) and the design of the India Office has been discussed by Lavinia Handley-Read in 'Legacy of a vanished Empire' (*Country Life*, 9 July 1970, pp. 110-12). Mrs Handley-Read describes the architectural sculpture by Armstead, Philip, Pfyffers and others in *Architectural Review*, vol. 148, 1970, pp. 272-79.

Christopher Hussey wrote his account as a protest against the then intention of the Government to demolish the building. This proposal was the subject of vigorous con-demnation and an official enquiry. Preser-vationists were delighted when, during 1972, it was announced that the Foreign and India Offices had been reprieved. They have now been cleaned of the century's accumulation of soot and grime.

What, however, of the proposals concerning the rest of the area? Pennethorne had pro-duced a scheme for placing a group of buildings on the site of the Old Palace of Whitehall, on the east side, along the river. Sir Charles Trevelyan a little later did the same, making the Banqueting House the focal point of several buildings which he suggested might be used by the War Office. Again, these plans were put aside.

In 1865-66 Colonel (later Lieutenant-General Sir) Andrew Clarke, RE, at that time Director of Engineering Works at the Admiralty, submitted a plan for the wholesale demolition of the west side of Whitehall and Parliament Street, from Parliament Square to Trafalgar Square. Even the Horse Guards building was to go. Clarke proposed that a unified building scheme, incorporating the new Foreign and India Offices, should be considered, together with buildings for the War Office and Admiralty, and barracks for cavalry and a battalion of Guards. On the eastern side of a very much widened Whitehall—a grand processional way from Charing Cross to Parliament—the Colonel made provision for 'first class residences'.

However, Colonel Clarke was not the only one with such ideas. Sir Henry Hunt thought the Board of Trade could be lodged in the Treasury building and Dover House, with splendid new houses for the Prime Minister and the Chancellor of the Exchequer, but he, at least, retained the Horse Guards, on the north side of which, between it and the old Admiralty, was proposed a new building for the Office of Works.

A. B. Mitford (later Lord Redesdale), of the Office of Works, took elements from the plans of both Clarke and Hunt, and proposed to demolish Drummond's Bank and other property at Charing Cross, as well as extending the Mall into Trafalgar Square. The Admiralty, he suggested, could be placed between Charles Street and Parliament Square.

Arthur Gates provided the Government with four alternative plans for using the land on the east side of Whitehall; and, while planning the extensions to the National Gallery, E. M. Barry asked that consideration should be given to a scheme for building a barracks on the river side of the Banqueting House.

By 1877 nothing at all had happened concerning the various proposals received by the Government. The *Builder* came up with another of its own, in which the Admiralty and War Offices were to be placed in blocks of buildings on the Embankment, built round courtyards and streets, through which a beneficial 'draught of air from the Surrey hills would be admitted'.

It was all so much wasted effort; no coherent plan was ever acted upon. In fact, proposals concerning the Admiralty and War Office were put into cold storage until towards the end of 1881, when the Government announced that 'after careful consideration' a new building for both departments was to be built immediately to the north of the Horse Guards, which would mean the demolition of the Paymaster-General's house and the old Admiralty building. Included in the scheme would possibly be official houses for the First Lord and the First Sea Lord in Spring Gardens.

The *Builder*, whilst welcoming the proposal, drew attention to the disastrous effect the new Thames Embankment was having on the Whitehall area. Sir J. Bazalgette had produced a section of the Embankment showing the sewer, miscalled 'the low-level sewer, which drains, or rather does not drain, the site of the new buildings', as it was 7 to 10 feet higher than the low-water level at which the 'ancient sewers of Westminster made their escape into the river. The consequence of this most disastrous choice of level has been the penning back of an unknown amount of damp, wet and old—if not recent—sewage over the whole

area between the Thames and the Park. To this, to a considerable extent, the insanitary state of the present Government offices can be traced'. The Government was, therefore, urged to do something before concentrating more civil servants in the area. It was believed that a special 'sewage lift' had been installed in Marlborough House to cope with the problem.

In general, the choice of this site for the new Admiralty and War Office did not meet with approval, and opinion inclined to the site originally proposed by Mitford, down beside Parliament Square. For the RIBA, J. Macvicar Anderson and William White put forward the view that the site was too small for a building of the size proposed. The Office of Works persisted in its choice and acquired the land. The *Builder* (22 July 1882) condemned the system whereby, in its view, a First Commissioner of Works could be ambitious to do something to distinguish his term of office, and carry out schemes of his own at the cost 'both of architectural propriety and of money and time previously expended in initiating other projects . . . The present holder of the office appears to labour under a dangerous amount of ill-directed zeal; and if things go on in this way, there is no knowing what costly mistakes may be made before another turn of the political wheel brings in another amateur architect to pull the metropolis about as he pleases.'

The history of the Admiralty building during the last two decades of the 19th century is even more bizarre than that of most of the Whitehall buildings during the previous thirty years, and the result was probably worse. The choice of the architect was to be determined by competition, but the Government, apparently having learnt nothing from any of the previous contests, decided to hold not merely one, but two. An announcement to this effect was made during September 1883, in which architects were invited to submit designs. From the competing architects, ten of them would be selected, and invited to produce further drawings for the second competition. The lucky architect who was thus selected would receive £600 for his competitive drawings, and a further £25,000 for the entire work, which, it was proposed, would be carried out in stages.

The First Commissioner of Works appointed two architects, Ewan Christian and P. C. Hardwick, and two members of the House of Commons, as well as himself, to assess the various designs, which had to be submitted by 1 March 1884. In all, entries were received from 128 architects, who obviously had also not profited from previous example. Just a month later, the result was made known. The selection committee had not been able to find even ten worthy architects, but could name only nine, most of

them unknown. This, of course, result extensive bickering, just as had every pre competition organized by the Govern Where, it was asked, were all the estab men? Were their designs too awful? Ha judging been too hasty? Had there been it be said, favouritism? To dampen susp the Government was urged to arrange a exhibition of all the designs received, a of action which it apparently had abso no intention of carrying out.

Instead, the planned arrangements ahead. The nine 'fortunate' architects (& Salter, H. Hall & W. H. Powell. Th Porter, Verity & Hunt, Aston We Ingress Bell, Spalding & Auld, all of Lo together with Leeming & Leemin Halifax, Maxwell & Tuke of Manchest Malcolm Stark junior & James Linds Glasgow) were given only about seven to prepare their drawings for the final jud The *Builder* thought the time was very 'A committee may find it easy to go light heart through several hundred dra but the two architects on the com ought to know very well, if their colle do not, that a complete set of plans for a building cannot be devised, though and executed by the 24th of June (the fixed), without either painful overwoi hasty and incomplete thought and exec The time ought to be extended, if justic be done to the building and to the archi

This type of pleading in the archite press had always been ignored hitherto there was no exception this time, for the result was announced during July 18 was stated in the judges' report that 'after careful examination of these de selected three as possessing especial m namely those of Messrs. Leeming & Le . . . Messrs Verity & Hunt . . .; Mes Webb & E. I. Bell . . . After further sideration of these three designs, the j were unanimously of opinion that, taki plans and elevations together, and h regard to the conditions of the compe Messrs. Leeming & Leeming have pro the best design', and consequently thi the recommendation that went through Government.

The *Builder*, however, was able to s a glance' that the design by the two Lee was not the best—architecturally at Their drawings were, nevertheless, 'o the most admirable pieces of purely tectural draughtsmanship which we rem to have seen', and it was thought tha judges had been seduced by them. Christian, indeed, commented that the 'drawings of the most remarkable de which may have been equalled, but nev

*General view of the government offices a Houses of Parliament. Courtesy, Aerofilm*

CENTRAL LIBRARY - FINE ART LIBRARY

39

my knowledge, surpassed for perfect execution'. The design itself was pretty universally condemned; a tall tower was so placed as to dwarf William Kent's Horse Guards, and was 'objectionable', details of one storey appeared 'to belong to a building of quite different scale', and other features of the building were 'very odd'.

Faced with this almost overwhelming criticism of a building for such an important site, facing as it did on to St James's Park, Whitehall, and the Mall, even the Office of Works took fright, and the two Leeming brothers were told to amend their design. The alterations were complete by April 1885, when models were placed on 'private' view and then deposited in the Houses of Parliament for inspection by the Lords and Commons. Critical alarm was not lessened by these changes, so at length the Government was forced to appoint a Select Committee in April 1887, to reconsider the building as presented, and also to report whether some, or all, of the old Admiralty buildings could not, with advantage, be retained. This Select Committee reported with a vengeance, recommending that the scheme was abandoned entirely, in spite of Christian's earlier view that 'It is a little short of wonderful that whatever its fault of detail may be, so fine a plan and so good an elevation should have been entirely wrought out by men, solitary students in a provincial town, with no special advantages, untravelled, unknown to the world of art . . .'

By the spring of the following year, 1888, the same architects had been re-employed, and produced revised designs again, for the inspection of the House of Commons, which would cost, it was estimated, some £213,000. These were reproduced in the *Building News* on 6 and 13 April. The old Admiralty building was to remain unaltered, so that the Leemings had no Whitehall frontage to worry about. What they were given to do, in fact, was nothing more than an L-shaped extension towards St James's Park, flanking the Horse Guards, to which opened a large courtyard, known as Admiralty Gardens, enclosed by an open colonnade. The foundations for this extension were excavated during 1890, and the first portion of the building was ready for occupation in 1895. The following year, the second stage along the Mall was started. The third and final portion was not ready until the spring of 1906. This was probably the block on Horse Guards, enclosing the courtyard, and on the site of the colonnade. The design of this, it was stated at the time, followed that of the façade to St James's Park, which would 'always remain as a monument to the parsimony of Sir William Harcourt's short period of administration as Chancellor of the Exchequer'. This frontage is now invisible behind the Citadel, erected during the Second World War, but Sir Nikolaus Pevsner's comment on the building is 'unfortunate'.

The War Office building designs by William Young were published in March 1899, at the same time as those of a large new government office block by J. M. Brydon between the Foreign Office and Parliament Square. One contemporary comment was that neither could be described as 'brilliant or dashingly original'.

In recent years there have been various proposals for additional buildings to provide space for members of Parliament. They have all proved as controversial and, at the moment, as inconclusive as the 19th century Government Offices disaster which the *Builder* felt 'should never be forgotten by the profession of British Architects'.

Lit. *Br*, 1857, etc. 'The story of the Government Offices', *Br*, 25 August 1877, pp. 852-56. 'Her Majesty's Office of Works and Public Building', *Br*, 8 September 1877, pp. 897-99. 'The new Government Offices', *Br*, 25 March 1899, pp. 289-91; *BN*, 24 March 1899, pp. 397-98.

...es Fergusson
...vernment Offices, Whitehall, from
...ames's Park. 1857
...ter-colour, heightened with Chinese
...e $26\frac{7}{8} \times 40\frac{3}{4}$ (68.2 $\times$ 102.5)
...095-1886
...toria and Albert Museum

**7** James Fergusson
Government Offices, Whitehall. 1857
*Inscribed* Southern elevation in Great George St and Bridge St No 2 Dulcius ex Asperis. Scale 44 feet to one inch
*Brown wash heightened with Chinese white* 21 × 39½ (52.7 × 100.5)
D.947-1886
Victoria and Albert Museum

Fergusson entered a set of designs in the Government Offices competition in 1857, under the motto quoted above, as no. 195. They were not noticed by reviewers. Several of them were sub-sequently shown in the Architectural Exhibition of 1858, whe[n] present design was probably no. 193. He also showed 'Western [...] facing St James's Park', now probably that which is in the Mu[...] (948-1886), and also no. 194, 'Home Office-War Office-Trea[...] East façade in Gt. Parliament St'.

**8** Sir George Gilbert Scott
Elevation of the west side of the Quadrangle, of the Fo[...] Office
*Lettered with title etc., scale, and artist's name and addre[...]
Pen and ink and wash* 23 × 38¾ (60.5 × 99)
Lent by the Department of the Environment

George Gilbert Scott
...sign for the Foreign Office. 1864
...ter-colour $33\frac{1}{2} \times 68\frac{1}{2}$ (85.2 × 174)
...t by the Royal Academy of Arts

...Gilbert Scott exhibited this drawing
...the original design for the Foreign
...ce, at the RA, as showing the design 'in
...style desired by the architect'. Of it,
*Building News* said 'no-one interested
...he present revival of medieval archi-
...ure can look at this drawing without
...ing that the world of art is a world of
...ion. It is but a few years since this
...gn was conceived. But in those few
years a revolution has occurred in professional taste which has shaken old
theories, and set every man thinking for
himself'.

The *Builder* did not consider that this
particular drawing was worthy to be
compared with the original designs of
1857, which Scott had submitted to the
competition, and thought it 'splashily
coloured'. However, Scott had 'done well'
to leave a record of his original idea for the
building. Though not wishing to enter the
argument on style, the *Builder* took the view
that 'the details of the building now in progress are not improving as the work goes up.

There are faults in them which, Italian
though the style be, the study of *Gothic*
architecture should have made impossible.
In the design in the Academy . . . the architect is evidently master of his details'.

The Home Office extension to the
building was begun in 1870 and ready for
occupation during 1874. Scott had planned
cupolas to the Whitehall façade which were
not carried out, nor were the proposed
groups and statues on the parapet.

Exhib. RA, 1864, no. 786.
Lit. *Br*, 7 May 1864, p. 326; 14 July 1866,
p. 527. *BN*, 6 May 1864, p. 333.

**10** Lieutenant-General Sir Andrew Clarke

Model for the proposed rebuilding of Whitehall. 1869

*Plaster, wood and cardboard, painted* $11\frac{1}{2} \times 124 \times 48$ (29.3 × 315 122.5)

Lent by the Department of the Environment

Colonel Clarke, as he was at the time, proposed to demolish every building between Great George Street and Trafalgar Square, except the new Foreign and India Offices, and to widen Whitehall and Parliament Street. At the southern

end, nearest Parliament Square, was a large block around two interior yards. This was intended to house Government departments, the quarters of the Metropolitan Police to provide a barracks for a Battal Guards. Northwards of this was th Foreign Office of Sir Gilbert S Downing Street, swept away, wou incorporated into Horse Guards P with the Treasury on the easter linked by an open arcade across th of the Horse Guards building to ba and stables for four squadrons o Household Cavalry. These barracks form part of a large complex aroun courtyards, for the Admiralty and Office, with official residences fo ministers, the Commander-in-Chie First Naval Lord, and three Secre Clarke proposed that all the bui would be intercommunicating at floor level along the whole of Whi

On the east side of the street he gested that, besides isolating the Ban ing House in the middle of a street Embankment, the rest of the site s be laid out for first-class houses and gardens.

Assistants who worked on the were E. I. Woodhead and G. L. Brig

Lit. *Br*, 13 March 1869, pp. 200-02, arrangement of the Public O London,' with a ground plan.

Lieutenant-General Sir Andrew
Clarke
Model showing a portion of a
proposed government office. 1869
*Wood, paper, and glass* $5\frac{1}{2} \times 6\frac{1}{4} \times$
$8\frac{1}{4}$ (13.9 × 15.7 × 20.9)
A.14-1973
Victoria and Albert Museum

The model is cut away to show the
arrangement of floors, light-wells, etc.

**11** John and Joseph Leeming
Model showing the proposed
Admiralty and War Office, Whitehall.
1885
*Wood and cardboard, painted* $15\frac{1}{2} \times$
$26 \times 34$ ($39.5 \times 66 \times 86$)
Lent from the Palace of Westminster

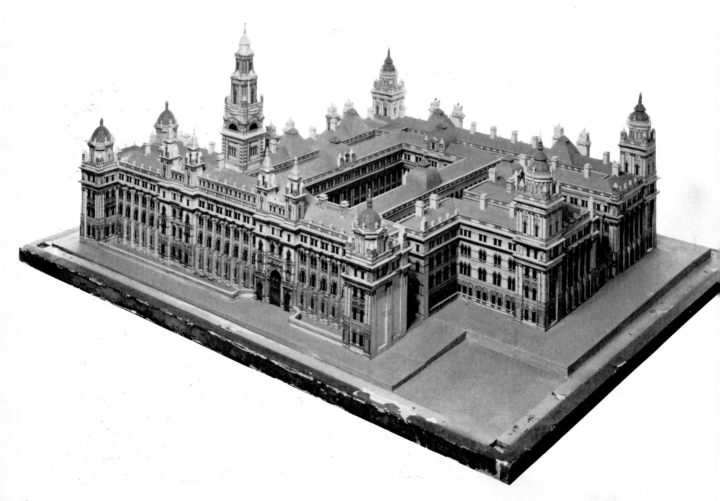

John and Joseph Leeming
Model showing the
proposed south-western
tower of the Admiralty and
War Office, Whitehall
1885
Plaster and wood 50 × 22
× 22 (127 × 56 × 56)
Lent from the Palace of
Westminster

beautifully executed model
a portion of Messrs.
Leeming & Leeming's
intended design for the new
Admiralty and War Offices
. has been on private view
this week at the studio of
Messrs. Mabey, Brothers,
Storey's Gate, Westminster,
previous to being exhibited
the Houses of Parliament,
for which purpose it has been
made under the direction of
the architects and the Office
Works. The model, carried
out to the ample scale of four
feet to the inch, comprises
the S.W. angle or pavilion of
the park front, including the
chief entrance to the suite of
rooms for the Secretary of
State for War, and likewise
furnishing the first three bays
the façade facing the
guards parade ground, or
strictly speaking, south elevation. The merits of the
design, judged as a specimen
monumental architecture,
are certainly brought out by
this "study in the round"
.'(BN, 3 April 1885, p. 547)
All the designs for this
building by the various competing architects were
criticized for attempting to
squeeze too many offices onto
restricted area, though it
was appreciated that they
were only following the requirements laid down by the
Board of Works, which left
margin for courts and
open spaces of suitable sizes.
This is painfully evident in
the accepted design . . . A
court 219 ft. long by 80 ft.
broad is not a favourable
proportion, and yet it has
only left . . . a width of 25
for the corridor court;
s court on the Spring
Gardens side is only 30 ft.

wide, and will form a long
dark hole . . . It is much to
be regretted, therefore, that
at the first start an area so
limited in space should have
been decided on for requirements of so extensive a
character. It has left little
opportunity for a display of
architectural effect, and, what
is more important, has resulted in the curtailing of the
proper width of the office
rooms, and an insufficiency of
light and air in the areas and
courts' (Br, 9 August 1884,
p. 182).

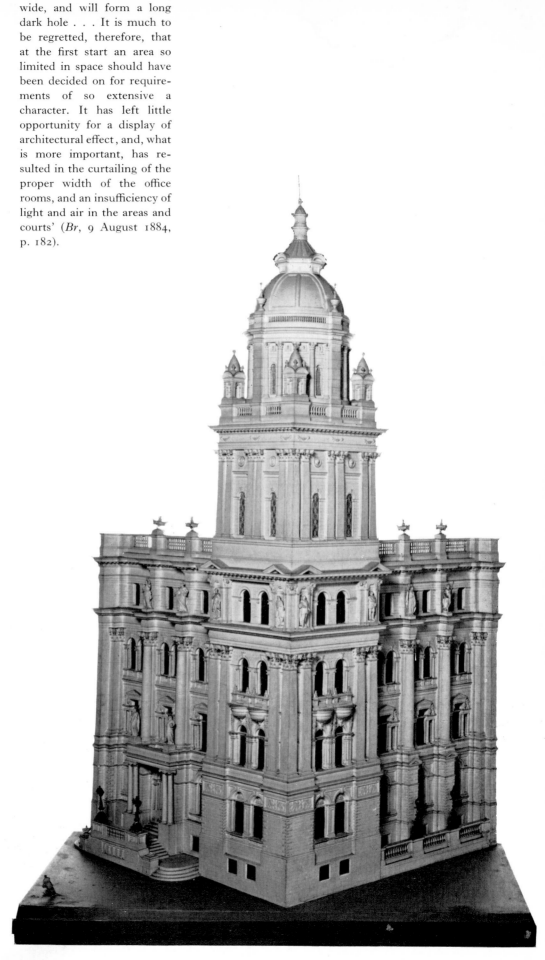

**13** Richard Norman Shaw
North elevation, New
Scotland Yard, London
1888
*Inscribed* Metropolitan
Police New Central Offices
R. Norman Shaw, RA
Archt. 29 Bloomsbury Sq.
W.C. etc., *and with scale
and date*
*Pen and ink and wash*
$19\frac{1}{2} \times 27$ (49.5 × 68.5)
Lent by the Royal
Academy of Arts, London.

At the same time as the
argument over the Admiralty
and War Office building at
the north end of Whitehall,
the Government offered the
Metropolitan Police a site for
their headquarters on the
Embankment, almost op-
posite the Foreign Office, in
1883. The plot of land had
originally been earmarked
for a National Opera House, and
this building, designed by
Francis H. Fowler, was to be
larger than the theatre in
Covent Garden. The foun-
dation stone was laid by the
Duke of Edinburgh during
December 1875, at which
time it was hoped to complete
the theatre within two years.
However, lack of funds called
a halt after the completion
of the foundations.

The Home Office did not
make up its mind about this
site for a considerable time,
but agreed to it in August
1886, a decision welcomed by
the *Builder*, which warned
that a building in so important a position would have to
be something 'very far superior' to ordinary police
buildings. The Receiver for
the Metropolitan Police District, A. R. Pennefather, did
not want to waste time on
probably inconclusive public
competitions, but advocated
that the Police Surveyor
should prepare plans, which
would be vetted by a pro-
fessional architect. Norman
Shaw was brought in for this,
but it seems that almost from
the first he assumed the
position of architect, sho
his design for the new b
ing at the Academy in
which was then describ
'an exceedingly solid-lo
building . . . and it is gr
ing to find the auth
going to an architect
Mr. Shaw for such a bui
instead of inflicting o
architecture on us'. The
headquarters was read
partial occupation by
police during Nove
1890.

Lit. S. Beattie, 'New Sc
Yard', *Architectural
tory*, vol. 15, 1972
68-81 (illus.).

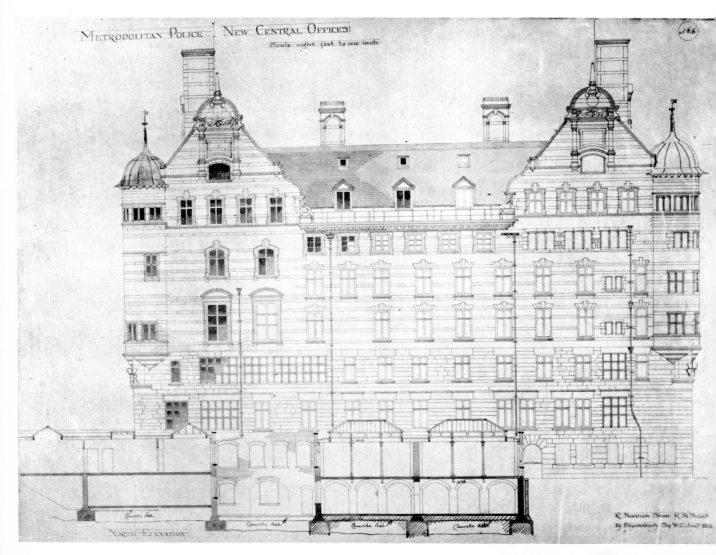

# The Law Courts

For many hundreds of years the courts of law had been centred on Westminster Hall, and, though Sir John Soane had provided additional buildings, these soon proved to be inadequate. The destruction of the Palace of Westminster by fire in 1834, with the exception of the Hall, made the situation even more inconvenient, and a few years later Sir Charles Barry produced a design for a building in Lincoln's Inn Fields. This project fell through.

By 1857 the situation was regarded as critical and various legal authorities were urging the Government to do something about it. At first there was no agreement on a site for a new building, nor even on the provision of the necessary money for it. It was generally agreed, though, that the new Courts would have to be nearer the Inns of Court, and attention became centred on an area near the river close to Somerset House, or alternatively on a site north of the Strand. It was not, however, until as late as 1865 that the site between Carey Street and the Strand was decided upon.

With the example of previous abortive architectural competitions in mind, the First Commissioner of Works, William Cowper, settled for a limited competition between six invited architects. These were E. M. Barry, Gilbert Scott, P. C. Hardwick, Alfred Waterhouse, G. E. Street, and T. H. Wyatt. Two of them, Wyatt and Hardwick, declined, and were replaced by Raphael Brandon and T. N. Deane. Not long afterwards Barry and Scott withdrew, their places being offered to H. B. Garling and Somers Clarke. The latter was not interested, so John Gibson was approached and accepted.

At this point the House of Commons intervened, and decided that a competition between only six architects was far too restricted, and the number was increased to a dozen. As a result Barry and Scott were asked to reconsider their decision, which they did, and decided to compete, and, in addition, others who accepted the Government's approach were Seddon, Burges, H. F. Lockwood, and H. R. Abraham, though Gibson eventually withdrew due to pressure of other work. All the competing architects were convinced Goths, and it was assumed, though no specific instructions were issued on the subject, that the new building was to be Gothic, in spite of the battle that was at that very time taking place between Palmerston and Gilbert Scott over the design of the new Foreign Office.

The architects were instructed to provide plans for about 683,000 square feet of accommodation, within the cost of £750,000. When the various designs were exhibited in New Square during 1867 it was, as Sir John Summerson says, 'a harvest of mid-Victorian Gothic invention such as had never been seen before and would never be seen again'. The exhibition aroused public interest and all the designs were engraved in the architectural journals of the day, with their spires, pinnacles, towers, domes, vast cathedral-like halls, and so on. Everyone had his own favourite design, so that the difficulties facing the judges may well be imagined. There was a wrangle involving among others, the RIBA, the Government, and A. Beresford-Hope, and when the result was announced, it was a decided non-event. There was no winner, just as had happened in the National Gallery Competition. The judges, William Cowper, Gladstone, Sir Alexander Cockburn (Lord Chief Justice), Sir R. Palmer, Sir William Stirling-Maxwell, John Shaw and George Pownall, preferred the plan provided by Barry, but not his architecture, naming instead that of G. E. Street, while the lawyers thought that Scott or Waterhouse served them better. At any rate, it was recommended that the commission be offered to Barry and Street jointly.

Once again—it seems to have happened with every major competition—there was uproar, all the competitors protesting vigorously. Eventually Street was named as the sole architect, and E. Barry had to be content with designing a new National Gallery, which in the end he was not allowed to build, but only to adapt.

Street, though, in his turn, had no easy time of it. Almost immediately the opponents of the Carey Street site revived the idea of the building on the Embankment. As this had the support of a new First Commissioner of Works, A. H. Layard, Street had to start preparing new plans. No decision was taken for a considerable time, and when at last it was for Carey Street, Layard departed for Spain as Ambassador, leaving Street to contend with the odious Acton Smee Ayrton as First Commissioner, who did his utmost to alter and reduce the design of the building. In spite of all difficulties, Street persevered, though he died in 1881 before the Law Courts were complete. He was succeeded by his son A. E. Street and Arthur Blomfield.

Lit. Sir J. Summerson, 'A Victorian Competition. The Royal Courts of Justice' in *Victorian Architecture, four studies in evaluation*, 1970, pp. 77-117. M. H. Port, 'The new Law Courts competition,' *Architectural History*, vol. 11, 1968 pp. 75-93, pls. 17-24. All the various designs are reproduced in these publications.

**14** Alfred Waterhouse
Perspective design for the Royal
Courts of Justice. 1866-67
*Pen and ink wash* 27½ × 52½ (69.9
× 133.4)

Lent by the Royal Institute of British
Architects

The *Building News*, reviewing the competitive designs, thought that, as far as the general public was concerned, Waterhouse was at a considerable advantage, as his drawings were finished 'in such a thoroughly artistic manner that not only do they far transcend the perspectives of all the other competitors, but might very fairly take rank among the architectural drawings of any water-colour exhibition'. Sounding a warning that many would be seduced by the attractiveness of the drawings, the *Building News* went on to suggest that most other architects could profit from Waterhouse's example as 'much of the best architectural thought of the present day begins and ends on paper because of the inaccurate, we may even say slovenly, manner in which it is expressed'.

The scheme proposed by Waterhouse for the Law Courts is described at length in *Building News*, 8 February 1867, pp. 95-6.

John Pollard Seddon
Monumental Halls, Westminster,
London. 1890
*Water-colour* $24\frac{1}{2} \times 35\frac{7}{8}$ (64.4 × 91.7)
RAN 15/c/1,1
Lent by the Royal Institute of
British Architects

The Monumental Halls were intended to accommodate the monuments in Westminster Abbey. With few exceptions, the monuments in the Abbey were confined to the eastern chapels until the beginning of the 18th century. Guelfi's memorial to Secretary Craggs, quickly followed by those to Newton and Stanhope by Rysbrack, began an invasion of white marble effigies into the transepts and nave. By the middle of the 19th century, therefore, almost all available space was filled, and concern began to be expressed. There were those who advocated the removal of everything, while others were of the opinion that, as the Abbey could be considered to be a national mausoleum, something more positive should be done to provide accommodation for both the bodies and memorials of such future persons whom it was desired to commemorate there.

In 1854 Sir Gilbert Scott presented a report to Lord John Thynne, the Sub-Dean, in which he said: 'Nothing can be done effectually for the improvement of the interior till a large proportion of the more offensive monuments are removed.' He proceeded then to categorize these monuments. There were those which 'as works of art are so contemptible as to be unworthy of a place in any good building'; others were 'fine works of art, but in bad taste'; and thirdly those which were not objectionable as works of art, or from the point of taste, but which were out of character with the Abbey, as they presented no 'religious sentiment.' On the face of it, Scott seems successfully to have condemned every monument later than that of Henry VII.

His proposal was that a 'wide and lofty cloister of great length' should be erected behind the old houses (now demolished) in Abingdon Street, into which these despised marbles could be cast. A few years afterwards Scott came up with another suggestion which involved the demolition of all the houses south of the Abbey between Abingdon Street and College Street, facing the new Houses of Parliament. Nothing came of either of these suggestions.

By 1890, however, public disquiet was such, that a Royal Commission was appointed to enquire into the lack of space in the Abbey, its members being

the First Commissioner of Works, David Plunket; Sir A. H. Layard; Sir Frederic Leighton, PRA: the Dean, Dr Bradley; Louis Jennings; and Alfred Waterhouse, RA, the President of the RIBA. The Commissioners heard a great deal of evidence, even from the Archbishop of Canterbury, E. W. Benson, who felt strongly that any new building should be a chapel, and attached somehow to the Abbey church. 'If it is to be a secular building, it had better not be anywhere near Westminster Abbey. I cannot give any opinion as to what should be done if it were a secular building.' Moreover, stated the Archbishop, he would object to any monument being removed from the Abbey. 'If you disturb the sentiment that the great man is laid to rest there for ever, you will disturb the satisfaction that is felt in placing great men there at any time. This higher effect of the monuments is very real, and on that account it is undesirable to disturb them.' He also thought that no monument should be discarded on grounds of taste, as he felt that the mixture of styles in the monuments had a great effect in drawing out the beauty of the architecture. 'Therefore I doubt whether, though you would gain space if you took away for instance Lord Mansfield's monument, you would gain really. You would see another arch, but that is a less advantage than you have in the different outlines. I do not know whether that is heresy.'

The Royal Commissioners inspected plans and drawings of various proposals put forward by the Abbey's Surveyor, J. L. Pearson, by Somers Clarke, E. J. Tarver, and L. Harvey and J. P. Seddon. The scheme by the latter joint-architects was divided into four parts. First they proposed a cluster of six chapels radiating round the Chapter House; the restoration of the Norman ambulatory and opening it to the cloisters and the new chapels; the building of a new ambulatory eastwards; and finally the construction of a huge Campo Santo along Abingdon Street, on the site suggested by Sir Gilbert Scott, of which they said, 'the cost would, no doubt, be very great'.

Harvey and Seddon, indeed, priced themselves completely out of the scheme, because their buildings worked out at the very large sum of £480,000, of which £200,000 was for the Campo Santo, on to which had to be added an estimated £100,000, for buying up the property in Abingdon Street.

When the Royal Commissioners presented their final report in 1891, they were in disagreement. Plunket, Jennings and Waterhouse recommended that a new monumental chapel should be built on the site of the Abbey's former refectory, while Layard, Leighton and the Dean thought that a site elsewhere should be chosen. The subject was debated for a while in the press, and then forgotten, though still today an occasional voice is raised in protest against the monuments.

Lit. Royal Commission on Westminster Abbey, *First Report*, 1890; *Final Report*, 1891.

**16** Sir Charles Barry
Highclere, Hampshire. 1840
*Water-colour* $19\frac{1}{2} \times 37$ (49.6 $\times$ 94)
Lent by the Royal Institute of British
Architects

Highclere was inherited in 1833 by Henry George Herbert, 3rd Earl of Carnarvon, who employed Barry to remodel the 18th century house. Barry's first design, dated 22 May 1838, was in a similar Italianate style to that which he used at Trentham Park, with the addition of small corner turrets in place of a tower. Lord Carnarvon wanted something richer and in May 1840 Barry produced a second design in what he called an 'Anglo-Italian' style, in other words the type of Elizabethan and Jacobean architecture which included strapwork, obelisks, carved panels and other decoration derived from Italian models. This much richer design underwent some further slight modifications, and the Earl finally approved Barry's third design, submitted in February 1842. Alterations continued to be made to the form of the tower, and the foundation stone was finally laid on 24 June 1842. Barry also made several schemes for decorating the interiors, which with the exception of the main staircase were never carried out. The main hall and possibly the Library were eventually decorated by Thomas Allom (see p. 53) in the early 1860s, and the entrance lobby possibly by Sir Gilbert Scott about 1870.

Barry's brief involved very little alteration to the existing fabric; both the fenestration and floor levels were kept and the original brick walls preserved beneath the stone skin. The *Civil Engineer and Architects' Journal* considered that this restriction prevented them 'from considering this a specimen of what he would do if left entirely to his own ideas for such a subject: still we should have expected from him greater freedom and taste in the application of that styl[e] its details, which he seems here to merely copied, without attempti[ng] infuse into them any originality or degree, refine them. It is far too s[ ] faithfully to that style to be much [ ] taste'. Barry's son, Alfred, recorde[d] 'the building thus transformed was [ ] his [father's] favourite works'. Whi[le the] sources of many of the details ca[n be] traced, and the overall outline is [remi]niscent with its central tower and corner turrets of Wollaton Hall [ ] Nottingham, the proportions and m[odel]ling are essentially Early Victorian.

Exhib. Possibly RA, 1840, no. [ ]
    RA, Bicentenary, 1968, no. 246.
Illus. *Architectural drawings fro[m* ]
    *Collection of the Royal Institute of [* ]
    *Architects*, 1961, pl. 27.
Lit. M. Girouard, *The Victorian c[ountry ]
    house*, 1972, pp. 68-70. *CE&AJ*[ ]
    1840, p. 188.

**Thomas Cubitt**

Osborne, Isle of Wight. 1845. Early design for the landward elevation

*Signed* T. C. *and dated* 1845

*Water- and body-colour* 20 × 33½ (50.8 × 80)

*Lent by Her Majesty The Queen*

After Queen Victoria's marriage in 1840 it became clear that none of the official residences was really suitable for the Royal couple and their young children. In March 1844 Prince Albert visited Osborne, the property of Lady Isabella Blachford, one of several houses which were suggested to him as possibilities for a new Royal residence, and arrangements were made to take the house on a lease with an option to purchase. Victoria first visited the property five months later, writing 'I am delighted with the house—which is so complete and snug—with some alterations and additions for the children it might be made an excellent house.' The Prince Consort employed Cubitt to survey the property, who reported that it would be cheaper to rebuild than to convert it, and in March 1845 he went over the house with the Prince discussing this possibility. By May Cubitt had drawn up plans for a new residence, called the Pavilion, attached by a corridor to the old house which was to be remodelled, and on 23 June the Queen laid the foundation stone. By September the building was up to the third floor, and on 1 March 1846 Queen Victoria recorded that 'the staircase and ceiling are in, and it will be quite delightful. I can hardly believe that we shall be living in this charming house built by ourselves in a few months'. They eventually moved in on 14 September 1846.

The Pavilion is depicted on the left in Cubitt's design. Plans for alterations and additions to the remainder of the property, and a model, were prepared by December 1846. The work was well in hand by 1848, when the *Builder* regretted the cement facings, and it was completed in 1851.

Many of the designs for interior decoration in both parts of the house were supplied by Ludwig Grüner. It is difficult to know how much of the work was designed by Cubitt and how much by the Prince Consort, since they worked closely together. The Italianate style is reminiscent of many of Cubitt's other works, some of which, like the Albert Gate Mansions, the Prince had carefully studied before employing him. Mrs Hobhouse has pointed out that the treatment of the loggia connecting the household wing to the Pavilion in Cubitt's design is plainer than that which was eventually carried out. It is less Italianate in style and closer to the vernacular English country house style of Cubitt's own house in Clapham Park. This alteration may have been the result of the Prince's intervention.

Lit. H. Hobhouse, *Thomas Cubitt Master Builder*, 1972, ch. 18, 'Our Cubitt-Osborne'.

**18** Augustus Welby Northmore Pugin
The Grange and St Augustine's
Church, Ramsgate, Kent. c. 1846
*Inscribed* A Prospect of St Augustines
*Pencil, pen and ink* 12¾ × 19 (32.6 ×
48.5)
D.124-1890
Victoria and Albert Museum

Ferrey records that Pugin bought the
land on the West Cliff at Ramsgate
about 1840-41 and that the choice of the
site was guided primarily by his love of
the sea and by a desire to be near his aunt
Selina Welby. The size of the Grange,
built 1843-44, and its arrangement reflect
the needs of Pugin's growing family, and
may have been influenced by his wife.
Pugin described it as 'a folio edition' of
his previous house, St Marie's Grange,
near Salisbury. Although a chapel was
attached to the Grange, this was not
sufficient for Pugin, who from 1846 built
from his own designs, and at his own
expense, the Church of St Augustine. The
spire shown in this drawing was not built.

The Grange was altered after Pugin's
death by Edward Welby Pugin, Mrs

Pugin and Cuthbert Pugin. The kitchen
and service quarters were rebuilt and
enlarged, a greenhouse added to the
drawing room, a long glazed corridor to
the main entrance included, and the
outbuildings completely rebuilt. It is
possible that the chimneys, roofs and
dormers were also altered.

Mrs Stanton describes the house as
'simple, dignified and comfortable'. The
massing and fenestration reflect the
internal arrangements—a tall two-storey
hall into which the living rooms open
directly thus avoiding the need for
corridors—and in that sense and in the
sense that it included no features which
were not 'necessary for convenience, construction or propriety' the house may be
seen as a forerunner of Philip Webb's
Red House (23). Pugin certainly found
the plan convenient, for he used it
again at The Glebe, Rampisham, and at
the Parsonage at Lanteglos, near Camel-
ford.

Another bird's-eye view of the Grange
and St Augustine's by Cuthbert Welby
Pugin, 1873, formerly in the possession of
Charles and Lavinia Handley-Read was
exhibited at the Royal Academy in 1879

and in the Handley-Read Exhibiti
the Royal Academy, 1972, Catalogu
B.136. An engraving by Pugin o
Grange alone is in the Departme
Prints and Drawings (E.78(7)-1970).

Lit. B. Ferrey, *Recollections of ⸺
Welby Pugin*, 1861. P. Stanton, ⸺
1972. J. Summerson, 'Pugin at ⸺
gate', *AR*, vol. ciii, April 1948
163-66.

Alfred Stevens

Drawing Room, Deysbrook, West Derby, Liverpool, Lancashire. 1847

*Pen and ink and water-colour* 19 × 26
(48.3 × 66)

586.B, purchased at the Alfred Stevens Sale, 1879

Victoria and Albert Museum

The dining room and drawing rooms of Deysbrook were decorated by Stevens for the Blundell family in the same year that he resigned his teaching post at the School of Design. Stannus records that 'The rooms were required for a special purpose at a given time; his [Stevens's] friend the late Mr. L. W. Collmann through whom he received the commission had given a long notice: and when the time drew nigh, became very anxious; but to all reminders he returned answer "they will be ready"; until there remained less than a fortnight, and Collman was in despair and troubling in his mind how he could treat these important panels in default of figures. Then Stevens arrived with a carpet-bag, a small portfolio of sketches, and a colour box; and executed them in something less than one day each. They were sketched on the walls in red chalk; and thinly painted in Parris' medium without models of any kind, which later fact may account for the peculiarity of the crination.' Towndrow, however, points out that full-size measured drawings for the decorations now in the Tate Gallery prove that Stevens worked out the whole scheme carefully before travelling to Liverpool and that, while he reserved the figure panels to himself, the remainder was carried out by assistants to his designs. The figurative panels in Stevens's essentially Pompeian scheme represent on the ceiling such attributes as 'Friendliness', 'Cheerfulness', 'Liberality', and 'Contentment', and on the walls 'Watchfulness', 'Trust', 'Arithmetic', 'Sculpture', and 'Geometry'. Some of the panels were moved at the time of the villa's demolition to the Walker Art Gallery, Liverpool.

Lit. H. Stannus, *Alfred Stevens and his work*, 1891, p. 8. K. R. Towndrow, *The works of Alfred Stevens*, Tate Gallery, 1950, p. 65.

**20** Robert Richardson Banks and Charles Barry, Junior

Cottages, Bylaugh Park, Norfolk. 1852

*Signed, and dated* 28 May 1852. *Inscribed* Bylaugh. Plans and Elevations of the proposed new cottages in lieu of those removed, *and with notes etc*

*Pen and ink and wash* $18\frac{3}{4} \times 29\frac{1}{8}$ (47.5 × 74)

M.P.A. 66(C. 103/3)

Lent from the Public Record Office

The mansion at Bylaugh was designed by Banks and Barry for Edward Lombe, and its construction, by Messrs Piper of Bishopsgate, begun in 1849 and finished in 1852, cost £29,389. It was then reported that Piper had entered into a second contract for the formation of the terraces, the enclosing of the park within a brick wall with several lodges, and other work. W. A. Nesfield was commissioned to lay out the park and gardens. 'The formation of the park and the erection of the . . .

accessorial buildings will take about years and, when all shall be com and the trees shall have attained growth, the property will form no least beautiful and perfect among many seats of the English nobility gentry.' The house is now a derelict

Lit. *Br*, 14 August 1852, pp. 51 M. Girouard, *The Victorian co house*, 1971, p. 177.

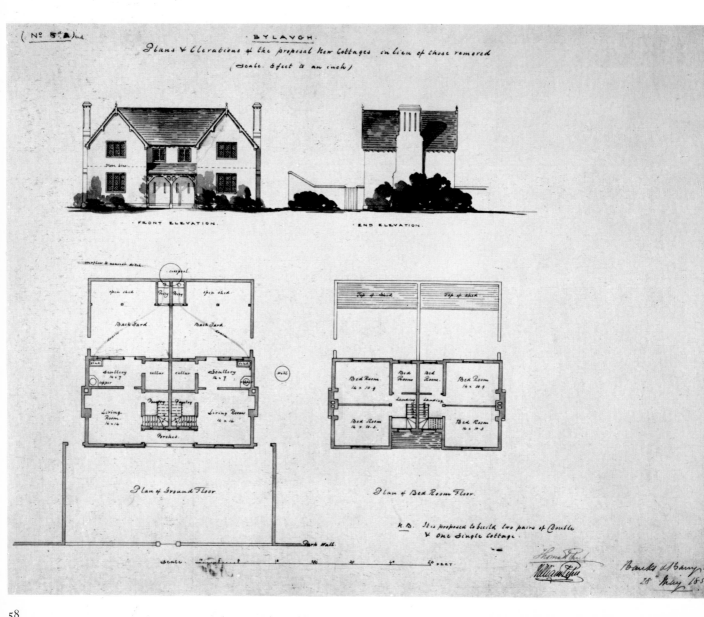

ilip Brown

ownsea Island Castle,
orset. c. 1852

*ater-colour* 29½ × 52
.9 × 132.1)

nt by Sabin Galleries
d

e castle began as a block
use, completed in 1547-48
Henry VIII as part of
South Coast defence
tem, remains of which still
vive in the basement of
present house. Many
erations and additions were
de by William Benson, Sir
rard Napier Sturt, and his
phew Humphrey Sturt,
, until by the end of the
h century the castle con-
ted of a four-storey castel-
ed central block with low
ngs and Venetian fen-
ration. In 1817 the Island
ssed to Sir Charles Chad,
umphrey Sturt's only son,
o in 1852 sold it to Colonel
lliam Petrie Waugh.
augh believed that the
and contained a rich bed of
ina clay calculated to be
rth about £1 million, and,
nvinced of the certainty of

an enormous income, im-
mediately put in hand
extensive building works.
These involved re-fronting
the castle in Portland stone
in a Tudor Gothic style apparently to Philip Brown's
designs, lavishly decorating
the interior with oak carvings,
building a jetty, the watch
towers and a sea wall facing
the north east. The clock
tower and the nearby church
of St Mary, completed in
1854, were also his work. At
this time he also established
the Branksea Clay and Pottery
Company, and on the west of
the Island erected a village,
which he called Maryland,
for the workmen operating
the clay pits.

By 1870 Waugh's company
had gone bankrupt and in
1896, during the occupancy of
Major Kenneth Balfour, a
fire broke out which gutted
the interior. Balfour undertook the rebuilding in the
following year, and it was
eventually completed by
Charles Van Raalte, who
purchased the castle in 1901.
The castle as it survives

accords broadly with Brown's
perspective although some
bright red brick refacing was
incorporated in 1897 in place
of the earlier stone work.

Exhib. 'A House in the
    Country', Sabin Galleries,
    1971, catalogue no. 2.
Illus. *Country Life*, 11
    November, 1971, p. 1259.
Lit. J. Newman and N.
    Pevsner, *Dorset*, 1973, pp.
    117-18. *Country Life*, 9
    April 1921, pp. 430-36.

**22** Robert Lewis Roumieu
House for Owen T. Alcer, Bushey
Heath, Hertfordshire. c. 1855
*Paper watermarked* 1855
*Pen and ink and water-colour* $18\frac{1}{2} \times 24$
$(48 \times 61)$
Z 5/23/4
Lent by the Royal Institute of British
Architects

Other drawings in the Royal Institute of
British Architects indicate that Roumieu
prepared alternative schemes for the
remodelling of an earlier house. Unlike
this Tudor design they were Italianate in
style. It is not known whether the work
was ever carried out. Other equally
frivolous designs by Roumieu were
executed, however, at 33-35 Eastcheap,
which Pevsner has described as 'one of
the maddest displays in London of
gabled gothic brick' and as 'utterly
undisciplined and crazy'; and at Milner
Square, which Summerson has compared
with the experience of 'an unhappy
dream'.

**23** Philip Webb
Red House, Bexley Heath, Kent
*Signed* Philip Webb Archt. 7
Ormond Street, Queens Sq., L
*and dated* April 1859. *Inscribed*
to be built at Upton near B
Kent for W Morris Esqr., Sect
c-d and South elevation. E
scullery. Elevation of West
North elevation. This is one
plans referred to in the Co
signed by me this 18th day of
1859 Witness P. Webb, William
*Pen and ink and wash* $20\frac{1}{2}$
$(52 \times 63.5)$
E.60-1916, given by Lady B
Jones
Victoria and Albert Museum

The fame of Red House rests mai
Lethaby's assessment of it as th
English 19th century building to ab
past styles, and on its resulting as
tion of the premier position
chronology of the Modern mov

Lethaby saw the building in terms of the country house and the large commission generally, but more recently it has been shown that Webb's inspiration was provided by the humble buildings such as schools, cottages and parsonages designed by his master Street and his idol Butterfield. William Morris, for whom Webb designed the house, wanted it to be 'very Mediaeval in spirit' and interpreted the half-hipped gables and pointed relieving arches as of the 13th century, but the revealed brick construction and segment-leaded windows, later to be so much a part of the Queen Anne style, testify to Webb's awareness of the 18th century also. What is essentially modern about Red House is that the internal arrangement appears to have dictated the form of the external elevations, although this too has earlier precedents, in for example the work of Pugin at Ramsgate (18) or Salisbury. Webb preferred to work alone, refusing to allow his name to be put forward for the Royal Academy and rarely permitting any scheme to appear in a contemporary periodical. Furthermore he refused Eastlake's request to describe his work in *A history of the Gothic Revival*. Illustrations of Red House were not published until 1900, when under pressure from friends including Lethaby, Webb allowed photographs to appear in *Country Life*; consequently, what contemporary accounts survive are not those of architects. Rossetti described it as 'More a poem than a house—but admirable to live in too', while Lady Burne-Jones remembered 'how successful the laying out of the garden was, and that the house never looked *bare*'. At one time Morris proposed making additions as a flat for the Burne-Joneses, and drawings by Webb for two alternative schemes survive in the Museum (E.65-71-1916), but these were never carried out.

The interiors of Red House were originally decorated by Morris and his friends, the pièce de résistance being the drawing room open to the roof, with a ceiling covered with floral designs, and the walls painted by Burne-Jones with scenes from the medieval romance of Sir Degrevaunt. Some of this work still survives though most has been swept away; it is remembered primarily today for providing the inspiration which led to the founding of the firm of Morris & Co.

Lit. J. Newman, *West Kent and the Weald*, 1969, pp. 155-59. R. Brandon Jones, 'Philip Webb' in P. Ferriday, *Victorian architecture*, 1963, pp. 250-51.

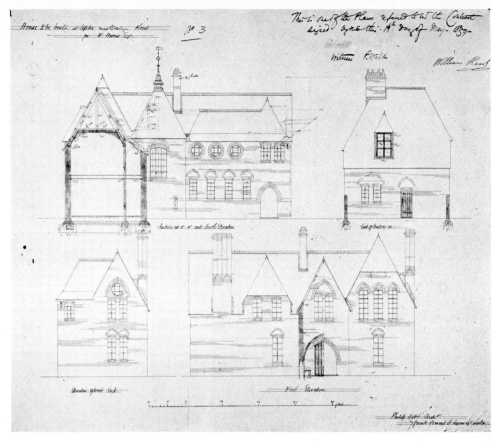

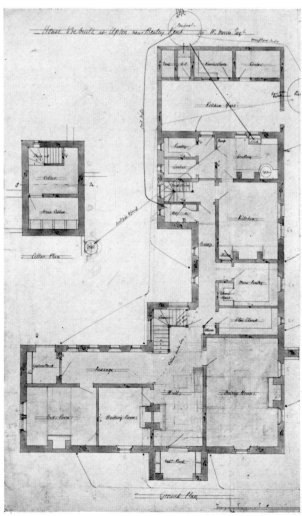

*Ground Plan, V & A M E.59-1916*

**24** Samuel Sanders Teulon
Elvetham Hall, Hartley Wintney, Hampshire. 1859
*Indenture, schedules and specifications of works on 50 leaves of vellum, and 17 contract drawings mounted on linen (one detached), bound into a volume lettered* Contract for additional buildings and alterations at Elvetham Hall *and dated* 1859. *The detached sheet signed* S. S. Teulon Archt., *and inscribed* The Right Honble. The Lord Calthorpe, Elvetham Hall, proposed alterations and additions. South West elevation. S. S. Teulon Archt. 9, Craigs Court, Charing Cross, London. This is one of the drawings referred to in the foregoing contract. Witness to the signature of Samuel Sanders Teulon, Henry Mills the elder and Henry Mills the younger *signed* Henry Mills, Henry Mills Jnr., J. C. Gregory *and* Thomas Soden.

*Numbered* 12
*Pen and ink and wash. Size of volume* $20\frac{7}{8} \times 16\frac{1}{2}$ (53.2 × 41.9). *Size of detached Sheet* $20\frac{1}{4} \times 28\frac{3}{4}$ (51.3 × 72.1)
Lent from Elvetham Hall

Mark Girouard has described Elvetham as 'the holiest or unholiest of zebras, being not only striped, but also zigzagged and diapered all over with bricks, and slates of different colours. The contortions of its roofs, plan and detailing defy analysis, there are no firm outlines of dominant shapes, everything is dissolving. Verticals shoot off into diagonals, or are disguised by fearful zigzaggings in coloured brick. The innumerable brick arches, instead of carrying the eye down to the ground are interrupted at their springing by blocks of elaborately engraved stone. The cornice line is broken up into restlessly notched brickwork, the roof is chopped up into dozens of little pieces. Inside there are no simple rectangular

rooms; they are always breaking o breaking through into different sh projections or adjacent spaces. Every face is busy with patterns or figures c or in stained glass — and what does add up to? The idea of a building so b up that it appears to be quivering all like an enormous multi-coloured je an intriguing one (though whether T was thinking that is purely surmise).

Teulon was apparently as mu mystery to his own generation as he the 20th century historian. The *Engineer and Architects' Journal* rem in July 1862, 'The mention of Teulon's name is quite sufficier prepare one for seeing some cu achievement, in the way of novelty a rate. But novelty is not to be soug any risk; and redundance of orna tation, however good in itself is conducive to beauty—far from it. much less worthy then is that fertil mere whim which can claim little than this facility! Yet under this ba

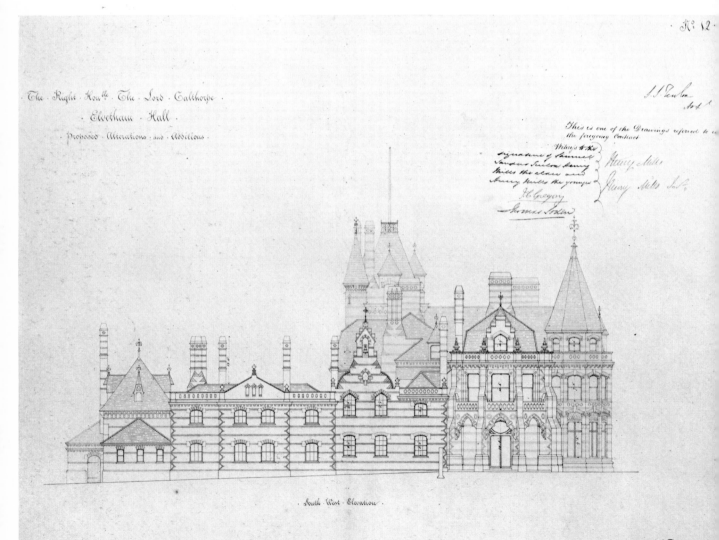

forced to include many of Mr.
.on's productions.' The *Builder* said
.lvetham 'the details, including the
.r, are grotesque rather than archi-
.nic'.

.he care taken by Teulon, both over
.contract and the drawings associated
. it, the consistency of his work and
.imilarity to that of Thomas Harris,
.erick Pilkington, and other con-
.poraries appears to evince that the
.n of Elvetham was stimulated by
.h more than a 'mere whim'.

.arious additions to the house were
.e in 1901, 1910-13 and later.

M. Girouard 'Acrobatic Gothic',
.untry Life, 31 December 1970, pp.
.83-87. *BN*, 1 June 1860, p. 431.
.26 May 1860, p. 331; 2 June 1860,
.345.

*.ective view from the* Builder, *26 May
.0, p. 331*

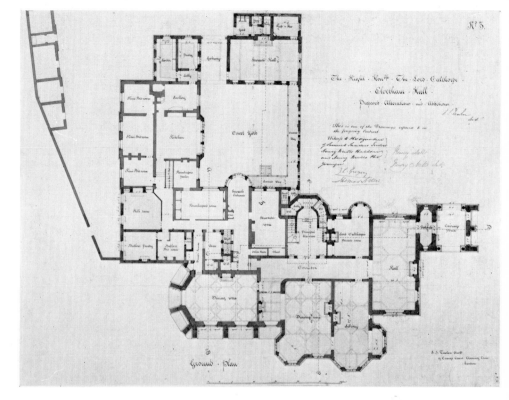

**25** Albert Jenkins Humbert
Sandringham House, Sandringham,
Norfolk. c. 1862
*Signed* A. J. Humbert and *inscribed*
(Study) Sandringham
*Water-colour* 20½ × 34 (52 × 86.3)
W11/6/7, given by the Rev. L. M.
Humbert
Lent by the Royal Institute of
British Architects

The Sandringham estate was purchased
by Albert Edward, Prince of Wales, in
1861 as a hunting-seat. In the following
year he employed Humbert, probably
because of the work Humbert had
previously done for his father, the Prince
Consort, to draw up plans for a new
house to replace the existing one. The
subsequent sequence of building is
complex, but it would appear that
Humbert's original design primarily for
an addition to the old house was not
finally completed until after 1870. In
1864 the *Builder* reported that many
improvements had been made to the
gardens and out-buildings, and three
years later that great progress had been
made in completing the new kitchen and
offices. At this time they also noticed
that 'The old conservatory adjoining the
house is being rapidly converted into a
billiard-room, and an American bowling
alley, 100 ft. long is being built; the wall
on one side is of concrete and has every
appearance of being as hard as rock. This
alley and billiard room will be li[g]
with gas. The whole of the building w
have been carried out by Messrs. G
contractors, of Swaffham, under
direction of Mr. Humbert, architect

Later alterations to the house incl
in 1892 the addition of another stor
the bowling alley. Previously, in 18
ballroom designed by Colonel R.
Edis was added to the main house,
after a fire, another storey and fu
ornamentation in 1891 in the
Jacobean style as Humbert's ori
design.

Lit. *Br*, 24 December 1864, p. 9[3]
November 1867, p. 807; 1 Feb[?]
1868, p. 73. N. Pevsner, *North Wes[t]
South Norfolk*, 1962, p. 301.

William Eden Nesfield

Plans, elevations and sections for an entrance lodge to Kew Gardens *Signed W. E. Nesfield [& Shaw deleted] Architects 30 Argyll Street Regent St. W. London and dated Decr. 1st. 1866. Numbered 3 and inscribed with notes etc. and signed Mess. Street & Son 14 Jany. 1867. Stamped by the Office of Works and* dated Jan 3 1867

*Pen and ink and wash* $20\frac{1}{2} \times 19\frac{1}{2}$ (52.4 × 49.6)

D.1332-1907, given by E. J. May, FRIBA, for the Phené Spiers Collection of architectural drawings
Victoria and Albert Museum

'As for the lodge at Kew, with its cut brick pilasters, high-pitched roof, tall carved chimney, pedimented dormers, plaster cove and classic detail, it is a bit of fully-fledged "Queen Anne" as it was called in those days—thirty years ago, be it remembered—when the Architectural world was still floundering in the throes of the Gothic revival . . .'

Lit. J. M. Brydon, 'William Eden Nesfield, 1835-1888, Part I', *AR*, vol. i, 1896-97, p. 239, illus. on p. 238.

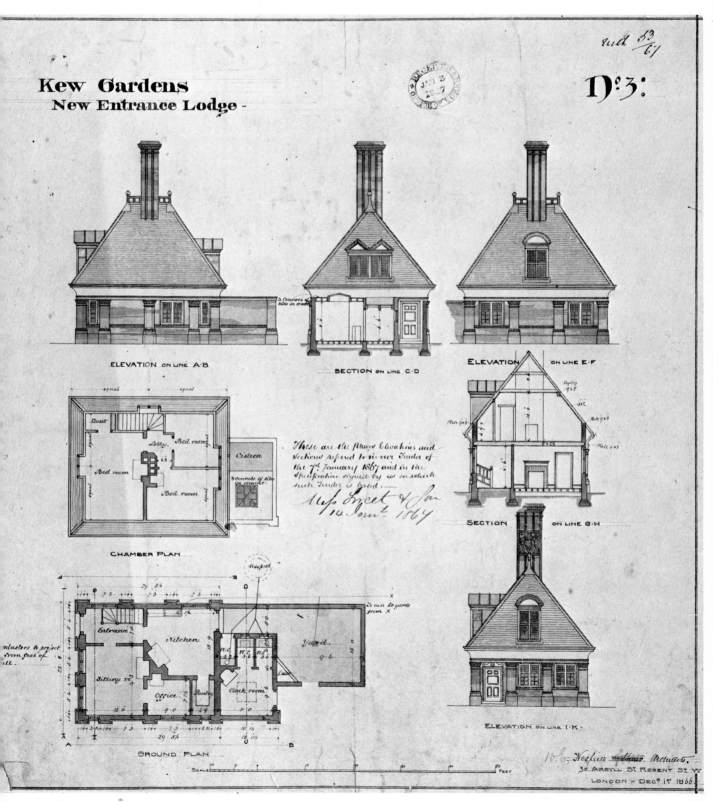

**27** Professor Robert Kerr
Model of the staircase
tower, Bear Wood,
Berkshire. c. 1867
*Wood* 30 × 16 (76.2 ×
40.6)
Lent from Bearwood
College

The tower, which contains
the main staircase, and has an
additional spiral 'Bachelors'
Stairs', is some 30 feet square
at the base, and nearly 90
feet high. It is open within,
and the upper part acts as a
lantern. Bear Wood is an
extremely large and complex
house, designed in an
'Elizabethan' style by Robert
Kerr, Professor of Archi-
tecture in King's College,
London, for John Walter,
MP, proprietor of *The Times*.
Begun in 1865, the tower
dates from c. 1867. The
building was complete externally by June 1868, when
Walter threw a party for the
380 workmen. At this dinner
'proposing the health of the
architect, Mr Walter said
that it was from the perusal
of Mr Kerr's book, *The
Gentleman's House*, he had
been led to seek that gentleman's assistance'. Kerr, in
subsequent editions of the
book, reproduced plans of
the house, as does Sir
Nikolaus Pevsner in
*Berkshire*.

These show that the house
is built round a courtyard
which, with a glazed skylight,
acts as a picture-gallery,
rising through two storeys.
Except in the main rooms,
one obtains the impression
that the sexes, whether the
servants or the house-guests,
were rigidly segregated. The
'young ladies' rooms' are
divided from those of the
'Bachelors' by a solid wall,
and there are separate staircases for them. The men
servants were in like manner
kept well away from the
women, who appear to have
been guarded by the House-
keeper.

Bear Wood was built of
'superior red brick, made on

he estate, and the dressings
re of brown Mansfield stone
f Mr. Lindley's quarries'.
Valter built his own gas-
orks to provide illumination,
nd installed twenty-two
athrooms, which, as Mark
Girouard comments, was 'a
ery generous supply for a
Victorian house'. It was not
ntil 1874 that everything
vas completed, and the final
ill totalled £120,000, which
vas double Kerr's original
stimate. It is not at all
urprising, therefore, that
vhen the architect asked for
n additional commission, he
vas rebuffed by Walter, who
gnored the request. This
uge house is now a school.

it. *Br*, 6 June 1868, p. 406.
*A*, 9 July 1870, p. 21.
M. Girouard, *The Victorian
country house*, 1971, pp.
121-24.

**28** William Burges
Design for the Clock
Tower of Cardiff Castle
*Signed* William Burges.
Archt. 15 Buckingham
Street Strand. W.C.,
*lettered* Cardiff Castle
New Tower: No. 9,
*inscribed with scale*, *notes*,
The Tower is 25 feet
square *etc.*
*Pen and ink and wash*
$69\frac{1}{2} \times 25$ ($167.5 \times 63.6$)
Lent by the Lord Mayor
and Corporation of
Cardiff

The association between the
third Marquess of Bute and
William Burges began in
1865. The Marquess was
then only 18 years old and
possessed immense wealth
derived from the docks of
Cardiff and estates in Wales
and Scotland. Both he and
Burges were obsessed with
medieval antiquarianism, and
Bute had the money which
enabled Burges to indulge in
his fantasies on a scale which
probably no other patron
would have supported.
Besides building the fairy-
tale Castell Coch, a few miles
to the north of Cardiff,
Burges and the Marquess also
set about rebuilding the
Castle. At this time the Castle
consisted mainly of ruined
walls and a late 18th century
Gothic house by Capability
Brown. Coming straight from
his failure to win the Law
Courts competition, Burges
set to work with enthusiasm
in 1868 on the first portion,
the clock or Bachelor's
Tower.

This present drawing, first
reproduced in the *Architect*
in 1882, forms part of a
magnificent collection of
many hundreds of designs by
Burges for the Castle which
are now in the possession of
Cardiff City Corporation.
This unrivalled collection of
fantasy comprises not only
architectural sections, plans
and elevations, but sketches,
water-colours and full-size
cartoons for decoration—

carved woodwork, door-
handles, stained-glass, tiles,
chimney-pieces, painting, and
so on.

The Clock Tower is a
typically idiosyncratic, top-
heavy tower by Burges; even
the Law Courts design had
a similar one. At Cardiff, the
exterior gives no hint of the
splendour of the rooms within, one on each floor. It was

more or less complete by
1874-75. On either side of the
clock faces are niches containing large coloured statues
of the Planets, the work of
Burges's favourite sculptor,
Thomas Nicholls.

Inside, the two lowest
rooms were for servants and
are not decorated. Above
these is the Winter Smoking
Room, richly decorated with

stained glass and pair
The vaulted ceiling dis
the signs of the Zodiac
occupations of the Sea
A typical Burges chin
piece is carved with grou
Lovers in Winter, with a
a figure of Cupid. A
painted and gilded.

The room over this
bedroom, with a bath a
ent. The decoration

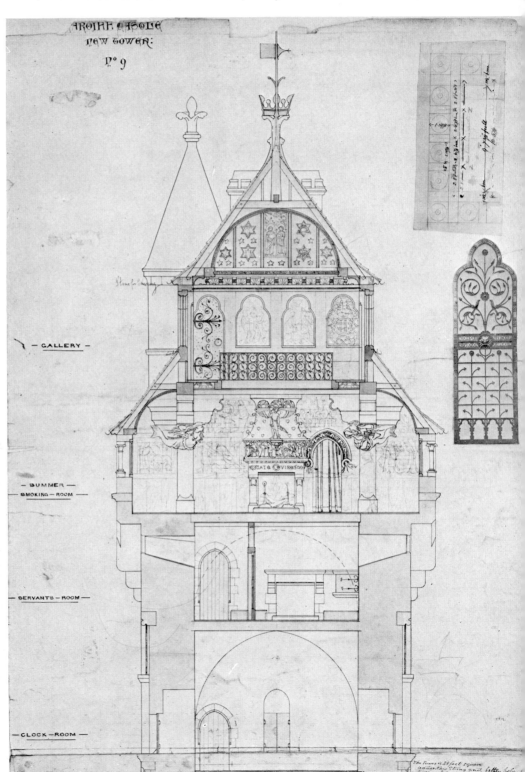

68

impler, the walls being painted with scenes connected with precious stones and metals. Continuing upwards, the clock room is reached, with a kitchen above, and then on to the top room, the Summer Smoking Room, with its magnificent views over Cardiff, and across the Bristol Channel to Somerset. There is another highly carved chimney-piece, this time the subject being Lovers in Summer, the hood being peppered with Love Birds. Mark Girouard describes this room as 'perhaps the strangest and most wonderful of all rooms'. It extends through two storeys with a clerestory. Not an inch of walls, ceilings, or floor is left undecorated. From the crystal-studded roof hangs a large golden chandlier representing the sun, in the centre of which is Apollo.

A correspondent to the *Architect* in 1874, having been over the Tower considered the Winter Smoking Room 'warm, homelike (*sic*), and in a word, comfortable', and the Summer Smoking Room 'cool, lofty and well-lighted'. The divans shown in the room in the designs, are still there, though somewhat mouldy and the worse for wear.

Burges and the Marquess went on to build other towers and to fill them with strange rooms—the Arab Room, the Chaucer Room and others. In this castle there is much to see, so much exquisite decoration, in tile, inlay, glass, painting, carving, as to render adequate description impossible. It is a quite unforgettable experience to wander through the rooms, which are open to the public, though at the moment certain of them are occupied by a college of music.

Illus. *A*, 1 April 1882. *The architectural designs of William Burges A.R.A.*, ed. R. P. Pullan, 1883, pl. 32.

Lit. M. Girouard, *The Victorian country house*, 1971, pp. 125-30.

**29** William Burges
Design for the Great Staircase of
Cardiff Castle. Drawn by Axel Haig.
1874
*Water-colour* $24\frac{1}{2} \times 19\frac{3}{4}$ (62.3 × 50.2)
Lent by Mr Derek Edwards

Burges exhibited his design at the Royal
Academy in 1874, where it was received
with a certain amount of surprise. The
*Builder* thought it a very fine drawing
of a 'wonderfully elaborate piece of work
of barbaric splendour . . . The mass of
gilded balustrade, and the rather awk-
ward-looking pedestal cropping up at the
stair angle, and carrying a Gothic man on
a Gothic horse, altogether produce a
combined effect of such a nature that we
are not surprised that the draughtsman
should have thought it necessary to
array the figures in Medieval costume, for
no modern dress, any more than modern
habits and culture, would harmonise with
this startling specimen of interior decoration. It is less out of character at Cardiff
Castle than it would be in many places,
and we fully admit the skill exhibited;
but it may be questioned whether the
same amount of labour and expense might
not have produced something of more
permanent artistic value.'

The *Architect* was slightly more lyrical
over the 'clever and elaborately-tinted
drawings', in which Burges's love of
brilliant colour was 'wonderfully displayed'. The reviewer continued, 'Here
we have a really clever design, somewhat
bold perhaps in detail, overladen with one
great blaze of gold and showy coloured
decoration, in which red is predominant.
The drawing shows an elaborate staircase
of French Gothic character, simply
treated in detail, but with an open
quatrefoil arrangement of balustrading
that is anything but happy, and the whole
covered with the most brilliant coloured
decoration. The vaulted roof springs from
a rather weak central shaft, while the
surrounding arcaded work is full of
detail and figure sculpture, the flat
surfaces being treated with figure decoration, brilliant in colouring and clever in
design, although wanting in repose and
harmony—reminding almost of a mid-
summer's night's dream, with all its
gorgeousness of gilding and colour, and
yet withal stamping the artist as one of the
most talented and original of modern
designers.'

In contrast, the *Building News* was of
the opinion the design was 'one of the
least happy that we have seen from Mr.
Burges's pencil. No definite system is
visible in his colouring, and the contrasts
of colour are more startling than pleasing.
Mr. Burges evidently labours under the
extraordinary impression that the main
purpose of architecture is to serve as the
basis for the display of colour.'

R. P. Pullan, writing in 1883, says that
the decoration of the staircase was then
incomplete. Subsequently, following an
accident in 1928, Lord Bute transformed
the hall, and all Burges's work, including
the staircase, was swept away.

Exhib. *RA*, 1874, no. 1146.
Lit. *A*, 23 May 1874, p. 286. *B*, 16 May
1874, p. 409. *A*, 4 July 1874, p. 6.
Illus. *A*, 4 July 1874; 1 April 1882.
*The architectural designs of William
Burges, A.R.A.*, ed. R. P. Pullan,
1883, pl. 33.

William Eden Nesfield

Plans and perspective view for an entrance lodge to Broadlands, Romsey, Hampshire.

*Signed* W. Eden Nesfield Architect o Argyll Street Regent St. W. *and ated* Decr. 1871. *Inscribed with scale nd* Broadlands No 61 Survey. October. 1871

*Pen and ink and wash* 20½ × 23 52.1 × 58.4)

.1340-1907, given by Mr E. J. May RIBA, for the Phené Spiers Collection f architectural drawings ictoria and Albert Museum

Lit. J. M. Brydon, 'William Eden Nesfield 1835-1888, Part I', *AR*, vol. i, 1896-97, pp. 235-47. The lodge as built is illustrated on p. 235, and the perspective design on p. 240.

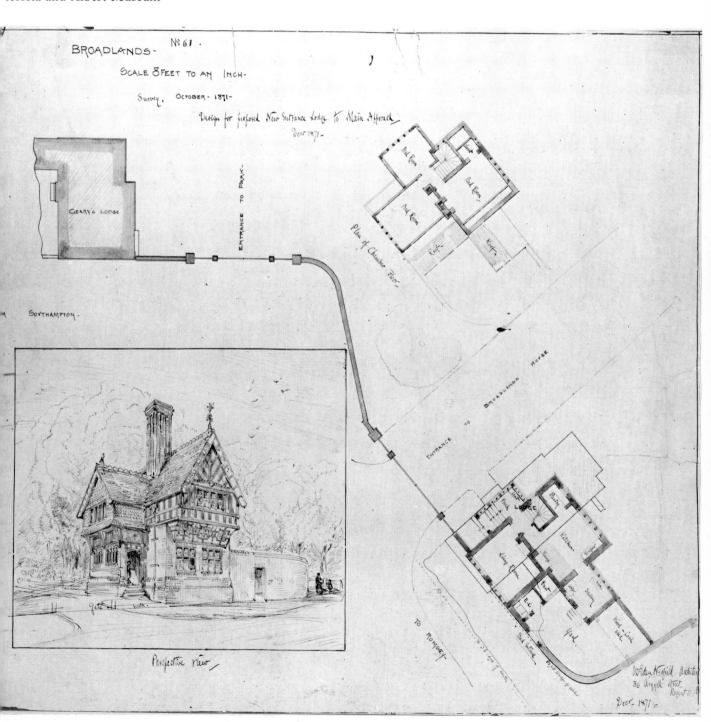

**31 Alfred Waterhouse**
Clock Tower and Chapel, Eaton Hall, Cheshire. 1875
*Signed* A. Waterhouse *and dated* 1875
*Pen and ink and water-colour* 24 × 17⅛ (64 × 44.5)
D.1880-1908, given by Mr P. Waterhouse, MA, FRIBA
the Phené Spiers Collection of architectural draw
Victoria and Albert Museum

In 1803-12 Viscount Belgrave, created 1st Marquess of V
minster in 1831, employed William Porden to rebuild his
century house, designed by William Samwell, as a specta
gothic mansion. Further alterations were carried out bet
1845 and 1854 by William Burn for the 2nd Marquess and bet
1870 and 1883 by Waterhouse for the 3rd Marquess, create
Duke in 1874. At a cost of £600,000 Waterhouse remodelle
house in a style 'which though owing something to the
century and something to France was an outstanding expre
of Victorian originality'. By comparison with the main
(demolished in 1961) the chapel and clock tower, which
survive, are reasonably subdued; only the gable-formed
minations to the staircase turret in the south east corner, and
clock tower, testify to Waterhouse's inventiveness in other
of the house. The *Building News* described Waterhouse's
spective as 'a beautiful but sketchy drawing—[which] repre
a picturesque cluster of buildings, consisting of a private c
for Eaton Hall, with a high pitched roof, flanked by a sl
staircase turret; while detached, but still forming part of the
stands a square clock tower of very considerable size and
with clock faces contrived in the same manner as those at
minster, and surmounted by a picturesque high roof.
Waterhouse's usual mastery of outline and skill in compo
are well seen in this clever view, and this small drawing, wh
in water-colours and no doubt by his own hand, fully kee
Mr Waterhouse's reputation as a colourist.' The interior
chapel is decorated with mosaics and glass designed by Fr
Shields and made by Heaton, Butler and Bayne; other furnis

ere designed by Waterhouse. The contractors were Messrs
George Smith & Co.

xhib. R.A. 1875, no. 945.

Ilus. *Br*, 9 August 1879, p. 888. J. Mordaunt Crook, *Victorian
architecture, a visual anthology*, London, 1972, pl. 224.

Lit. N. Pevsner and E. Hubbard, *Cheshire*, 1971, pp. 207-10.
*BN*, 7 May, 1875, p. 509.

Richard Norman Shaw
The Manor House, Adcote, Shropshire. 1875-76
*Inscribed* Adcote, West elevation. *Numbered* 12
*Pen and ink and water-colour* $19\frac{1}{8} \times 25\frac{7}{8}$ (48.5 × 65.7)
E.1697-1908, given by Norman Shaw for the Phené Spiers
Collection of architectural drawings
Victoria and Albert Museum

Adcote, like Flete of 1878 and Dawpool of 1882, shows that Shaw
was quite content to continue building in an Elizabethan and
Jacobean manner many years after Queen Anne had become
fashionable. The *Builder* approved what was termed the 'late
Gothic protest' but was nevertheless unable to accept certain of
its more picturesque elements: battlements, for instance, it found
'unnecessary and incongruous'. Adcote, built for Mrs Rebecca
Darby, a relative of the iron-founding Darbys of Coalbrookdale,
was said to be nearing completion in December 1878. Girouard
suggests that the concept of medieval great hall which has been
added to in the 16th century may have been inspired by Southwick
Hall in Northamptonshire which Shaw sketched in the late
1850s. The house was built by Messrs Hale & Sons of stone from
a quarry on the estate and the walls, so thick as to be convincingly
medieval in plan, were lined on the inside with cement faced with
brick and ashlar. The great hall, entered from a central corridor
under a gallery, measures some 60 × 32 feet and is panelled to
a height of 13 feet. The timber roof is carried by three stone
arches, a motif possibly derived from Ightham Mote in Kent.

Mark Girouard has said of Adcote that 'Shaw is the maestro in
complete control, who knows just what he is capable of and never
puts a foot wrong. It is a cold masterpiece, there is a slight sense of
unreality about it, and one has the uneasy foreknowledge that this
kind of brilliance is heading down a dead end, and will lead to the
slick and sterile competence of millionaire Elizabethan houses of
the 1920's. But it is still a masterpiece.'

Lit. M. Girouard, *The Victorian country house*, 1972, pp. 158-60.
*BN*, 20 December, 1878, p. 640. N. Pevsner, *Shropshire*, 1958,
pp. 52-3. *Br*, 10 May, 1879, p. 504.

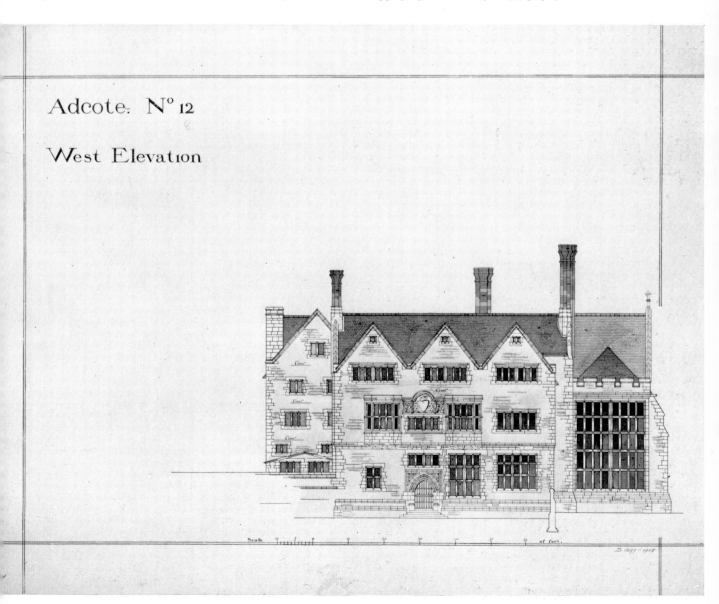

Adcote. N° 12

West Elevation

**33** William Eden Nesfield
Loughton Hall, Loughton, Essex. 1878
*Signed* W. Eden Nesfield Archt. 19, Margaret Street,
London, W. *Inscribed* Loughton Hall, No. 6. Entrance
Front. Garden Front. Memo., The chimney stacks to Main
Building are to be 2 feet less in height than shewn.
*Initialled* J. B. This is one of the Drawings referred to in
the contract agreement bearing date Oct. 14th, 1878, and
signed by me *signed* John Bentley. *Two alterations to the
original design are each inscribed* This alteration to drawing
was made before the Contract was signed *and initialled* J.B.
*Pen and ink, water-colour and pencil* 18¾ × 25 (47.7 × 63.5)
D.1352-1907, given by Mr E. J. May, FRIBA, for the Phené
Spiers collection of architectural drawings
Victoria and Albert Museum

The House was designed for the Rev. J. W. Maitland, w
sister was married to Nesfield's cousin Osbert Salvin. Gird
has described it as 'Nesfield's most likeable country h
altogether delightful in its Queen Anne mixture of 17th-
century motifs and sash windows, lead lights, gables, cu
oeils-de-boeuf, white painted balustrades, plastered gables,
roof and tall chimney stacks.' Pevsner notes the similarity
Norman Shaw's only Essex building, a house at Chigwell o
same date. Apropos the influence of Shaw on Nesfield it is v
noting that Nesfield uses at Loughton Hall the 'Ipswich'
which Shaw had used in 1875 at Old Swan House (43) an
1877 at New Zealand Chambers.
    Loughton Hall is now a school.

Lit. M. Girouard, *The Victorian country house*, 1972, pl. 4€
Pevsner, *Essex*, 1954, p. 262. AR, vol. i, December
    pp. 293-94.

*Top. An earlier design by Ne*
*(1871). V&AM D.1354-190*
*Bottom. Ground Plan. V&A*
*D.1349-1907*

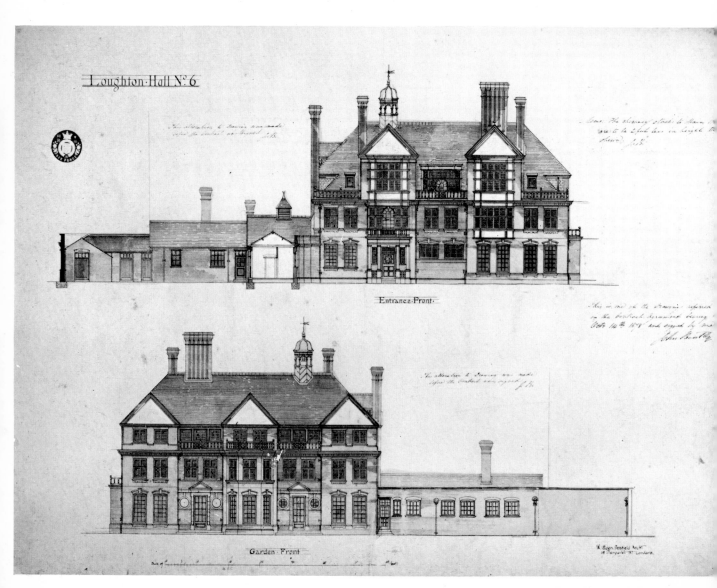

Loughton·Hall·Nº·6

Entrance·Front·

Garden·Front·

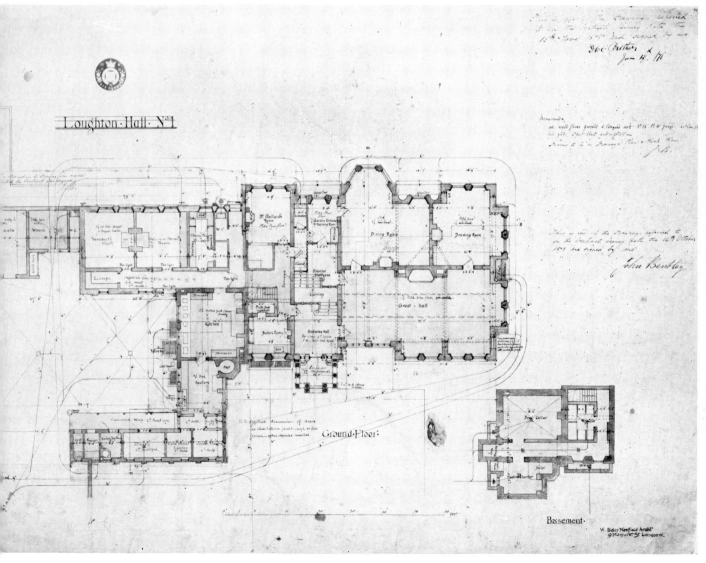

Loughton·Hall·Nº1

Ground·Floor·

Basement·

**34** John James Stevenson
The Grand Saloon, Ken Hill,
Snettisham, Norfolk. 1880
*Signed* A J Adames Delt. *and dated*
1880. *Inscribed with names, etc.*
*Pen and ink* 18½ × 22¾ (47 × 57.7)
D.1789-1908, given by Mrs J. J.
Stevenson, for the Phené Spiers
Collection of architectural drawings
Victoria and Albert Museum

Edward Green, the younger, acquired
the Snettisham estate in 1877 and built
Ken Hill as essentially a house for shooting holidays, since he spent most of his
time in London and Yorkshire managing
the family business. His father had
earlier employed Thomas Jeckyll to
restore the family house, Old Hall near
Wakefield, and his son would almost
certainly have employed Jeckyll again,

but in 1877 Jeckyll had become mad, and
in 1881 died. So Green asked Stevenson
to design Ken Hill instead. Stevenson was
rather a surprising choice, since his
reputation was based on town rather than
country houses. Although the asymmetrical form and plan of Ken Hill are
Gothic in derivation, and the house is
constructed in the local brown carstone
rather than brick, the detailing is undeniably Queen Anne. In his two volume
*House architecture*, published in the same
year that Ken Hill was built, Stevenson
set down his views about the importance
of the grand saloon, 'the place of great
reception rooms might in many cases be
supplied by a Hall of the old type, which
would have even greater dignity, without
their dismal character when out of use.
Such a hall forms a charming feature
even in a moderately sized country house.

It is much better than a drawing roo
dancing and games; for the oak floo
be left exposed opposite couche
fireplace, and instead of the quanti
fragile furniture and ornaments
which a drawing room is usually e
bered, a few oak benches and tabl
all that is required.' The saloon and
main living rooms at Ken Hill are si
on the first floor, probably to impro
view from the windows across the
flat surrounding parkland. The esta
next to Sandringham (25) and the
of Wales visited Green for shooting p

Exhib. RA, 1880, no. 1088.
Illus. *BN*, 25 June 1880, p. 744.
Lit. M. Girouard, *The Victorian c*
*house*, 1972, pp. 161-64. M. Gir
'Ken Hill, Norfolk', *Country*
21 December 1967, pp. 1654-56

KENHILL : NORFOLK.
EDWARD GREEN ESQUIRE    GRAND SALOON    J·J·STEVENSON, F
ARCHITECT

**35** Charles Francis Annesley
Voysey
Broadleys, Cartmel,
Lancashire. 1898
*Signed* C. F. A. Voysey, 6,
Carlton Hill, NW *and
dated* July, 1898. *Inscribed*
Broadleys Windermere for
A Currer Briggs Esq. ⅛th
scale 2nd set
*Pencil, and water-colour*
29 × 20½ (73.7 × 52.1)
E.252-1913
Victoria and Albert
Museum

Hitchock has said of
Broadleys that 'in its horizon-
tality, its concentration of
fenestration and its avoidance
of mediaeval feeling this
house represents the extreme
point of innovation and
originality in Voysey's work'.
Broadleys was one of several
houses designed by Voysey in
1898 for the Windermere
area. All have steeply pitched
roofs and wide eaves and an
austere severity which may
reflect the harsh climate and
barren landscape in which
they were set. All Voysey's
designs, unlike many of those
of his contemporary, Shaw,
were structurally simple, the
internal walls passing through
both floors, and relatively
inexpensive to build. Horace
Townsend, when writing
about Broadleys in the *Studio*,
related that Voysey had told
him that he had chosen Bath
stone dressings, green slates
and rough cast for their cheap-
ness. The central bay window,
glazed to its full height,
helped to compensate for any
loss of light in the drawing
room caused by the verandah
which runs along one end of
it. In a very similar design,
also of 1898, for a house for
H. Rickards, Voysey omitted
a verandah and reduced the
importance of the central bay
window, making the two
outside bays dominant.

The *Builder*, when noticing
a drawing of Broadleys which
Voysey showed at the Royal
Academy in 1899, remarked
that this style of drawing in
pencil with 'whity green'

washes was something 'which
Mr. Voysey has invented'. It
soon became the accepted
mode among many of his
contemporaries.

Lit. *Br*, 10 June 1899, p. 563.
H. R. Hitchcock, *Archi-
tecture, 19th and 20th centuries*, 1958, pp. 276-78.
*Studio*, April 1899, p. 158.

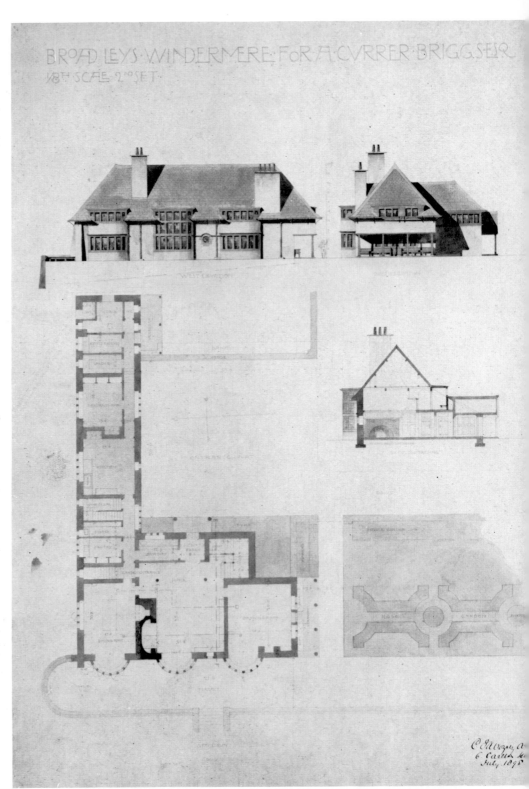

*ogue 36*

**36** Owen Jones (*previous page*)
Drawing room ceiling, No. 8, Kensington Palace Gardens, London. 1843
*Water-colour* Octagonal 18½ × 18½
(47 × 47)
8352
Victoria and Albert Museum

As a result of the recommendations of a committee appointed in 1838 to enquire into the financial state of the royal gardens, in 1841 the land now occupied by Kensington Palace Gardens was detached from Kensington Palace and prepared for sale on building leases, in order to pay for improvements to the garden at Frogmore. James Pennethorne and Thomas Chawner as architects to the Commissioners for Woods and Forests drew up plans providing for a broad road of detached villas. The plots were advertised in 1842 and eventually an offer from John Marriott Blashfield, a partner in the firm of building materials manufacturers Wyatt and Parker, was accepted.

Within days of making his offer to the Crown Commissioners (see 37) John M. Blashfield forwarded plans, elevations and details prepared by Owen Jones for a villa on plot 6, later no. 8. To all intents and purposes the designs adhered to the fashionable Italianate style; the only real indications of Jones's authorship were in the detailing. The façades were richly and prettily encrusted with cement ornamentation in his favourite Moorish style and the balcony walls and the parapets pierced with fretwork designs. Pennethorne reported to the Commissioners that the house was larger than they had originally conceived. 'As regards the elevations. We have to observe that from the general forms, and the richness of ornament, the design will probably produce an appearance equal to that originally intended for this site and we do not feel that we ought to object to the peculiarity of the proposed Moresque enrichments though hitherto not much adopted in this country.' The stipulations laid down by the Commissioners did not permit Jones to use any colour on the exterior; inside, however, his specifications called for the ceilings of the ground floor rooms to be 'painted and decorated in colours' and the principal staircase and hall to be 'paved with ornamental floor tiles'. The first and second floor rooms were 'plastered and papered' and 'whited with plain cornices'. The house appears to have been completed by 1845 but it remained untenanted until 1852, when a Mrs Matilda Murray bought it from Blashfield's mortgagees for £6,300, less than half of the £15,000 required to build it. Mrs Murray immediately converted the house into two flats and so it remained until it was demolished in 1961.

Jones's decoration is not simply based on Moorish precedents; it also derives from other sources particularly medieval illuminated manuscripts, which he had carefully studied in connection with his c printing business.

Lit. M. Girouard 'Town houses fc wealthy', *Country Life*, 11 Nover 1971, p. 1269. G.L.C., *Survey of don*, vol. xxxvii, Northern Kensir 1973. Files in the Crown Estate C

**37** Thomas Henry Wyatt and L Brandon
Entrance gates to Kensington P Gardens, Bayswater Road, Lor 1845
*Inscribed on the back* Perspective of the North Entrance to Kensir Palace Gardens erected for J. Blashfield Esqre from the design under the superintendence of M Wyatt and Brandon, April 1845
*Water-colour* 19½ × 36⅝ (49.5 × Lent by The Royal Boroug Kensington and Chelsea

The site of Kensington Palace Ga was made available for building in by the Commissioners for Wood: Forests (see 36), and J. M. Blas undertook to erect a road of villas Commissioners had originally statec they would be responsible for the er of the entrance lodges to the roa Blashfield requested permission to them himself on the understanding he be allowed to sell the gravel exca

during the preparation of the foundations of his houses, to which the Commissioners agreed. In the event Blashfield, who eventually went bankrupt, realized only £1,000 from gravel sales and the entrance lodges cost £2,000 to build.

Blashfield employed several architects to supply him with designs for houses including H. E. Kendall, Owen Jones, C. H. Lewis and Wyatt and Brandon. Besides designing the entrance lodges, the latter partnership was also responsible for the two houses in an Italianate style in the foreground on the right hand side of the road and the first on the left. Other houses were later built in the road by James Knowles, James Murray, Banks and Barry, S. Smirke and P. Hardwick.

Exhib. RA 1845, no. 1104. 'Pictorial Kensington: The Old Court Suburb', Leighton House, 1951, no. 449.

Illus. *Country Life*, 11 November 1971, p. 1268.

Lit. M. Girouard, 'Town houses for the wealthy', *Country Life*, 11 November 1971, p. 1270. G.L.C., *Survey of London*, vol. xxxvii, Northern Kensington, 1973, illus pl. 92a.

## 38 Sir Charles Barry
Bridgwater House, St James's, London. c. 1845
*Inscribed* Bridgwater House, Town Residence of the Earl of Ellesmere, South Elevation
*Pen and ink and wash* $17\frac{1}{2} \times 28\frac{1}{2}$ (44.5 × 72.5)
Lent by the Royal Institute of British Architects

The house was begun in 1847 for Lord Francis Egerton (created Earl of Ellesmere and Viscount Brackley in 1846) and was named after his grandfather, the canal-building Duke of Bridgwater. Barry's first design, exhibited at the Royal Academy in 1841 (no. 981), with a Grand Corinthian order was rejected as too expensive. An intermediate design followed in an 'Anglo Italian' style similar to that which he had used at Highclere (16), but that was also rejected in favour of this design in the more fashionable High Renaissance style of his club houses (see 96). Charles Barry junior recorded in his diary that his father continued to refer to this later design as 'Anglo-Italian', and he noted, 'This will I think be a very grand mansion, but one that will excite much animadversion on account of its style as being far from a pure one.' The statement is difficult to understand, because, while the style is certainly not as pure as that of the Travellers' and Reform Clubs, it is not on the other hand particularly debased. The foundations of the new house were commenced in January 1846 and building began in July 1847. The carcase was finished by September 1848, although the final plan of the interior was not settled until 1849. The great picture gallery was opened to the public in May 1851, but the remainder of the house was not completed until 1854. The builders were Messrs Baker; and C. H. Smith, John Thomas and Richard Westmacott junior were employed for decorative work. The saloon was decorated after the death of the first Lord Ellesmere in 1857 partly to the designs of J. Götzenberger.

The house was damaged during the war and restored by Robert Atkinson and Partners in 1948-49.

Lit. G.L.C. *Survey of London*, vol. xxx, The Parish of St. James, Westminster, 1960, pp. 496-509, pl. 239a.

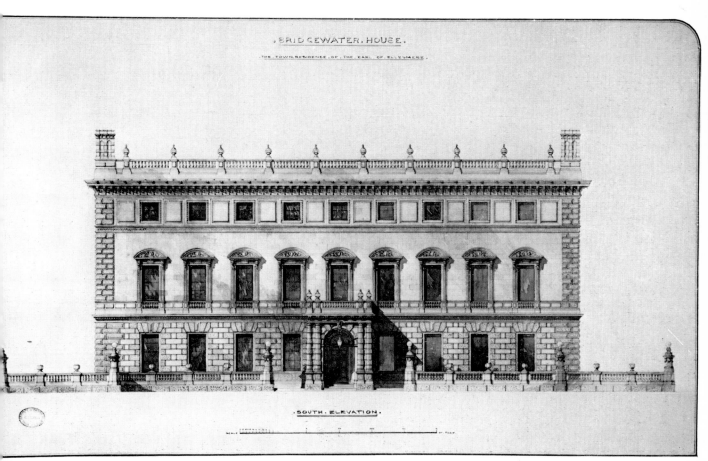

BRIDGEWATER HOUSE.
THE TOWN RESIDENCE OF THE EARL OF ELLESMERE.

SOUTH ELEVATION.

**39** Owen Jones
Room in an unidentified house. c. 1860
*Water-colour*
E.1691-93, 1706-1912
Victoria and Albert Museum

Jones's rich Pompeian decorations were almost certainly adapted
from the designs illustrated in Wilhelm Zahn's *Die schönsten
Ornamente und merkwürdigsten Gemälde aus Pompeji, Herkulanum
und Stabiae*, published from 1829. He had a copy in his library
and is known to have greatly admired it.

Leonard Collmann
Ironwork, 20 Arlington Street, London. After 1869
*Signed on the back* L. W. Collmann Esq., 75 Grosvenor St.
*Lettered* 20 Arlington Street. Ironwork to Park Front.
*Scale* $\frac{1}{2}$ in = 1 ft
*Watermark dated* 1869
*Pen and ink, pencil and water-colour* $32\frac{3}{8} \times 23\frac{1}{8}$ (82.6 × 59.1)
593. G
Victoria and Albert Museum

The design, which is reminiscent of much earlier ironwork at places such as Brighton, was prepared for the Marquess of Salisbury. It is one of the few designs in the exhibition for decorative, as opposed to structural, ironwork.

20 ARLINGTON STREET.
IRON WORK TO PARK FRONT.
Scale ½ in = 1 ft.

**41** John Gregory Crace
Ceiling decoration, Grosvenor House, London. c. 1870
*Stamped* John G Crace & Son, 38 Wigmore Street. *Inscribed in pencil* at Grosvenor House, J G Crace
*Water-colour over preliminary pencil* $12\frac{3}{4} \times 12$ (32.2 $\times$ 30.5)
E.1829-1912, given by Mr J. D. Crace
Victoria and Albert Museum

In his book *The art of colour decoration*, 1912, John Dibblee Crace recorded that his father made the design about 1870 for 'a room that contains some of the fine paintings of the owner's collection of "Old Masters" on walls hung with dark red silk. The general colouring of the ceiling is in the low tones of cream-colour, verging on drab, with gold; but its leading forms are marked out by a quiet dark red, which occurs in larger mass in the angle panels. Thus, while there is a recall of the wall colour and of the gilding of the frames, the quiet general tone gives full value to the skies and lights in the pictures, in which they have been necessarily mellowed by time.' The *Art Journal* noted that the ceiling 13 feet high and that 'the colour scheme is applied to the mo relief of the plaster work'.

Grosvenor House was probably built some time before 17 the Duke of Gloucester, when it was known as Gloucester H On the death of the Duke in 1805 the property was taken ov the 2nd Earl Grosvenor, who had succeeded to the title years earlier and who in 1831 was created Marquess of minster. Crace's decorations were probably carried out fo third Marquess, created Duke in 1874. Some addition alterations to the house were carried out in 1842 by Th Cundy junior (1790-1867) and it was eventually demo during the present century.

Illus. *Art Journal*, 1906, p. 202. J. D. Crace, *The art of decoration*, 1912, p. 83.
Lit. E. Beresford Chancellor, *The private palaces of London*, ch. xii.

John James Stevenson

The Red House, No. 3 Bayswater Hill, London. 1871

*Signed* John J Stevenson *and* J. Kinnimont (?). *Dated* March 1871 *Inscribed* House No. 3 Bayswater Hill. Front elevation. *Numbered* 5

*Pen and ink and water-colour. Sight size* $14\frac{1}{4} \times 18\frac{7}{8}$ (36.1 × 48)

D.1764-1908, given by Mrs J. J. Stevenson, for the Phené Spiers Collection of architectural drawings Victoria and Albert Museum

Ground plan
V & AM
D.1761-1908

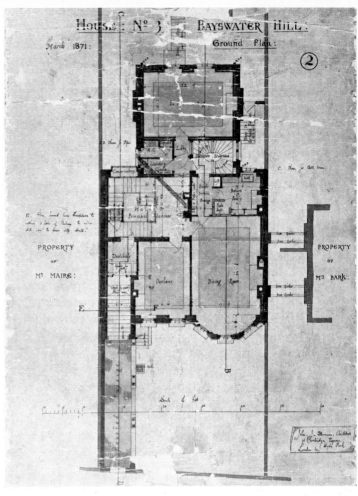

The Red House with its long narrow segment-headed windows and Dutch gables is generally accepted as being one of the first buildings to be erected in the 'Queen Anne' style so popular in the last three decades of the century: it certainly preceded the numerous similar buildings which Stevenson later built in Kensington and Knightsbridge. He appears to have evolved this type of brick design about 1870 with E. R. Robson, a fellow pupil under Scott, after returning from a winter's study in Paris. Stevenson's work predates Norman Shaw's in the same style but not that of Nesfield, or even Webb. Stevenson built The Red House for his own use and it became the meeting place of a large circle of friends prominent in art and literature, such as Alfred Singer, George MacDonald, Sir W. Q. Orchardson, J. H. Middleton, William Morris and Prof. Robertson Smith. The Red House received surprisingly little notice in the press at the time of its erection and these associations and the building's prominent position undoubtedly help to account for the large number of commissions which Stevenson later received.

A design for the staircase was shown at the Royal Academy in 1874, which does not appear to have been considered as of sufficient interest to note mention by critics of the exhibition. Stevenson's own views on the Queen Anne style were expressed in a paper read before the Architectural Conference in June 1874 entitled 'On the recent reaction of taste in English Architecture', in which he said that he thought Queen Anne would be more appropriately called 'Free Classic' or 'Re-Renaissance' (reprinted *BN*, 26 June 1874, p. 689). The Red House has now been demolished.

*Lit.* N. Pevsner, *London, except the Cities of London and Westminster*, 1952, pp. 308-09.

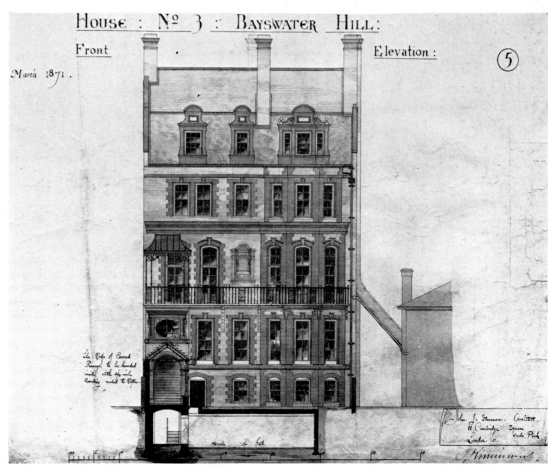

**43** Richard Norman Shaw
Old Swan House, No. 17 Chelsea Embankment, London. 1875
*Signed* R Norman Shaw ARA, Architect. 30 Argyll Street, Regent Street, W. *Dated* January 4th 1876. *Inscribed* W Flower Esqre, Chelsea Embankment, No. Front elevation. Section thro entrance hall etc. Scale $\frac{1}{8}''$ to 1 foot. This is one of the drawings referred to in the contract signed by me bearing date 21st December 1875. Signed Charles Jarrett. Witness Ernest Newton. Approved George Vulliamy Archt. July 7 1876
*Pen and ink and water-colour* 20 × 26$\frac{7}{8}$ (51 × 68.5)
D.1653-1908, given by the artist for the Phené Spiers Collection of architectural drawings
Victoria and Albert Museum

Old Swan House abutted Cheyne House, which Shaw had built in the previous year, and it seems likely that his design was influenced by the earlier house, since the drawing of Old Swan House shown at the Royal Academy in 1877 (no. 1103, illustrated *BN*, 15 June 1877, p. 592) clearly depicts both. Thus the attenuated second floor windows were probably conceived, not only as a means of giving a strong vertical accent to the upper half of the building, and thereby relieving some of the weight from the windows beneath, but also as a foil to the similar, lower windows in no. 18. Shaw's ingenious plan involved a drawing room running the entire length of the building, which was lit by three large picturesque oriel windows, often called 'Ipswich' oriels, since they probably derived from Sparrowe's house at Ipswich of c. 1670. Three years earlier he had used similar windows at New Zealand Chambers and in 1877 repeated them again on Chelsea Embank[ment] though on a smaller scale, in a hou[se de]signed for Mrs Erskine Wemyss. His f[ormer] partner, Eden Nesfield, also used s[imilar] windows in 1878 at Loughton H[all,] Essex (33).

Pevsner has said of Old Swan [House] that it displays 'an originality, a fe[licity] of invention and combination, an[d an] elegance completely new at the tim[e . . .] [Shaw] defeated the grossness o[f the] High Victorian and reintroduced [deli-]cacy, sensitivity and a nice sen[se of] composition and proportion.' It is [there-]fore perhaps not surprising that [con-]temporary accounts of the house [were] somewhat critical.

'The light oriel windows seem [op-]pressed down by the heavy overha[nging] storey above them, this is hard [to] build in truth.' 'The three bays su[ppor-]ting the overhanging superstructu[re are] quaint, but the effect of the whole is [. . .]

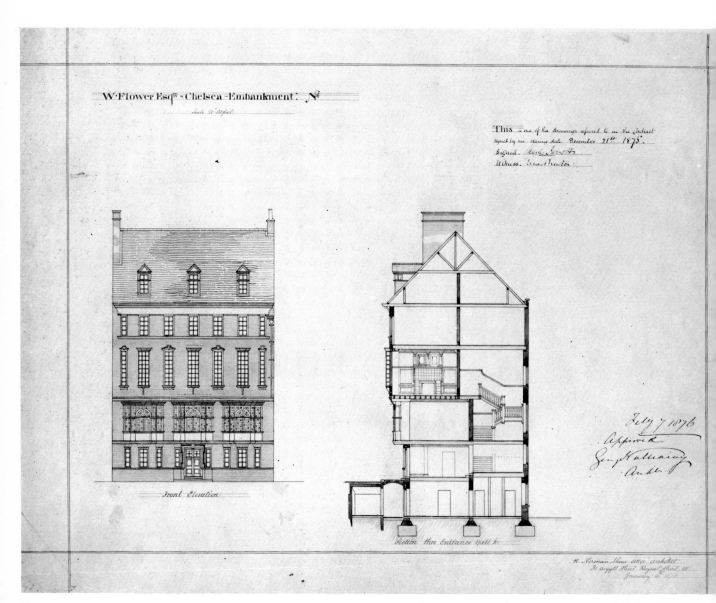

nd we cannot call the architecture
tisfactory.' In 1888 William Morris
rote of Shaw's 'elegantly fantastic houses
Chelsea' achieved by 'a quite selfcon-
ious and very laborious eclecticism'.
The very narrow segment-headed
indows are in the 'Queen Anne' style
hich Shaw had helped to establish with
s Lowther Lodge in Kensington Gore,
ow the Royal Geographical Society, of
873. This building undoubtedly owed
mething to the earlier work of Nesfield
nd Stevenson, but Old Swan House is
more original, very personal statement
ade during Shaw's most interesting
ears.

it. N. Pevsner, 'Richard Norman Shaw'
in P. Ferriday, *Victorian architecture*,
1963. *Br*, 12 May 1877, p. 475. *BN*,
15 June, 1877, p. 589.

. *V & AM D.1652-1902*

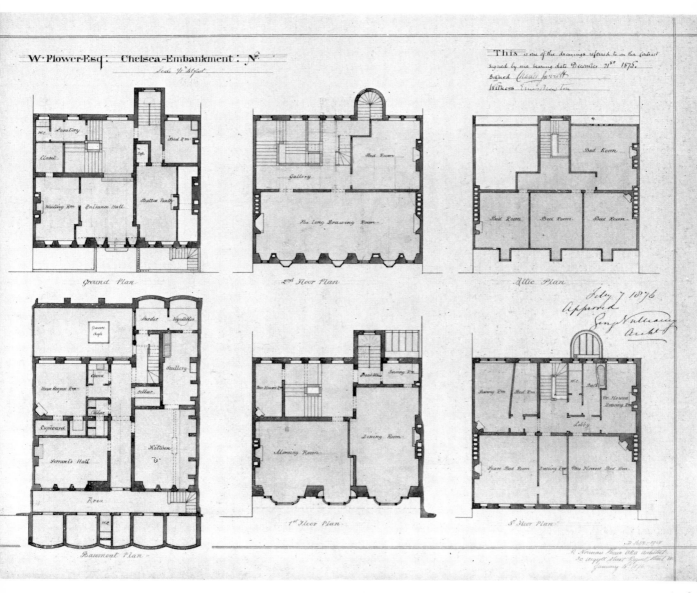

**44** Edward William Godwin
The White House, Tite Street,
Chelsea, London. 1877
*Signed* Edd. W. Godwin F.S.A.
Archt, *and dated* Sep. '77. *Inscribed*
Tite St. or Front Elevation of House
for J. A. McN. Whistler esqr. Chelsea
*Also signed* B S (?) Nightingale *and
dated* Nov 6th '77
*Pen and ink and water-colour, height-
ened with Chinese white* 15¼ × 22
(38.8 × 56.1)
E.540-1963, given by Mr Edward
Godwin, son of the artist
Victoria and Albert Museum

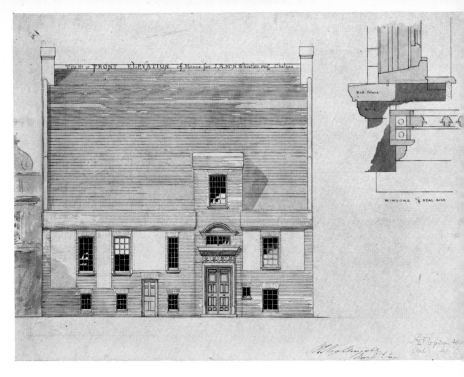

The White House was designed for
Godwin's friend, James McNeill Whistler,
who wanted it to serve as an atelier for
students, with large and small studios, and
to provide living accommodation for
himself and his mistress. On 23 October
1877 Whistler signed an agreement with
the Metropolitan Board of Works for a
double plot in Tite Street on which to
build the house and also undertook to
submit Godwin's designs to the Board for
their approval. In point of fact he started
building without having previously obtained permission and although George
Vulliamy, the Board's architect, sanc-
tioned the design, noting that it possessed
'some novel features', the General Purposes Committee rejected it. On 28 June
1878 Godwin forwarded further designs,
which were also rejected. In the meantime
Whistler continued to build until the
house was almost completed. The Board
could in theory have taken back the site
since the original agreement had been
violated but they decided instead to
press Whistler to make various ornamental additions, for which Godwin
provided further designs. In the event
Whistler's libel action against Ruskin
caused him to go bankrupt in May 1879
and in September of the same year he
sold the house to Harry Quilter, who
made several alterations not included in
Godwin's designs.

The White House, which was recently
demolished, reflects the same care in the
precise arrangement of the windows, door
and roof in relation both to the minimal
ornament and to the overall form as the
Japanese designs which Godwin so much
admired.

Lit. M. Girouard, 'Chelsea's Bohemian
studio houses', *Country Life*, 23 November 1972, p. 1370.

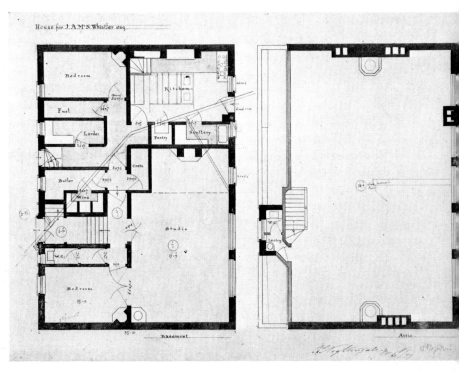

*Basement and attic plans. V & AM E.541-1963*

Richard Phené Spiers
Studio and Stable, Chelsea, London, 1878
*Inscribed* Rt. Hon. Sir Robert Collier. Proposed residence
studio and stables. Chelsea. Studio and stables elevation.
*Pen and ink and water-colour* 13¾ × 25 (35 × 63.5)
E.1603-1925, given by Mr A. T. Bolton, FSA, FRIBA, for the
Phené Spiers Collection of architectural drawings
Victoria and Albert Museum

The studio and stables are situated at the rear of the main house,
also designed by Spiers, built on the Thames Embankment facing
Battersea Park, and were connected by a covered passage at
ground floor level. The exterior elevations involved not only the
use of red brick in the moulded quoins and heads to the windows,
but also terra-cotta supplied by the Architectural Terra Cotta
Company from Spiers's designs. This caused the *Building News*
to remark that a perspective view of the house which Spiers showed
at the Royal Academy in 1879 was 'a very red drawing'. The
architecture, they noted, was 'Queen Anne of much refinement
and character'. The contractors for the work were Messrs Kirk &
Randall of Woolwich.

Sir Robert Collier (1817-86), later Lord Monkswell, was a
judge. The studio was built for his son, the portrait painter John
Collier (1850-1934).

Lit. *BN*, 2 May 1879, p. 468; 27 June 1879, p. 720.

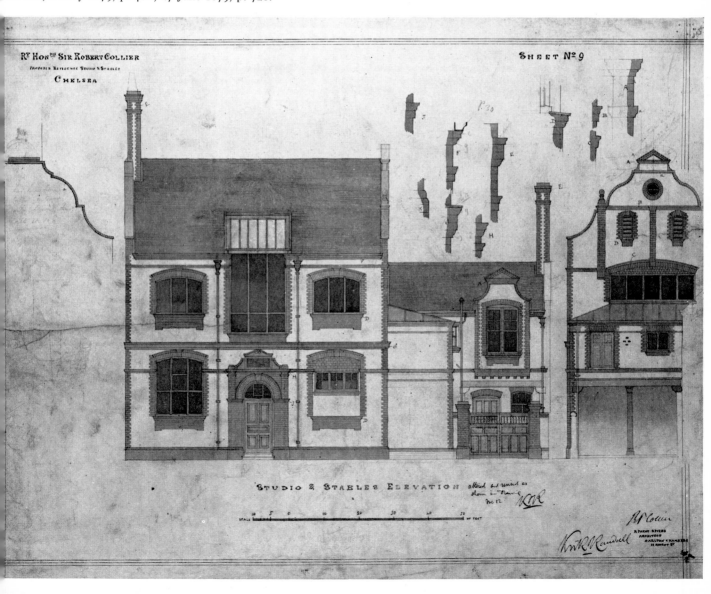

**46** George Aitchison
Arab Hall, Leighton House, Holland Park Road, Kensington, London. 1880
*Signed on the mount* George Aitchison ARA 150 Harley St, W, *and dated* March 1880. *Inscribed on the back* Arab Hall, at Sir Frederick Leighton's House, Kensington, from a drawing kindly lent by George Aitchison Esqre. A R A Architect, *and on the mount* Arab Hall, Kensington W, Sir F Leighton Bart. P R A
*Water-colour and gold heightened with white* 25 × 17¼ (63.4 × 43.7)
Presented by the executors of Aitchison's estate
Lent by the Royal Institute of British Architects

Sir Frederic, later Lord, Leighton (1─96), the painter and sculptor, commissioned his life-long friend Aitchison design the house in 1866 and subsequently employed him to make several alterations and additions. These were mainly inspired by two tours which Leighton undertook in the East in 1868 in 1873. After the first he employed Aitchison, to supply designs for Arabian windows, and after the second to design the Arabian Hall. Leighton had acquired a large collection of original tiles during the second tour and these with contemporary examples made by William De Morgan, were incorporated into the Hall and entrance corridor leading to it. The *Building News* noted that Aitchison had received 'Carte Blanche—to produce a really beautiful hall, whose only use should be to contain the beautiful collection of Eastern which Sir Frederick Leighton was fortunate enough to possess.' The result which remains among the most successful of its type, was complete by 1880, when the *Builder* noticed Aitchison's drawing at the Royal Academy, stating that it did 'of course come under the head of imitative art, as far as the details concerned; there is room however special effects in combinations, and opportunity has not been neglected.

According to Aitchison and Walter Crane, the design of the Arab Hall based on the palace of La Zisa in Palermo. Some of the capitals of the columns modelled by (Sir) J. Edgar Boehm Aitchison's designs and others partly Randolph Caldecott. The mosaic was designed by Walter Crane. builders were Messrs Woodward of bury; Harland and Fisher executed painted decorations and Burke Company the mosaics.

The drawing may have been 1891 before being sent for exhibition Chicago.

Exhib. RA, 1880, no. 1176 or Possibly Chicago 1893, no. 989. Bicentary, 1968, no. 289.
Illus. *Catalogue of the Drawings Collection of the RIBA*, vol. A, fig. 20.
Lit. *Br*, 1 May 1880, p. 554. *BN*, 30 1880, p. 506. C. F. Stell, 'Leighton House, Kensington', *Archaeological Journal*, vol. cxiv, 1959, pp. 12─ G.L.C., *Survey of London*, vol. x Northern Kensington, 1973, p. 1

Sir Ernest George

Harrington Gardens, Kensington, London. 1883

*Inscribed* Harrington Gardens, W. S. Gilbert, Hon. H. Coke & Others. Ernest George & Peto, Architects

*Pen and sepia ink* 19⅞ × 32⅞ (50.5 × 83.5)

E.4256-1909, given by the artist for the Phené Spiers Collection of architectural drawings

Victoria and Albert Museum

The drawing illustrates not only George's fascination with Netherlandish architecture—variously described as 'Franco-Flemish of c. 1500 with Early Renaissance terra cotta decoration' and as 'Renaissance of the Low Countries', which he is said to have 'discovered for the 19th century', but also both his keen sense of the pictorial and the high quality of his draughtsmanship. Goodhart Rendel once remarked about the latter 'The charm of these sketches became legendary, although rival architects might disagreeably suggest that the task of providing their happily-imagined exteriors with convenient and constructable plans for every floor would often cause a good deal of trouble in the master's office.' The *Builder*, when noticing the drawing at the Royal Academy, was scathing: 'We are led to insist on that latter quality [homogeneity] in regard to the ridiculously patched appearance of some designs exhibited (if that can be called 'design' which seems to aim at appearance purely by accident), such as the sham antique collection of buildings called Harrington Gardens with the names of architects, one of whom at least ought to know better. Old streets do occasionally assume this kind of appearance of pieces of buildings in ever so many different manners all muddled together, and they have a picturesque suggestiveness then, but to go about to make this kind of thing deliberately is child's play.' It is of course quite possible that no. 19, designed for W. S. Gilbert, composer of the Savoy operas, was made intentionally whimsical.

George is recorded as never having felt the need to look deeply into any problem set before him, and yet his intuitive feeling for design produced a style of architecture, particularly as evinced in his many large country house designs, which was an alternative to that of Shaw and the Queen Anne.

Exhib. Probably RA, 1883, no. 1201.
Lit. N. Pevsner, *London, except the Cities of London and Westminster*, 1952, p. 267. *BN*, 11 May 1883, p. 616. *Br*, 5 May 1883, p. 596.

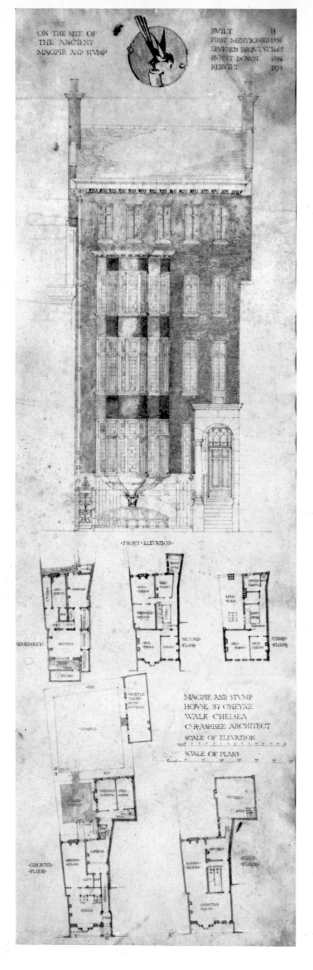

**48** Charles Robert Ashbee
Magpie and Stump House, 37 Cheyne Walk, London,
*Lettered* Magpie and Stump House, 37 Cheyne W
Chelsea. C. R. Ashbee architect. On the site of the ar
Magpie and Stump, built 14 . First mentioned
Leveret's bequest 1662. Burnt down 1886. Rebuilt 18
*Pen and ink and water-colour on vellum* 32½ × 10½ (
× 26.9)
E.202-1965
Victoria and Albert Museum

The house was built on the site of the old Magpie and Stump
which had burned down in 1886, and was used by Ashbee
own residence until 1917, when he left England to take
appointment as Civic Adviser to the City of Jerusalem. From
when Ashbee had moved the Guild of Handicraft to Chi
Campden, he lived in the house only spasmodically. At the
the drawing was exhibited at the Royal Academy the *I*
*Architect* noted 'a long crumpled piece of vellum in a fram
ingeniously designed plans, and agreeably simple brick ele
containing an effective three storey oriel and adequate con
The *Building News* noted that this apparently Shaw-inspire
was 'peculiar in plan—a semi-circle projecting from the
face of a semi-octagon'.

Between 1898 and 1899 Ashbee designed nos. 38-39 Cl
Walk, which adjoined Magpie and Stump House and
contrasted strongly with it, having much freer flat façade
steeply pointed roofs. Later he designed nos. 71-76 C
Walk and prepared designs for nos. 115-116 and 'Da
Tower', which were not carried out.

The drawing was sold with the house in 1921. The hous
demolished in 1968.

Exhib. RA 1895, no. 1487.
Lit. *BN*, 24 May 1895, p. 362. *Br*, 25 May 1895, p. 362
catalogue of Hampton & Sons and Andrews Hitch, 18 Oc
1921.

# Catalogue

## 4 Commercial Buildings

**49** Charles Robert Cockerell
Branch Bank of England, Castle
Street, Liverpool, Lancashire. 1845
*Inscribed* Liverpool Branch Bank of
England. Elevation in Castle Street
*Pen and ink on tracing paper* 14¾ ×
18¼ (37.6 × 51)
E.2089-1909, given by Mr F. P. and
Mr L. P. Cockerell, for the Phené
Spiers Collection of architectural
drawings
Victoria and Albert Museum

In 1844 Cockerell, as architect to the
Bank of England, was commissioned to
design branch banks at Plymouth, Manchester, Bristol and Liverpool. All were
similar in plan and in their main elevations, which have a pediment crowning
the attic storey and an attached order
ornamenting the lower storeys, and were
all derived very obviously from his

Westminster Life and British Fire Office
in the Strand of 1831-32. Unlike the
banks at Plymouth, Manchester and
Bristol, however, the Liverpool bank was
situated on a corner site and consequently
provided an opportunity for Cockerell to
design two façades. The side elevation in
Cork Street has three tripartite giant
windows under arches. These, like the
corner piers in Castle Street, are boldly
rusticated. Both fronts were executed in
Darley Dale stone with granite plinths,
and the main entrance was surrounded
by a polished red granite fascia. The
jambs were made from single blocks of
stone over twelve feet long, two feet wide
and one foot deep. The contractors for
the building, which cost £23,135, were
Messrs Holmes, who were also the contractors for St George's Hall (see 79-81).

Most contemporary and modern critics
agree that the bank was one of Cockerell's
finest works, but Hitchcock has pointed

out that the diagonal view of front
side together was not so success
considered as in the Sun Life Offic
Threadneedle Street of 1839-42, w
Cockerell placed the entrance acros
corner. He also points out that 'The s
Ionic columns flanking the central wi
of the second storey and the arched
mould (for such it amounts to) abov
rather shallow niche in which this wi
is set cannot but appear somewhat p
But the projection of the characte
first-floor balconies into the plane o
colonnade on the front, and well out
the wall plane on the side, is both str
and effective.'

Lit. N. Pevsner, *South Lancashire*,
p. 170. H. R. Hitchcock, *Early
torian architecture in Britain*,
pp. 357-59. E. M. Dodd 'C
Robert Cockerell' in P. Fer
*Victorian architecture*, 1963, p. 1

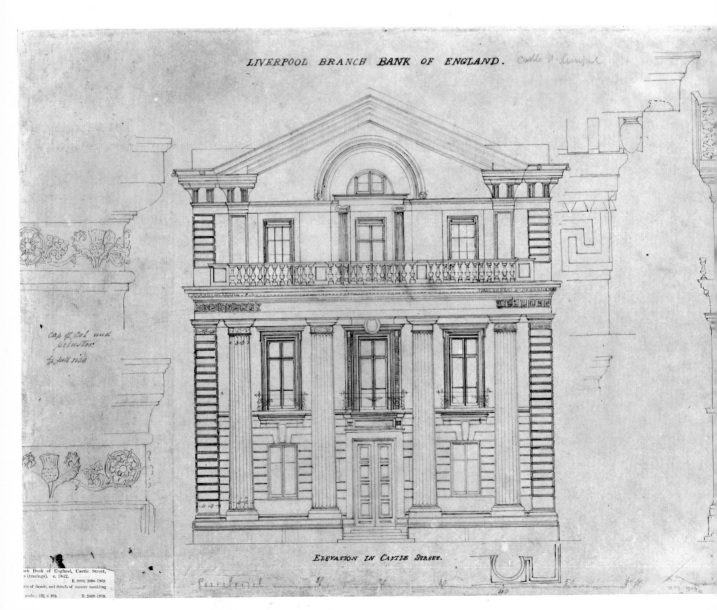

LIVERPOOL BRANCH BANK OF ENGLAND.

ELEVATION IN CASTLE STREET.

James Bunstone Bunning

The Coal Exchange, Lower Thames Street, London. 1847-49

*inscribed* New Coal Exchange, section

*pen and ink and wash* 29⅛ × 47½
(74 × 120.7)

Plan Drawer 1 Roll 20 No. 472

*lent from the Corporation of London Records Office*

The Coal Exchange, Bunning's first important building for the Corporation, was commenced in 1847 and opened officially by the Prince Consort on 30 October 1849. The complex plan involved two rectangular blocks radiating from a quadrant portico half their height, surmounted by a circular tower in three stages 109 feet high. The most notable feature of the building was the rotunda occupying the position of a central court-yard and rising to the full height of the surrounding blocks. Unlike them it was constructed almost entirely in iron, some three hundred tons being used, with a roof of glass supported on 32 ribs. The panels between the ironwork were painted with 'Raffaelesque' decorations by Fredick Sang representing various aspects of mining and other subjects.

Those at the base of the dome, depicting botanical specimens found in coal, were drawn by Bunning's pupil Melhado. The iron work was cast by Messrs Dewer and

the building construction superintended by William Trego. The total cost was £40,000.

Pevsner has described the iron work, much of which was decorated with cable motifs, as 'immensely elaborate and crushingly tasteless!', an opinion which was shared by contemporary critics. The *Builder* wrote in 1863 'of the external details, Italian in character, and indeed of some of the internal, where the roll mouldings take the form of ropes, the less now said the better': other critics made jokes about architects who hanged themselves with too much rope. Hitchcock has pointed out that the rope pattern was particularly well suited to the casting process, and the ribbing which it provided strengthened the various members more effectively than merely thickening them. The contrast between this detailing in iron and the 'Italianate' detailing of the masonry façades emphasizes the very different tastes shown in the early Victorian period in the products of engineering and those of architecture. Bunning showed much less reluctance to unite the two in his more functional buildings for the New Metropolitan Cattle Market in the next decade (see 53).

The Coal Exchange was demolished in 1962, in the face of fierce protests, to make way for new buildings which have

not yet materialized. Parts of the iron work were acquired by the Victoria and Albert Museum, and have been lent to the Science Museum.

*Lit.* *ILN*, 3 November 1849, pp. 300-04. *Br*, 24 September 1849, p. 462; 7 November 1863, p. 783. H. R. Hitchcock, *Early Victorian architecture in Britain*, 1954, pp. 320-24. H. R. Hitchcock, 'The Coal Exchange', *Architectural Review*, vol. ci, 1947, pp. 185-87.

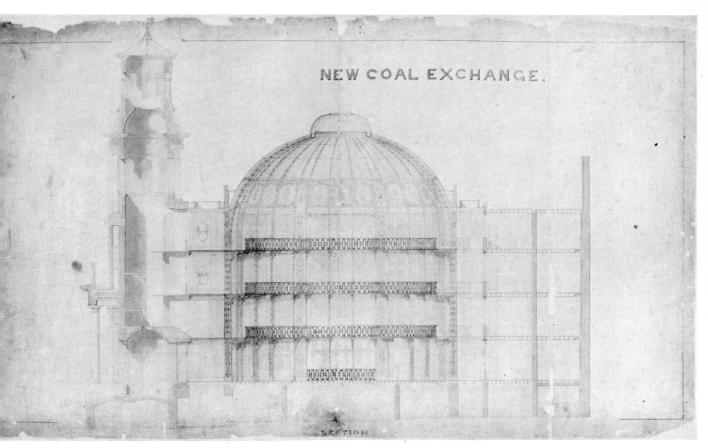

NEW COAL EXCHANGE.

SECTION

**51** George Wightwick
Tea Warehouse, Frankfort Street,
Plymouth, Devon. 1848
*Signed* Geo. Wightwick, Architect.
*Inscribed* Tea Warehouse no. 4.
*Pen and ink and wash* 14 × 20½
(35.5 × 52)
V 13/57
Lent by the Royal Institute of British
Architects

Wightwick's fanciful design with its Greek Key frieze and Chinoiserie detailing seems to relate more closely to mid-18th century precedents than to any of the more serious works he had earlier carried out at Plymouth with John Foulston. The design probably reflects Wightwick's interest in the theatre. In 1832 he had published *Remarks on theatres* and was apparently almost drawn to the stage after relinquishing his post as Sir John Soane's assistant in 1829. The comparison with a stage set is further supported by the manner in which the verandah has been imposed on a building with which it has no stylistic affinities and by the bright polychromy of the design. Nicholas Taylor remarks that the design is the architectural equivalent of the 'Willow Pattern' on china.

Illus. N. Taylor, *Monuments of commerce*,
RIBA Drawings Series, ed. J. Harris,
1968, pl. 11.

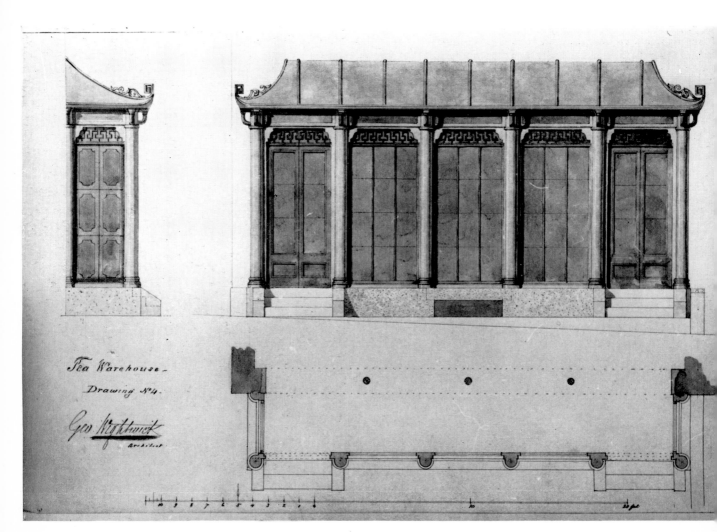

James Bunstone Bunning
Billingsgate Market, Thames Street,
London. 1850-52
Inscribed *Billingsgate Market No. VI.
Elevation in Thames Street. Signed
by the Contractor* John Jay.
*Pen and ink and wash* 23¾ × 38¼
(60.5 × 97.1)
Surveyors' Market Plans 739
Lent from the Corporation of London
Records Office

By 1850 the great increase in the quantity
of fish brought to London by train persuaded the Corporation that Billingsgate
Market should be increased in size.
Bunning as their architect provided plans
for enclosing the site of Billingsgate Dock,
which not only greatly increased the size
of the Market, but also provided a sub-
market for the sale of shell-fish. These
plans were adopted and work on a river
wall of Hayton granite sunk 14 feet into
the soil beneath the river bed was started.
This acted as one wall of the shell-fish
market and also provided part of the
foundation of the main market above. The
façades of the main market were designed
in red brick and Portland stone with open
arcades supported on cast iron columns.
The central feature of the river façade
was a clock tower which also acted as a
flue for the ventilation system. The latter,
like the cleansing system which operated
with pumped water, was supplied with a
steam engine installed by Bessemer. The
roofing over the main market of galvanized
corrugated iron supported on light cast
iron columns and girders with glass
skylights was erected by Walker, the
remainder of the work was carried out by
John Jay at a total cost of about £20,000.

The *Illustrated London News* noted that
the market was opened in time for the
oyster season in 1852, at which time the
main building was not completed. In
1875 alterations and additions were made
to the buildings by Sir Horace Jones.

The building is now threatened with
demolition.

Lit. *Br*, 3 January 1852, p. 1. *ILN*, 7
August 1852, p. 96. C. Booker and
C. Lycett Green, *Goodbye London*, 1973,
p. 123, no. 21.

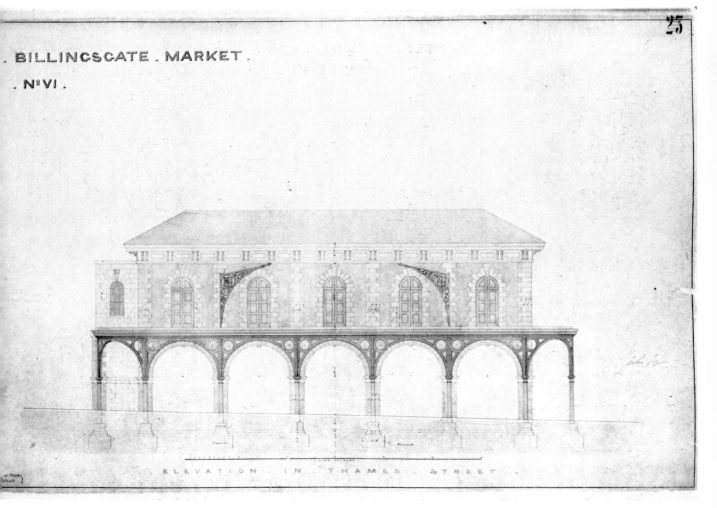

. BILLINGSGATE . MARKET .
. Nº VI .

. E L E V A T I O N . I N . T H A M E S . S T R E E T .

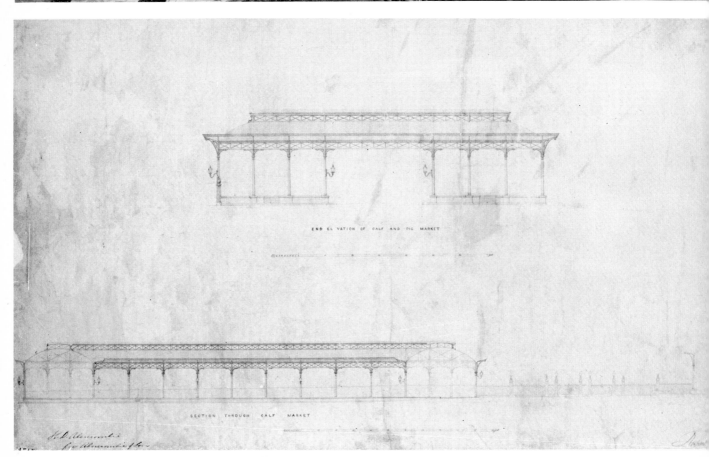

END ELEVATION OF CALF AND PIG MARKET

SECTION THROUGH CALF MARKET

James Bunstone Bunning

New Metropolitan Cattle Market,
Copenhagen Fields, London. 1854-55

Bird's eye view

*Inscribed.* Isometric view of the new
Metropolitan Cattle Market, Copenhagen
Fields. Erected at the expense of the
Corporation of London, under the super-
intendence of the Markets Improvement
Committee. The first stone of the clock
tower laid March 24, 1854 in the Mayor-
alty of the Right Honourable Thomas
Sidney, by Henry Lowman Taylor Esq.
The Chairman of the Committee. Opened
for business June 15 1855 in the Mayor-
alty of the Right Honourable Sir Francis
Graham Moon, Bart. Contractors Messrs
. Willson, R. W. Kennard, J. Jay, R.
Walker, etc. King litho. J. B. Bunning
Archt.
*Chromolithograph* 24¾ × 32½ (63 × 82.5)

Calf and Pig Market
*Signed* H D Abercrombie *and*
Richard Walker. *Dated* 20 June
1854. *Inscribed* End elevation of
Calf and Pig Market. Section
through Calf Market
*Pen and ink and wash* 22¾ × 35¼
(57.8 × 89.5)
Surveyors' Market Plans 1751 and
1515
Lent from the Corporation of
London Records Office

The New Metropolitan Cattle Market,
subsequently known as the Caledonia
Market, was Bunning's most important
work. On an irregularly shaped site of
more than 30 acres he made provision
for 42,000 sheep, almost 10,000 bullocks,
two taverns, a clerk's residence, two
inns, several banking houses, a clock
tower, covered pig and calf markets
with accommodation for more than
2,000 animals, public and private
slaughter houses, a railway station,
meat market, etc. By 10 May 1853
levelling of the site, laying of the sewers
and the foundations of the enclosures
had been commenced 'in earnest'. The
first stone of the clock tower and banking houses, which formed the central
feature of the market, was laid some
ten months later, at which time H. W.
Taylor expressed the hope that the
market would provide a 'pattern for the
whole world'. By this time houses were
said to be 'springing up in all directions
around the site'. Work progressed
rapidly and by 2 December the *Builder*
was able to report that they were 'fast
approaching to such a state of completion, as will admit of its being
opened for use'. The market finally
opened officially on 15 June 1855, when
the total cost was said to have been
£300,000.

Bunning's design involved the use of a
considerable amount of iron not just in
the utilitarian calf and pig sheds but in
the taverns where the balconies are
supported by brackets not unlike those
used in the Coal Exchange, and in the
ground floor arcades of the central
group of clock tower and offices. The
strangely Baroque scrolled buttresses
at the base of the tower were apparently
provided to serve as a visual link with
the offices beneath. The open loggia
and balcony at the top provided a
viewing platform for the market super-
visors, while accommodation beneath
was used by the Electric Telegraph
Company. Similar later towers by
Bunning, such as those at the Holloway
prison and at Billingsgate market, were
used to hide ventilation pipes.

Bunning's obituary in the *Builder*
recorded that the Market 'was the
result of much study [by Bunning] in
all details, as those of water supply,
paving, rails, and whatever else.—Mr.
Bunning had previously made a design
for remodelling the market on the
Smithfield site, or bordering it, at the
time when the Corporation were
desirous that the central position should
be retained.' Hitchcock records that
these amounted to an 'amazing number
of plans'.

Lit. *Br*, 10 September 1853, p. 584;
1 April 1854, p. 173; 2 December
1854, pp. 618-19; 16 June 1855, p. 286.
*ILN*, 16 June 1855, pp. 601-02. H. R.
Hitchcock, *Early Victorian architecture in Britain*, 1954, pp. 324-25.

lfred Waterhouse

inyon & Fryer Warehouse, Chester
treet, Manchester, 1855
igned A. Waterhouse, Archt. and
ated (18)55
en and ink and water-colour Sight
ze 19½ × 14⅜ (49.5 × 36.3)
.1886-1908, given by Mr P. Water-
ouse, FRIBA, for the Phené Spiers
ollection of architectural drawings
ictoria and Albert Museum

his drawing, done when he was only
years old, appears to be the first which
Vaterhouse exhibited. It was described
the Architectural Exhibition Catalogue
'Street front of fireproof offices and
ores now erecting for Messrs. Binyon
nd Fryer, sugar refiners, Chester Street,
Ianchester. Windows of offices deeply
cessed and walls above supported by
upled columns. Arches and cornices
rincipally composed of white brick.' It
a remarkably mature work for a young
an at the outset of his career. The
racketed cornice, polychrome brick-
ork and small windows in the upper
half of the building, and the arcaded
windows on the first floor were directly
inspired by the Doge's Palace. Their
arrangement, and that of doors and
windows on the ground floor, is precisely
indicative of the interior functions of the
building, storage in the top and offices
and showrooms in the bottom. The
drawing received little notice at the time
of its exhibition probably because it
appeared with two other Manchester
warehouses, one of which, by Travers &
Mangall, claimed attention since it had a
frontage of 300 feet and reputedly cost
£45,000. Three years later Waterhouse
confirmed the victory of Gothic in Manchester over the classicism of, for example,
Walters's Free Trade Hall, with his
Assize Courts begun in 1859. The varied
façade of the latter shows Waterhouse
breaking away from the tight Ruskinian
composition of the Fryer and Binyon
warehouse towards the more picturesque
massing of Scott.

Exhib. Architectural Exhibition 1855-56,
no. 63.
Illus. H. R. Hitchcock, '*Victorian monu-

*ments of commerce*', AR, vol. cv, 1949,
p. 61. S. Muthesius, *The High Victorian Movement in architecture, 1850-
1870*, 1972, p. 191.
Lit. *Br*, 19 January 1856, p. 26. *CE&AJ*,
January 1856, p. 3.

**55** John Burley Waring
Design for an unidentified group of
shops and offices. c. 1855
*Pencil, water- and body colour* 25¼ ×
38½ (64.2 × 97.5)
Bequeathed by J. B. Waring
Victoria and Albert Museum

This striking design has many similarities
with the premises in Macclesfield of
Arighi, Bianchi & Company, by an
unknown designer, of 1882-83, for which
it may have been the inspiration. Waring
manages to combine eclectic ornament
with iron, glass, sculpture and polychromy
in a unified design, which is quite the
most successful of his attempts to form
a new style of architecture representing
19th century achievements and requirements.

**56** Owen Jones
Osler's Gallery, Oxford Street,
don. 1858-60
*Pen and ink and water-colour*
$58 \times 40\frac{1}{4}$ ($147.3 \times 102$)
Lent by Mr P. A. G. Osler

Osler's Gallery was begun in 185
opened in June 1859. It was simi
form to the St James's Concert Ha
Crystal Palace Bazaar, which Jone
designed in 1855 and 1857 respec
and involved the use of similar ma
such as coloured glass, fibrous p
and iron. The *Civil Engineer and* 
*tects' Journal* commented 'In this 
the author's facility of invention 
use of several novel materials is des
of examination, as suggestive of hir
the future; also the mode of lightin
disposition of the polychromy—b
elaboration of the drawing consis
less in the specialities so profusel
played on the various counters and
Under the circumstances, the n
fidelity with which these are rende
quite allowable; otherwise it mig
questionable why so much labour s
have been incurred on so subordin
matter.' The *Builder* questioned w
'the effect from stained glass is favo
to correct opinions of the qualities d
in articles of white glass such as a
sale at Messrs Osler's.' Jones's argu
had been that in the case of the C
Palace Bazaar, the correct combi
of primary colours in the stained
roof produced a scientifically white
by which to examine the produc
sale.

The sense of infinitesimal space c
by the mirrors, and their reflecti
many small areas of bright light 
numerous facets of cut glass, produ
'fairy-like' effect and caused the
*Journal* to describe the buildin
'amongst the most attractive o
"sights" which the metropolis con
In 1862 Jones added a wing to the
gallery described as surpassing
'intrinsic beauty of effect': both
now been demolished.

Exhib. RA, 1860, no. 691.
Lit. M. Darby and D. Van Zanten, '
Jones' iron and glass designs 
1850's', *Architectura*, forthco
issue. *CE&AJ*, 1 July 1860, p. 18
2 June 1860, p. 345. *Art Jo*
1862, p. 211.

Cuthbert Brodrick
Unidentified board room
*Signed* Cuthbert Brodrick, Archt.
c. 1860
*Pencil and water-colour* 19½ × 23⅛
(49.5 × 58.7)
Presented by Mr H. Trevor Field
Lent by the Royal Institute of British
Architects

It is not known for whom Brodrick prepared this design. Nicholas Taylor remarks that 'with its sensible armchairs of red velvet and its "not too French, French" décor this is an epitome of the quiet luxury preferred by the commercial aristocracy (the older Forsytes), before new domestic ideals were commissioned from Shaw (or Bossinney). The Chairman and 16 directors round a semi-circular table are faced by a secretary or manager and two deputies.'

Illus. N. Taylor, *Monuments of commerce,* 1968, pl. 28.
Lit. *Catalogue of the Drawings Collection of the RIBA,* vol. B, p. 110.

**8** Richard Norman Shaw
Warehouse, Narrow Street, London.
c. 1862
*Pencil, pen and ink and water-colour*
$20\frac{3}{4} \times 14\frac{3}{4}$ (52.7 × 37.4)
Lent by the Royal Academy of Arts

It is not known definitely for whom the warehouse was designed, but it seems likely that it may have been for Shaw Savill, the shipping firm. This company had been founded in 1858 by Robert Shaw, Norman Shaw's brother, and Walter Savill. Robert Shaw died in 1864, at which time Richard Norman was asked to become a partner, but, preferring architecture, he declined, and James Temple, his cousin, was asked instead. The reasons for supposing that it may have been for this firm are twofold. Firstly, the warehouse has a weathervane in the form of a ship, and designs for similar vanes appear on Shaw's early drawings for Leys Wood designed for Temple, and, secondly, a set of contract drawings in the Royal Academy of Arts, associated with the perspective, were witnessed by Alfred Savill, Walter's brother. These drawings indicate that the warehouse was associated with a property on the other side of Narrow Street, to which it was attached both by a bridge and by vaults under the road. The contract, dated February 1863, was for the warehouse alone; Shaw subsequently increased the size of the adjoining property, preparing new drawings which are dated May 1863.

Shaw's design quite obviously owes its form to the earlier warehouse buildings like that depicted on the left in his drawing, but the details, particularly the tile hanging, appear to owe something to the Kentish tradition of vernacular building, which he had studied with Nesfield. Drawings dated 24 September 1862 for tile-hung Kent buildings are preserved in one of Shaw's sketch-books.

The warehouse drawings are inscribed by Shaw with the address 8 Albion Road, and were thus not only prepared before his association with Nesfield, but are among the first two or three designs which he completed. These included another warehouse in Coopers Row for the wine merchant Irvine.

George Somers Clarke the elder
The General Credit and Discount
Company, 7 Lothbury, London.
1866
*Water-colour* 47½ × 45 (120.7 × 114.3)
Lent by the Royal Institute of British
Architects

Much confusion has arisen over the fact
that Clarke designed buildings for the
Auction Mart Company and the General
Credit and Discount Company next door
to each other in Lothbury at approxi-
mately the same time. This drawing is not
in fact for the former, as often stated, but
for the latter. It was described by the
*Building News* in 1868 as not doing
justice to the building, 'which is one of
mark, and for which we are thankful, as
a relief from the usual vulgarity of the
City buildings—it is a delicate—almost
too delicate—version of Venetian Gothic.
We like particularly its bold chimneys,
but deplore the manner in which the
upper square-headed windows run up
into the cornice, and protest against the
elongated granite bosses with which it is
freely studded as carrying to excess the
style of ornament with which we were
already satiated in its milder forms.'
Taylor describes it as 'the finest example
of Venetian Gothic in London, with a
curiously American air of literal-minded
sumptuousness, as though shipped direct
from the Grand Canal.' Much of Somers
Clarke's detail is taken from the types
portrayed in Ruskin's *Stones of Venice*,
which appeared in 1853 and established
Byzantine and Gothic as appropriate
styles for commercial buildings. The
*Builder* thought the design too dependent
upon Venetian prototypes remarking 'the
exactitude of the reproduction detracts
greatly from the *art-* character of the
work.'

Exhib. Probably Architectural Exhibition,
　　1868, no. 72. RA, Bicentenary Exhi-
　　bition, 1968, no. 283.
Lit. *Br*, 15 September 1866, pp. 679-80,
　　793. *BN*, 26 June 1868, p. 427. *Cata-
　　logue of the Drawings Collection of the
　　RIBA*, vol. C-F, 1972, & fig. 19.
Illus. N. Taylor, *Monuments of commerce*,
　　RIBA Drawings Series, ed. J. Harris,
　　1968, pp. 50-1.

**60** Philip Speakman Webb
Atherton Colliery, Atherton, Lancashire. c. 1870
*Signed* Philip Webb, Archt., 1 Raymond Buildings, Gray's Inn Road, London. *Inscribed* Design for buildings at Atherton Colliery for Herbert Fletcher Esq. Scale ⅛th of an inch to a foot. Elevation of Chimney. Cross section of stage. Section through boiler house. Side elevation of engine house and stage. *Also inscribed with notes to the builders*
*Pen and ink and water-colour* 19¼ × 28½ (49 × 71.3)
E.110-1916, given by Mr Emery Walker
Victoria and Albert Museum

Atherton was the centre of an area of collieries, cotton mills and iron works, which one writer noted 'cover the surface of the country with their inartistic buildings and surroundings and are linked together by the equally unlovely dwellings of the people.'

Webb's colliery building is not mentioned in accounts of his work. The commission from Fletcher may have come through Sir Lowthian Bell, for whom Webb acted as consultant architect for industrial buildings in his ironworks and for whom he built Rounton Grange in 1872.

**61** Rowland Plumbe
25 Austin Friars, London. 1872
*Signed on the mount* Rowland Plur FRIBA Archt. 13 Fitzroy Sq.
*inscribed* View of No. 25 Austin F
*Pen and ink and water-colour* 14 10 (36.8 × 20.3)
W 3/15
Lent by the Royal Institute of Br Architects

Plumbe's richly polychromatic fa with its terra-cotta enrichments revealed iron construction provide interesting variation on the Ven Gothic theme of much comme building in the City at this date. single arch which frames the compos retains a sense of its structural deriv and is finished picturesquely wi stepped gable.

Exhib. Possibly RA 1872, no. 1261.

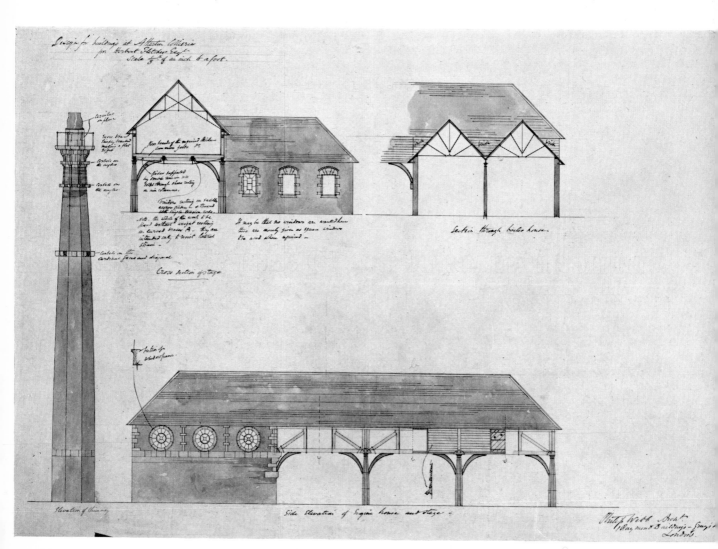

**62** Thomas Bellamy
Law Fire Insurance Office, Chancery
Lane, London. The rear façade in
Carey Street. 1874
*Pen and ink and water-colour* 20½ ×
23¼ (52 × 59)
U8/1/5, given by Bellamy's executors
in 1877
Lent by the Royal Institute of British
Architects

Speaking after Bellamy's death his friend
T. L. Donaldson remarked about the
Law Fire Offices that the façade in
Chancery Lane is 'simple and unpreten-
tious, but imposing from the breadth of
its composition and the purity of its details,
which are conceived in the finest style of
Italian Architecture of the best periods.
The interior is arranged with every
attention to business requirements, happily realising picturesque effects: for on
passing through the front office, which is
spacious and lofty, one is agreeably
surprised by a corridor leading to the
offices at the rear. This passage is flanked
on one side by an arcade of three arches,
supported by columns, and on the other
by the like arcade opening into a spacious
staircase—lighted from above and per-
ceptible from the front office. The whole
of the details are very simple, but each
feature and moulding is elaborately
studied to satisfy the most fastidious
taste. We see in this building how wisely
Mr Bellamy was guided by Italian art,
and could rise to the level of Palladio and
the other distinguished masters o
great school.' The *Builder* notic
June 1876 that the Carey Street
which is flanked on the right by th
façades of Vulliamy's Law Society
ing of 1831 and on the right by a
by Knowles of 1864, was complete
before Bellamy's death.

Illus. N. Taylor, *Monuments of com*
RIBA Drawings Series, ed. J. F
1968, pl. 6.
Lit. *Br*, 17 June 1876, p. 600. N. Pe
*London, the Cities of London &*
*minster*, 1962, p. 317. RIBA, *Jo*
1876-77, pp. 217-18.

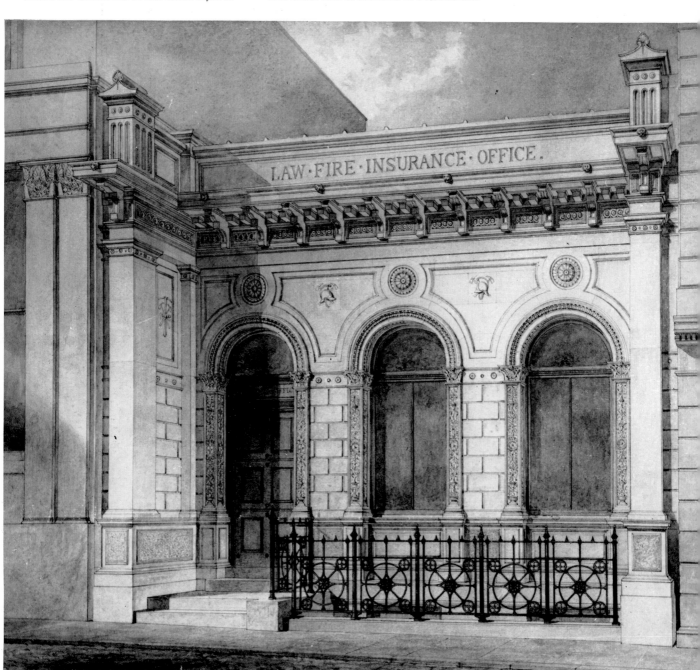

Edward William Godwin
McLean's Fine Art Gallery, 7 Hay-
market, London. 1884
Signed E. W. Godwin *and inscribed
with measurements*
*Pencil and water-colour* 19¾ × 12
(50.2 × 30.5)
E.629-1963, given by Mr Edward
Godwin, son of the artist
Victoria and Albert Museum

The design was certainly not carried out
above ground floor level and it is not
clear whether even that part was done,
although there are certain details in the
existing shop front, such as the position
of the numbers, which indicate that it
may have been. Three other sketches are
preserved in the Department of Prints
and Drawings (pp. 72 and 78 E.262-1963;
E.631-1963) and reveal that Godwin ex-
perimented with several designs, one of
which is Gothic in detailing. All, however,
are obviously inspired by his earlier
design for the Fine Art Society's premises
in New Bond Street and reflect his
saponnerie furniture and other applied
arts designs. The project is one of the last
architectural designs which he prepared
before his death and reveals that he was
content to develop orientalism in his
buildings in the face of the more fashionable Queen Anne, in which style he had
already produced furniture designs.

**64** George Aitchison
Royal Exchange Assurance Comp[
offices, no. 29 Pall Mall, London. [
*Water-colour* 18 × 23½ (45.8 × 5[
U1/10/1, given by G. Aitchis[
executors
Lent by the Royal Institute of Br[
Architects

Aitchison was commissioned in 188[
design new offices for the Royal Exch[
Assurance Company to replace the ea[
neo-classical building erected in [
The long narrow site overshadowe[
the left by the Junior Carlton Club [
on the right by the 18th century offic[
the Cunard Steamship Company ap[
ently influenced his use of careful deta[
and dictated the large expanse of win[
The *Builder* said of Aitchison's d[
that 'The architect has aimed at effe[
well-balanced proportions, with on[
moderate amount of carefully consid[
ornament. The panels of glass m[
between the trusses of the cornice fo[
somewhat novel and pleasing inci[
the green aventurine ground contra[
well with the pale red Mansfield an[
copper coloured ornament. The c[
tides afford a pleasing contrast to n[
of our architectural sculpture, they [
the work of Mr. Boehm, RA. The rai[
and the fine grille in the porch are [
cellent examples of decorative work [
the interior 'a harmonious but restr[
tone of colouring has been aimed at [
lower part of the walls being panelled [
walnut with a carved frieze, while a[
they are covered with green m[
mosaic: a green bronze cornice enri[
with gold and silver ornaments fin[
the walls, and above is a cream-colo[
embossed ceiling.'

Aitchison's plan included living [
commodation in the top half of [
building accessible from a rear entr[
in St James's Square. The Royal [
change Assurance Company occupie[
premises until 1907. In 1925 they [
acquired by the Junior Carlton Clul[
the formation of a ladies' annexe.

Lit. G.L.C., *Survey of London*, vol. [
St James, Westminster, Part I, S[
of Piccadilly, 1967, p. 326. *Br[
August 1885, p. 220 (plan and il[
29 April 1899, p. 404. *BN*, 28 [
1899, p. 565. *A&CR* 28 April [
p. 266

Charles Rennie Mackintosh
Extension to the Glasgow Herald
Building, Mitchell Street, Glasgow.
1894
*Inscribed* The 'Herald' Buildi[ng],
Mitchell Street, Glas[g]ow. John
Moneyman and Keppie. *Dated on a
drainpipe* 1894
*Pen and ink* $35\frac{7}{8} \times 23\frac{7}{8}$ (91.2 × 60.8)
Given by Sylvan MacNair
Lent from Glasgow University, Mac-
intosh Collection

It was thought for some time that
Mackintosh merely applied the details to
John Keppie's building, but two preliminary studies at the back of Mackintosh's Italian sketchbook show that he
was responsible for the whole design.
Howarth has stated that the prominent
corner tower was derived from Henry
Wilson's design for Victoria (BC) Cathedral of 1893, but Walker has more
recently shown that the inspiration was
probably provided by the angle turret of
James Maclaren's High School at Stirling.
Mackintosh re-used a number of features
that had first appeared in Maclaren's
designs in several of his buildings, as for
example the arrangement of balcony and
bay window at the Glasgow School of
Art, which Maclaren had used four years
earlier in his London houses at 10-12
Palace Court. Walker states that the
deep swelling form of the corbelling,
with elongated shields at the angles is
'unprecedented', and notices that the
swirling art nouveau forms of the top
floor pediments derive from 17th century
Scottish details.

The plan involved a road running
through the building on to which the
despatch room opened so that the news-
papers could be easily picked up for
delivery without blocking the street
outside. Construction was in red sand-
stone from Locharbugg's quarry and the
building was designed to be fireproof. A
'hydropneumatic' lift to take both goods
and passengers was fitted in to the stair-
well, the walls of which were lined with
glazed and pressed brick.

Exhib. Exhibition of Work by Charles
Rennie Mackintosh, Saltire Society and
Arts Council of Great Britain, Edinburgh, 1953. Charles Rennie Mackintosh, Centenary Exhibition, Arts Council, London & Glasgow, 1968.

Mus. *Academy Architecture*, vol. vi, 1894,
p. 89. *BA*, 8 February 1875, p. 94.
N. Pevsner, *Charles Rennie Mackintosh*,
1950, p. 63. R. MacLeod, *Charles
Rennie Mackintosh*, 1968, p. 34. *Charles
Rennie Mackintosh*, Centenary Exhibition Catalogue, 1968, pl. 10.
Lit. T. Howarth, *Charles Rennie Mackintosh and the Modern Movement*, 1952,
pp. 60-3. D. Walker, 'Charles Rennie
Mackintosh', *AR*, 1968, pp. 358-59.
A. Gomme and D. Walker, *Architecture
of Glasgow*, 1968, p. 220.

**66** Harry Bulkeley Creswell
Queensferry Factory, Flintshire. 1905
*Signed* H B Creswell Inv Architect *and dated* 10.11.05
*Water-Colour* 16½ × 36¾ (42 × 93.5)
RAN 8/D/1
Lent by the Royal Institute of British Architects

Exhib. RA Bicentenary, 1968, no. 301.
Lit. N. Pevsner, 'Nine Swallows—No Summer', *AR*, vol.
1942, p. 109. *Br.* 13 July 1901, p. 34; 1 December 1906, p
(illus.)

'The most advanced British building of its date. Why is it not just as famous as Peter Behrens turbine factory of 1909?' asks Pevsner. 'As far as functional logic, straightforward presentation and fearless novelty of form go nothing in Britain about 1900 emulates the Queensferry factory—the dignity of labour and the might of the machine are expressed strongly here.' The *Builder* illustrated the factory, which was designed for Williams & Robinson, manufacturers of water pipe boilers, in July 1901, stating that work was in progress. Subsequently Creswell made several alterations most noticeably in the form of the central tower. This had originally been designed to contain water tanks for the fire-hydrants, taps, etc., and a lift for coal trucks, but was enlarged and re-designed to enclose hydraulic accumulators necessary for the tube drawing process. The buildings were faced with purple brindled bricks from Buckley and the strings and courses made specially from hard vitrified purple brick from the same local source. The roofs of the large open sheds, of steel, boarded and slated, were constructed by Anderson & Son of Belfast, and the glazing carried out by Helliwell using his patented process. The general contractors were Foster & Dicksee of Rugby, where Creswell had done previous work. The *Builder* noted in 1906, when the factory had been completed, that the distinctive buttresses, which lend an air of Egyptian solidity and monumentality, were structurally necessary. 'The form of battered piers was suggested by a consideration of the possible lateral pressure on walls by the large area of light roofing floating on cast iron stanchions, and by the nature of the ground which called for shallow foundations. The spread of the piers at their base avoids the use of several courses of footings.'

# Catalogue

## 5 Schools, Colleges

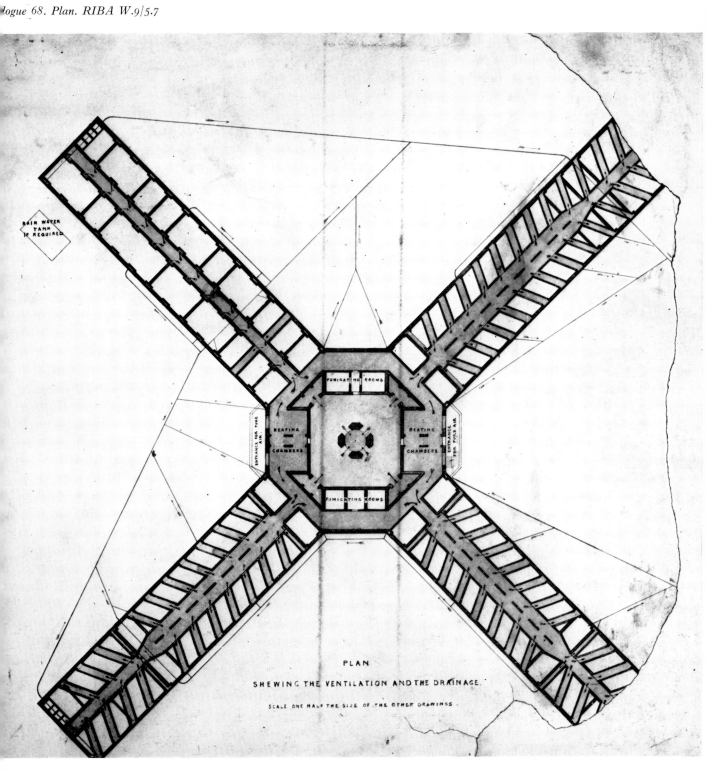

RAIN WATER
TANK
IF REQUIRED

FUMIGATING ROOMS

HEATING
CHAMBERS

ENTRANCE FOR PURE AIR.

HEATING
CHAMBERS

ENTRANCE FOR PURE AIR.

FUMIGATING ROOMS

PLAN

SHEWING THE VENTILATION AND THE DRAINAGE.

SCALE ONE HALF THE SIZE OF THE OTHER DRAWINGS.

**67** S. M. B.
School, Regent's Park, London.
*Signed* S. M. B. *and dated* Decr.
*Inscribed* Elevation and Ground
of proposed new school for Tr
district. The building is carried
the above height (28 ft.) in
effectually to carry away the sr
which, if the building is lower n
annoy the neighbours more thar
additional height of building.
upper part is intended as a comm
room, which it is desirable to ha
unobjectionable. Any alteration
Commissioners or the Duke of
land may suggest shall be attende
*Signed* H. Fitton, Churchwardo
Trinity Church
*Pen and ink and water-colour* 14 ×
(35.5 × 51.3)
LRRO 1/1050, no. 7. MPE 904
Lent from the Public Record Off

The ingenious plan provided ac
modation for 200 boys and 200 gi
two large lecture rooms, with s
rooms for the school master and s
mistress in the centre and a comr
room above. Four entrances ensuree
the sexes were rigidly segregated
within the building.

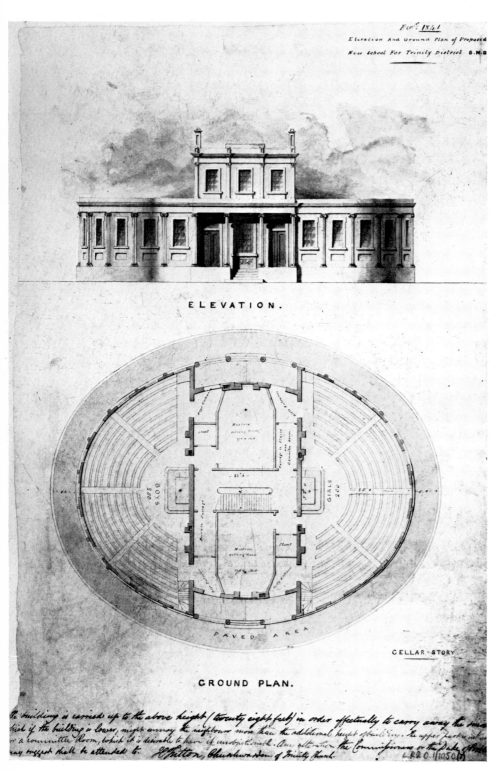

Decr. 1841

Elevation And Ground Plan of Proposed
New School For Trinity District S. M. B.

E L E V A T I O N .

BOYS
200

GIRLS
200

CELLAR STORY

PAVED AREA

GROUND PLAN.

The building is carried up to the above height (twenty eight feet) in order effectually to carry away the sm
which if the building is lower, might annoy the neighbours more than the additional height of building. The upper part is
for a committee Room, which it is desirable to have if unobjectionable. Any alteration the Commissioners or the Duke of
may suggest shall be attended to. H. Fitton, Churchwarden of Trinity Church      LRRO 1/1050

**68** Harvey Lonsdale Elmes
Pauper Schools, Kirkdale, Liver
Lancashire. 1841
*Inscribed with the motto* In Silen
Spe *and* Design for the new Pa
Schools, Liverpool. Girls. Comm
Entrance. Boys
*Pen and sepia wash* 24¼ × 37½
× 95.7)
W 9/5/8
Lent by the Royal Institute of B
Architects

Elmes entered a competition for the
pauper schools in 1841 but was appar
unsuccessful. His depressingly utili
buildings, which are not relieved b
diminutive central feature, pro
accommodation and schoolrooms
axial plan. Elmes was successful i
almost contemporary competition fc
Collegiate High School at Eve
Liverpool, which was opened in 184
which he provided a more pictur
Tudor Gothic design.

George Townsend Andrews

York and Ripon Diocesan Training School, now St John's College, Lord Mayor's Walk, York. 1845
*Signed* G. T. Andrews, Archt. York *and dated* April 1845. *Inscribed* York and Ripon Diocesan Training School *Pencil and water-colour* $10\frac{3}{8} \times 26\frac{7}{8}$ ($41.5 \times 68.2$)
E936.20
Victoria and Albert Museum

A York and Ripon Diocesan Training School for schoolmasters was opened in 1841 in Monkgate, York, as a residential training centre for the diocese of York. By 1844 these premises were found to be inadequate and designs for a new building in Lord Mayor's Walk commissioned from G. T. Andrews. In January 1845 the *Builder* reported that 'the subscriptions and donations towards the erection of these buildings already amounted to £2,500 but much more is needed to carry the original design into execution.' Further funds were subscribed by the government and by the National Society, and the school eventually opened later in the same year having cost a total of £11,955. Before 1859 a chapel was added and numerous further additions have been made in the present century. Andrews's use of brick and pointed gables, probably influenced by the cottages he was building from 1840 for the York and North Midland Railway, testify to his willingness to work in the Tudor style as well as in the Gothic of his churches and Classic of his railway stations.

Lit. N. Pevsner, *Yorkshire, York and the East Riding*, 1972, p. 138. *Victoria County History*, The City of York, 1961, pp. 452-53. *Br*, 11 June 1845, p. 21.

DESIGN FOR THE NEW PAUPER SCHOOLS.
LIVERPOOL

**70** James Bunstone Bunning
Freemen's Orphan School, Shepherds Lane, Brixton. 1852
*Signed* J L W *and* W J Leper (?). *Dated* Jan 12, 1852.
*Inscribed* New Orphan Schools Brixton. Front elevation.
*Numbered 6*
*Pen and ink and water-colour* 22½ × 35½ (57.1 × 90.2)
Surveyors' Institution Plans 1197
Lent from the Corporation of London Records Office

Responsibility for the founding of the school appears to rest with Mr Hale, Chairman of the Corporation's Education Committee, who in 1850 obtained an Act of Parliament, against some opposition, 'for the erection, maintainance and endowment of a school at Brixton'. The first stone of the new school was laid by Mr Alderman Hunter, the Lord Mayor, on 27 April 1852, and it was opened on 28 March 1854, having cost about £20,000, considerably more than was originally proposed. The school was designed to accommodate seventy boys and thirty girls with room for expansion if necessary. The *Builder* recorded that 'the entrance hall is large and spacious, so as to admit of a library in the gallery, as well as to provide spaces for paintings, which from time to time may be presented. There are excellent committee rooms, girls' school, and work-rooms, boys' school, rooms for the officials, bath rooms, and large play-grounds both for boys and girls. The building contains provision for ventilation, and every desirable convenience. Each end of the dining room is filled in with a large semicircular-headed glazed partition, so that the staircases are seen from the room. The dining hall itself is a very handsome and lofty apartment, with a skylight at the apex of the roof glazed with rough plate, which does not leave a dark corner for a mouse.' As at the Coal Exchange Bunning's design included much interior decoration and sculpture. The sides of the dining hall were provided with subjects in *alto relievo* by John Henning and his son illustrating the idle and industrious apprentices after Hogarth, and the staircases were decorated with sculptures of Helen Walker and Dick Whittington by W. Calder Marshall.

Lit. *Br.* 1 April 1854, p. 173; 22 April 1854, pp. 209-11.

**71** John Pollard Seddon and John Prichard
School, Llandough, Glamorganshire, c. 1861
*Inscribed* Llandough School, Glamorganshire. Front El[evation]. Ground Plan. Prichard and Seddon, Diocesan Ar[chi]tects, Llandaff & 6 Whitehall, London
*Pen and ink and water-colour* 20⅝ × 14¾ (52.5 × 37.4)
D.1356-1896
Victoria and Albert Museum

The school which was converted from a barn by the bui[lder] Mr Jarvis, at a cost of £350 was apparently completed by [1859] when the *Ecclesiologist* remarked 'the style is First Pointed al[l] too decided and elaborate for the size and destination of [the] building. The schoolroom is lighted by a First Pointed arca[de of] contiguous lancets richly moulded'. The *Building News* n[oted] when the drawing was exhibited at the Royal Academy, th[at it] had 'the good qualities which are incorporated with all [Prichard and Seddon's] designs. The dressings are of v[?] freestone, with occasional black blocks, the whole design si[mple] as it is, is worked out in a vigorous manner.' The building [pro]vided for a schoolroom on the left and a residence for the s[chool]master on the right. It should not be confused with the s[chool] which Prichard built at Llandaff and which was complete[d in] 1867 (*BN*, 1867, p. 510).

Exhib. Probably RA, 1861, no. 683.
Lit. *Ecclesiologist*, vol. xxi, 1859, p. 210. *BN*, 21 May 1861, p. [?]. 17 May 1867, pp. 340, 343 (illus.).

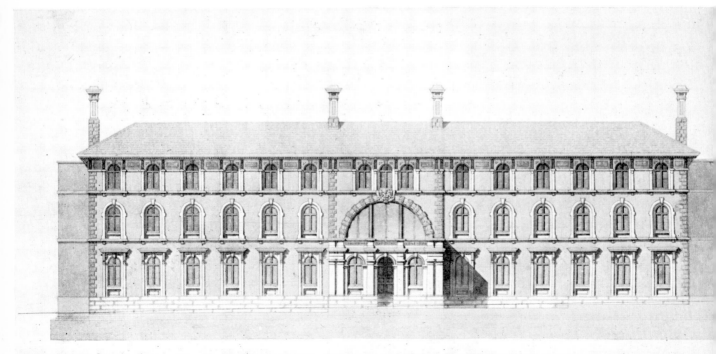

FRONT ELEVATION.

Llandough Schools

Glamorganshire

Scale 1/4 Inch to a Foot

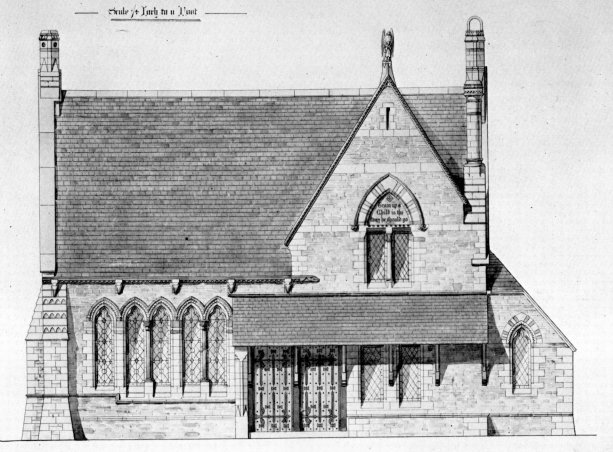

Front Elevation

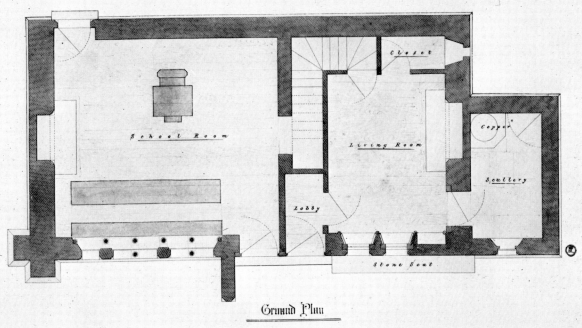

Ground Plan

School Room

Closet

Living Room

Copper

Scullery

Lobby

Stone Seat

Prichard & Seddon
Diocesan Architects, Llandaff
& 6 Whitehall, London.

D. 1856

117

**72** Alfred Waterhouse
Gonville and Caius College, Cambridge. 1869
*Signed* A. Waterhouse
*Pen and ink and water-colour* $25\frac{1}{8} \times 35$ (63.8 × 88.9)
D.1888-1908, given by Mr P. Waterhouse, FRIBA, for the Phené Spiers Collection of architectural drawings Victoria and Albert Museum

The College was founded by Edmund Gonville in 1348 and by Dr Caius in 1557. Waterhouse was responsible for rebuilding much of Tree Court in 1870, of which this drawing depicts the southern elevation. There had in fact been plans for rebuilding as early as 1822 by Wilkins which were never carried out. Modern historians have been very critical of Waterhouse's work, pointing out that it took no account of the neighbouring Senate House and Church of St Mary: Pevsner has said of it that 'from the street and especially the corner they [Waterhouse's buildings] are disastrous— the elevation is pretentious and in a characteristically High Victorian way utterly unconscious of the architecture into which it should fit.' 19th century critics were less harsh. 'Mr Waterhouse is constructing new buildings for Gonville and Cauis College Cambridge in a curious and somewhat heavy Jacobitish style. The view shows two fronts; one next a narrow street of low gabled houses, in which he introduces square oriels to every student's room on the first floor: he has an oriel at one corner of the building one storey high, and at the corresponding corner three stories high. There is a general appearance of heaviness every way, his oriels and other projections are not sufficiently well corbelled out to relieve them from an appearance of giving way from the weight.' 'This is really a good picturesque design, and the detail is in character with that of the old part of the college, and infinitely better than his versions of Gothic. We should prefer a simpler finish to the top of the otherwise good oriel window at the angle.' Alterations to Waterhouse's work in the master's lodge were made by E. S. Prior in 1889.

Exhib. RA, 1869, no. 975.
Illus. *Br.* 12 July 1873, p. 542. J. daunt Crook, *Victorian architectu visual anthology*, London, 1972, pl.
Lit. N. Pevsner, *Cambridgeshire*, p. 67. *Br*, 8 May 1869, p. 358. *B* May 1869, p. 404.

William Butterfield

Grammar School, Heavitree, Exeter.
1878

*Inscribed* Proposed buildings Grammar
School, Exeter. Elevation on the line
DD. *Numbered* 12

*Pen and ink, pencil and water-colour*
12⅝ × 20⅜ (32.7 × 51.8)

D.10-1908, given by Mr Halsey
Ricardo for the Phené Spiers Col-
lection of architectural drawings
Victoria and Albert Museum

The *Builder* noted in August 1879 that
on 30 July 'the corner-stone of the new
Exeter Grammar School in Victoria Park,
which is to take the place of the old
school building in High Street, was laid
by the bishop of the diocese. In style the
new building is said to be what is known
as Domestic Gothic of the fourteenth
century. It will be constructed of red
brick from Cum Davy, with Box Ground
dressings, and the roof will be covered
with Willand Abbey slates—the contractors are Messrs. Stephens and Bastow
of Bristol.' The original plan involved
two wings at right angles with residences
for assistant masters, matron, etc., in a
six-storey block at the corner. The North
wing contained dining hall, kitchens, etc.,
and the East wing class rooms, studies
and dormitories, for sixty pupils. Provision was made, however, for extending
this wing to include laboratories, etc.,
and a 'great schoolroom' in which meetings could be held, and for the addition of a
South wing to contain further class rooms

for another sixty pupils. Thompson
records that the building cost £13,568
exclusive of the North wing and a chapel,
which was added later.

Lit. P. Thompson, *William Butterfield*,
    1971, pp. 359, 435. *Br*, 30 August 1879,
    p. 980. *BA*, vol. xi, 1879, p. 57.

*Ground Plan*
*V & AM D.4-1908*

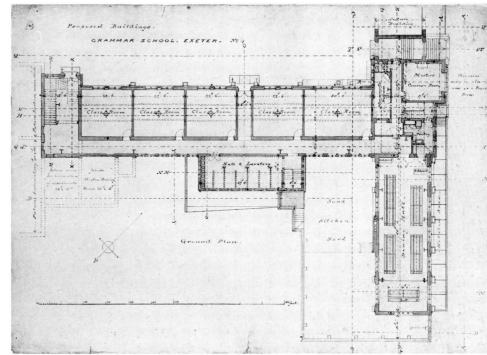

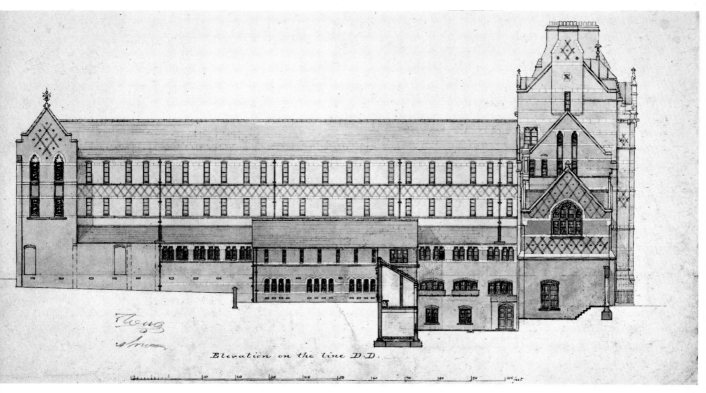

*Elevation on the line DD.*

**74** Robert Lewis Roumieu
School, Bushey, Hertfordshire. 1879 Unaccepted competition design
*Signed* Roumieu & Aitchison *and dated* July 1879. *Inscribed*
Design for Bushey Board Schools. West Elevation
*Pen and ink and water-colour* 13½ × 17¼ (34.5 × 44.2)
Z 5/41
Lent by the Royal Institute of British Architects

The local education board invited designs from seven architects early in 1879 for a new girls' and infants' school under one roof. In August the *Builder* announced that the design bearing the motto 'Success' submitted by H. H. Bridgman had been selected and that he had received instructions to obtain tenders.

Lit. *Br*, 16 August 1879, p 921. *BN*, 15 August 1879, p. 197.

Design · for · Bvshey · Board · Schools.

West elevation

Scale of feet

# Catalogue

## 6 Asylums, Prisons, Hospitals

logue 76
R.I.B.A. W.9/7.2

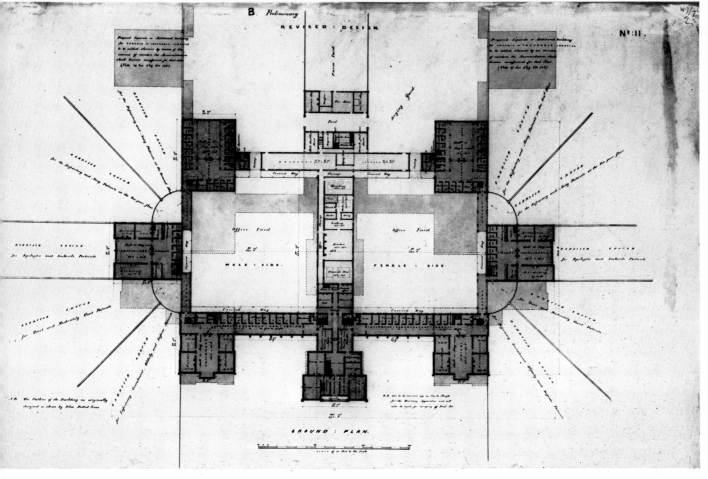

**75** Sydney Smirke
Bethlem Hospital (now the Imperial War Museum), St George's Fields, London. c. 1840
*Lettered on the mount* Principal front of Bethlem Hospital erected MDCCCXV, James Lewis architect. Enlarged MDCCCXI Sydney Smirke Architect
*Pen and ink and water-colour* 14 × 70 (35.5 × 177.8)
Lent by the Board of Governors of the Bethlem Royal Hospital and the Maudsley Hospital

By the end of the 18th century Bethlem Hospital found its accommodation in Moorfields inadequate. From 1801 various sites for a new building were examined until in June 1807 the President and Treasurer reported that a site in St George's Fields was suitable for their purposes. Negotiations for the land took three years, and in July 1810 an open competition for the building was announced in the press with premiums of £200, £100 and £50 offered for the three best designs. James Lewis, the hospital surveyor, George Dance the younger and S. P. Cockerell acted as adjudicators and awarded the First Premium to John Gandy. Subsequently all the competition designs were rejected in favour of a new design prepared by Lewis, who incorporated several of their better features. The foundation stone was laid by the President, Sir Richard Carr Glynn, on 18 April 1812, and the patients were eventually transferred to their new quarters in August three years later.

Smirke's first connection with the hospital came in 1835, when he was asked to undertake enlargements, to provide accommodation for nearly double the original number of patients, and workshops for the male patients, laundries for the employment of the female patients. He achieved this by building wing blocks at either end of the main façade, and two long galleried blocks across the gardens at the rear. The first stone of these additions was laid on 26 July 1838. The original building had a low cupola as its central feature but in the early 1840s Smirke was employed to enlarge the chapel beneath and replaced this with a larger copper covered dome, which was completed by 1845. Between 1866 and 1869 he was again employed by the hospital authorities to design a convalescent home at Witley. The main hospital remained at St George's Fields until 1926, when it moved to Monks Orchard near Addington. The Imperial War Museum first opened their galleries to the public in 1936, after the building had been considerably reduced in size.

The *Builder* remarked about Smirke's dome 'we totally disapprove. Three or four years ago, the façade of this pile was injured exceedingly by the addition of wings, which have a very unsatisfactory and indeed unhappy effect. Now to the summit of this edifice, which is in the very simplest style of Grecian Ionic architecture, this incongruous and ill-advised addition is proposed.'

Lit. G.L.C., *Survey of London*, vol. xxv, St George's Fields, 1955, ch. 9. *Br*, 1 June 1844, p. 271.

**76** Harvey Lonsdale Elmes
Lunatic Asylum, Rainhill, Lancas
1846
*Signed* H. Lonsdale Elmes, A. London, *and dated* November 1846. *Inscribed* Preliminary De for the West Derby Lunatic Asy South Elevation. No. XI
*Pen and ink and water-colour* 15¾ × (40 × 65.2)
W/9/7(13)
Lent by the Royal Institute British Architects

On 24 June 1847 Elmes wrote to Robert Rawlinson, the engineer later, with C. R. Cockerell, comp St George's Hall, from Ventnor in Isle of Wight, whither he had trav in an attempt to regain his failing h 'You may possibly have heard that I obtained the lunatic asylum at West D (for that division of the county) to b and that my plans have been h approved by H. M. Commissione Lunacy.' The asylum was event completed (like St George's Hall) Elmes's death, at Rainhill near St He in 1851. As originally built it prov accommodation for 400 patients, many later additions were made inclu a large annexe in 1886-87 by G Grayson, and in 1893 Burdett recc that 1,800 patients could be ac modated.
Elmes's first designs, dated Septe 1846, depict a Classical building. D October and early November these u went various revisions both in arrangement of the plan and the deta

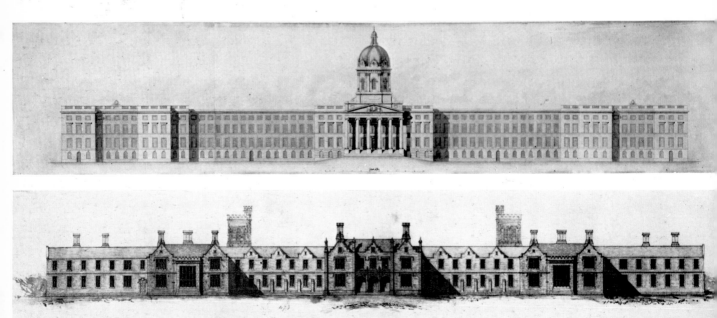

the elevations until this final design, in the Tudor style, was settled upon. A preliminary pencil sketch for this elevation is also preserved in the Royal Institute of British Architects (W9/7/12).

Lit. N. Pevsner, *South Lancashire*, 1969, p. 371. *Br*, 16 September 1854, p. 489. H. C. Burdett, *Hospitals and asylums of the world*, vol. ii, 1893, p. 85.

**77** James Bunstone Bunning
City Prison, Holloway, London. 1847
*Inscribed* City New Prison front elevation
*Pen and ink and wash* $30\frac{3}{4}$ × $47\frac{1}{2}$ (78.1 × 120.6)
Surveyors' Justice Plans 574
Lent from the Corporation of London Records Office

The radial or 'panopticon' arrangement of prisons whereby it was possible for the minimum number of staff to view a large number of cells, was first put into practice by the American architect, John Haviland, in his Eastern Penitentiary, Philadelphia of 1823-25. Charles Barry adopted a similar arrangement at Pentonville Prison in 1841-42, using only four arms instead of Haviland's seven, and either this, or Reading Gaol by Scott and Moffatt of 1842-44, was probably Bunning's model for Holloway. The 'castellated gothic' style, used by both Haviland, and Scott and Moffatt, like the alternative 'Egyptian' style, assisted in creating the impression of impregnability.

Holloway was completed at a cost of £100,000 at the beginning of October 1852. It included provision for sixty female and sixty-one juvenile prisoners in the front two wings, and two hundred and eighty-three male prisoners in the four radiating wings behind. The central tower, based on Caesar's Tower at Warwick Castle, contained a tube 'of boiler plate, five feet in diameter at bottom, and three feet at top' which was part of the ventilation system. A furnace in the bottom heated the air in the column, which was connected by side tunnels to the cell blocks. As the warm air passed out of the top so fresh air was drawn through the building to replenish it. The cells themselves, each 13 feet by 7 feet, were fitted up with water-closets, wash hand basins, cupboards, tables and stools, and were heated by hot water pipes laid in the corridor floors. Water was provided by a well 30 feet in diameter and 319 feet deep, and stored in tanks containing 14,000 gallons in towers over the central entrance. Pentonville had been erected on the principle of complete separation of the prisoners. It was thought that such a system, by its severity, would have the effect of lessening crime, but in practice this was not found to be the case. The City authorities were accordingly 'at a loss upon what principle to arrange their prison [Holloway], but they adopted a middle course, and they have now the means of confining the vicious in separate cells; and have a sufficient number of workrooms for classified association.'

Lit. *BN*, 14 June 1851, pp. 376-77.

**78** James Bunstone Bunning
Asylum for Pauper Lunatics, now Stone House Hospital and The Hollies, Stone, Kent. 1859
*Inscribed* Proposed new asylum for Pauper Lunatics for the City of London. Elevation of main buildings and male and female wings. Architect's Office, Guildhall. *Dated* 1859. *Numbered* 7
*Pen and ink and water-colour* 23 × 36½ (58.4 × 92.8)
Surveyors' Institution Plans 81
Lent from the Corporation of London Records Office

The building was complete by 24 February 1866, when the *Builder* reported 'The new lunatic asylum for the City of London, which has been erected at the cost of the Corporation at Stone, near Dartford, Kent, is now ready for the reception of patients. The asylum has been erected at a cost of about £65,000, and is intended to accommodate 250 patients. It is situated on an elevated piece of ground about a mile and a half from Dartford, overlooking the Thames, and commanding a view of the surrounding country for miles. It is fitted up with baths and lavatories, laundries and workshops, and surrounded by spacious grounds tastefully laid out. Bagatelle-boards and other games, and means of recreation are provided for the inmates; and in short, all the appliances for comfort and convenience which have been adopted of late years in the best regulated establishments for the treatment of persons afflicted with insanity in all its varied forms. Nearly five years have been spent in its construction.'

The red brick and stone Tudor design may have been influenced by Rogers's Almshouses, which Bunning built in the same style in 1858. The tall thin campanile 'madly corbelled out near the top' disguised a ventilation stack pipe similar to that which Bunning had used at the City Prison, Holloway, in the previous decade (see 77). By 1893 a detached hospital for infectious diseases had been added and the grounds increased by a further 107 acres. At that time the buildings provided 430 beds and 70 single rooms. A chapel was added at the north end by Andrew Murray in 1898.

Lit. *Br.* 24 February 1866, p. 135. *ILN*, 21 April 1866, p. 404, illus. p. 376. J. Newman, *West Kent and the Weald*, 1969, p. 527. Burdett, *op. cit.*, vol. ii, p. 86.

# Catalogue

## 7 Civic Buildings

*Catalogue 79*

## St George's Hall, Liverpool, Lancashire. 1839-51

**79** Harvey Lonsdale Elmes
Final design from the North East.
1839-40
*Pencil and water-colour* $16\frac{1}{4} \times 20\frac{1}{4}$
($41.3 \times 51.8$)
U13/48
Lent by the Royal Institute of
British Architects

Exhib. Selection of original drawings
from the Royal Institute of British
Architects, Collection 1910 Architectural Drawings from the Collection of
the Royal Institute of British Architects, 1961. Neo-Classical Exhibition,
London, 1972, no. 1080. RA Bicentenary Exhibition, 1968 no. 269.

Illus. W. Millard 'The Institute Collections', RIBA, *Journal*, vol. xvii, 1910,
p. 599. R. Dircks, 'The Library and Collections of the Royal Institute of British

Architects', RIBA, *Journal*, vol. xxviii,
1921, p. 88. *Architectural Drawings
from the Collection of the Royal Institute
of British Architects*, 1961, pl. 31. J.
Mordaunt Crook, *The Greek Revival*,
1968, pl. 40. P. Ferriday *Victorian architecture*, 1963, pl. xxxii. A. E. Richardson, *Monumental Classic architecture in
Great Britain and Ireland*, 1914, pl. xlix
(photo. from same point of view).
*Catalogue of the Drawings Collection of
the RIBA*, vol. C-F, 1972, fig. 49.

Lit. N. Pevsner, *South Lancashire*, 1969,
pp. 155-57. H. R. Hitchcock, *Early
Victorian architecture in Britain*, 1954,
pp. 309-12. J. Mordaunt Crook, *The
Greek Revival: neo-classical attitudes in
British architecture*, 1760-1870, 1972.

**80** Charles Robert Cockerell
Interior of the Great Hall. c. 1851
*Pencil and wash* $24 \times 30\frac{3}{8}$ ($61 \times 77$)
E.2018-1909, given by Mr F. P. and

Mr L. P. Cockerell for the P
Spiers Collection of architec
drawings
Victoria and Albert Museum

Lit. *Br*, 30 August 1851, p. 550;
January 1853; 1 January 1855, p

Elmes won the first competition
concert hall to be built by public
scription in 1839, and also won a fu
competition for Assize Courts held i
following year. Subscriptions were
forthcoming for the concert hall an
Corporation decided to incorpora
with the Assize Courts in one buil
which their surveyor Franklin wa
pointed to erect. After a protest
Elmes, however, supported by Fra
Elmes produced a further design,
bining his two earlier schemes, whic
accepted in 1841. Elmes, who was
25 years old when he entered for the
competition, died before the Hall

completed and it was finished by C. R. Cockerell and the engineer Sir Robert Rawlinson. Elmes's first two schemes derive very obviously from Greek prototypes and from the work of Schinkel and Klenze, which he had been to Berlin to study. His final design, however, owes much less to these sources, the separate elements of the earlier projects have been more skilfully combined, the rhythm is more even—essentially early Victorian—and the general effect one of monumental grandeur. It was recognized at the time of completion as one of the greatest buildings of its age, an opinion which time has confirmed. Pevsner has called it 'the freest neo-Grecian building in England and one of the finest in the world' and Hitchcock as 'one of the finest of all 19th century British monuments'.

Cockerell acted as Elmes's assistant from 1839, when work on the Hall was still in its initial stages, and, when Elmes died in 1843, he agreed to design those fittings for which no drawings had been left. In August 1851 the *Builder* reported that the building was still in a very incomplete state, the floor was not laid, the

walls were bare and the ceiling at an 'embryo' stage, the great hall was 'as yet a mere shell'. By January 1853 the interior was full of scaffolding, the walls being lined with polished marble, the ceiling painted, and the floor laid with Minton's encaustic tiles. At this time it was reported that 'Mr Willis has sent down a considerable portion of the framework of the organ, with the bellows, wind-chests, and a portion of the pipes. The Committee are about contracting for the case and platform, which will cost together about £3,000. The bellows will be worked by a steam engine, having two 8 inch oscillating cylinders turning about a crank, but without a flywheel, that the power may be under more rapid control. This is probably the first application of steam power to the production of music on record, except the frightful railway whistle. The organ will be the largest in the world—some think too large.' St George's Hall was finally inaugurated in September 1854 though work continued for another two years.

The position of the organ obscuring the Nisi Prius Court and impairing the

perspective of Elmes's interior, one which he considered important, led to criticism of Cockerell's design. The *Builder* explained that 'its position . . . must ever be lamented: but after extended deliberation, and the best advice on acoustics and musical convenience, it was finally decided to be placed at the north end of the hall. Pains have been taken by its form and structure, to play into the lines and perspective and uses of that part of the hall.' Cockerell's most successful work in St George's Hall was the circular concert room involving, not only bright polychromy like his work in the Great Hall itself, but also new materials such as iron and fibrous plaster.

**81** Thomas Hathaway
Model of the Hall before Cockerell's
modifications. 1845-46 (*bottom*)
*Cardboard and other materials on a
wooden base* 10¼ × 5¾ (26 × 14.5),
H. 2⅝ (6.6)
51:61:1, given by Mrs Dargie of
Beaumaris, a descendant of the maker,
1951
Lent from the City of Liverpool
Museums

*A later model of St George's Hall,
Liverpool City Museums*

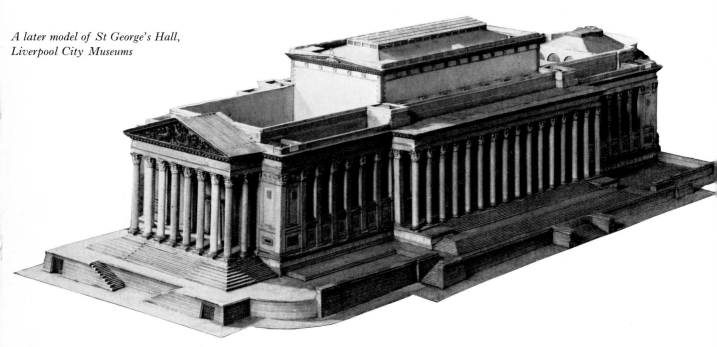

Thomas Henry Wyatt and David Brandon
Model for the Assize Courts, Cambridge. c. 1840
*Wood and cardboard* 7¼ × 26¾ × 36 (18.5 × 67.9 × 91.4)
Lent by the Royal Commission on Historical Monuments (England)

Early in 1840 it was decided that Cambridge needed new Assize Courts, but there was some opposition to the selected site on Castle Hill, particularly from the Mayor and Corporation, who favoured building instead on part of the Old Botanic Gardens in Downing Street. In the end, they lost the battle, and the Castle Hill location was settled, even though it would mean the demolition of the surviving fragments of the castle itself. Wyatt and Brandon were commissioned to produce designs, The first estimates for the building were £8,344 if it were in Whitby stone; Portland stone worked out at some £400 more expensive.

The Committee appointed to see the project through commissioned a cardboard model at a cost which was not to exceed £70. The total expenditure on the building was £12,571, which included more than £400 for sculptured figures.

The *Illustrated London News* (1 April 1843) presented an engraving of the new Courts which did not have any sculptured ornament at that time. 'The style selected', reported the paper, 'is Palladian, and the façade somewhat novel and decidedly effective. It reminds the spectator of Palladio's loggie at the Basilica, Vicenza. It is not, however, a servile imitation of its Italian predecessor; there are many variations and these certainly are in favour of the English building. The sameness and poverty of the original are avoided by compressing the details, a richness being thus gained which tells favourably for the general effect . . . The total length of the front is 136 feet; the entrance leads into a hall 30 feet square, and this communicates with the two courts . . . each of these

is 51 feet by 32 feet. Rooms for the judges and the grand jury, with other apartments are also conveniently placed . . .' There was an underground tunnel connecting the Courts with the adjacent gaol.

On the parapet of the façade were four sculptured figures; Mercy and Justice by a Mr Smith, and Law and Power by Edward Davis. The latter exhibited a figure 'Power of Law' in 1844 at Westminster Hall (no. 182). The *Art-Union* of that year described it as 'a female figure with a chain, but extremely heavy in character and coarse in execution, insomuch as to amount to nothing beyond a sketch.'

The Assize Courts were demolished during the 1950s.

Exhib. Great Exhibition 1851, Cl. VII, no. 220.

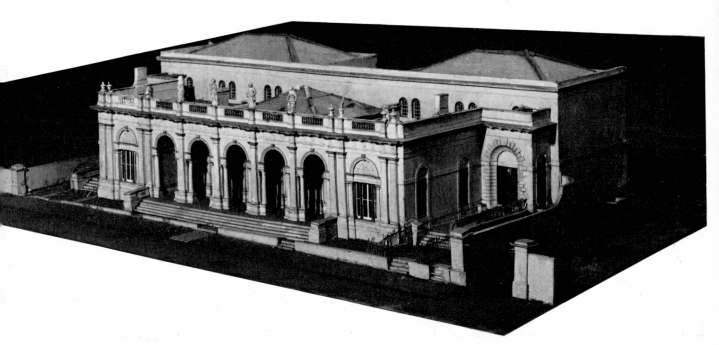

**83** Cuthbert Brodrick
The Town Hall, Leeds, Yorksh
1854
*Signed* CB *and dated* 1854
*Water-colour* $25\frac{1}{8} \times 36\frac{1}{8}$ (63.9 $\times$ 9
Lent from Leeds City Art Galleri

Designs for the new Town Hall wer
vited in an open competition in 1852
sixteen plans were received. These
judged by Sir Charles Barry, who
commended in December that the
prize should be awarded to Brod
who had entered under the pseudo
'Honos alit artes'. Brodrick was at
time virtually unknown outside
native Hull, and the Council expre
disappointment that a more fan
architect had not been selected, as
Barry if it was safe to entrust such a
to one who was only thirty years of
Barry replied that he had faith in P
rick's 'talent and genius', and only
did the Council officially appoint hi
their architect.

Brodrick's original design did not include a tower but did provide for a giant colonnade completely surrounding the rectangular building, broken by projections at the corners, and standing on a heavily rusticated basement. The tower was apparently suggested by Barry and appears in Brodrick's designs for the first time in 1853 when the scheme was noticed by the *Building News*. At this time it was stated that, although the foundation stone had been laid on 17 August, the tower formed no part of the present contract. In fact it was not finally decided to add it until 1857, by which time Brodrick had revised the design to include a dome in place of the previous lantern, and replanned the South vestibule and Council Chamber to provide stronger foundations for it. The tower remained unfinished when Queen Victoria opened the Hall on 7 September 1858. At this time Prince Albert is reported to have said, 'When I first saw the building, Mr Brodrick, I said to the Queen "Magnificent! Magnificent! Beautiful proportion!"'

The Hall, said to have been esteemed in its day, by American visitors, as highly as the great medieval cathedrals, reflects the increasing desire of provincial towns to rival in their public buildings those of London. The most obvious precursor for Brodrick's scheme is Elmes's St George's Hall (79-81) then nearing completion, and it is worth noting that Elmes had originally included a tower in his design for the Assize Courts of 1839-40. A more direct inspiration was that of the Royal Institution at Hull, which Brodrick had designed only a few months before the Leeds competition, and various French buildings, particularly the Paris Bourse designed by A. T. Brongniart in 1808, which Brodrick sketched during a continental tour in the 1840s, and the publications of Durand.

Exhib. Possibly International Exhibition, London, 1862, Cl. xxxvii, A, 1516. Possibly International Exhibition, Paris, 1867, Group I, Cl. IV, 6, 11. Institute of Advanced Architectural Studies (St John's Church, Ousebridge), York, 1967.

Illus. *BN*, 6 August 1858, p. 795 (slight alterations). *Journal of the Royal Society of Arts*, January 1971, p. 75 (detail).

Lit. *Br*, 16 October 1858, p. 693; 11 September 1858, p. 624; 18 September 1858, p. 633. *BN*, 6 August 1858, p. 785 (illus. incl. plan); 20 August 1858, p. 841; 17 September 1858, pp. 935, 937; 31 December 1858, p. 1289.

**84** Edward William Godwin

The Town Hall, Northampton. 1861
*Signed* E. G. *Lettered* Section XX *and*
back elevation. *Inscribed on the back in*
*pencil at a later date.* Competition
drawings, Town Hall, Northampton,
*and dated* 1860
*Pen and ink and wash* $16\frac{1}{8} \times 25\frac{1}{8}$ (40.8
$\times$ 64)
E.579-1963, given by Mr Edward
Godwin, son of the artist
Victoria and Albert Museum

The competition for Northampton Town
Hall was held early in 1861. On 9 March
the *Builder* announced that six designs
from the forty submitted had been
selected for further consideration. By
April these had been further reduced to
three, which were forwarded by the
Mayor to William Tite for his professional
opinion. In a letter reprinted in the
*Builder* (27 April, p. 28) Tite recommended that the Council accept the
design signed 'Circumspice', placing
Godwin's design, signed 'Non Nobis
Domine' in second place. This decision
was later reversed by the Council, who
implied that Godwin's Gothic design
fulfilled their requirements better than
the other Italian design. Construction
began later in the year under the superintendence of John Watkin, and was
completed in May 1864.

Tite remarked about Godwin's design
that he had 'some doubts about the
possibility of executing the roof of the
Great Hall in the manner indicated; and
I am disposed to think that the room
itself will not have good acoustic properties. The sessions court would be,
however, very convenient, and it solves
the problem of extension very satisfactorily.
As to the elevation towards St Giles

Square, I would suggest that the slender
columns bearing statues under niches
might be very advantageously omitted:
and that the dormer windows in the roof
are made needlessly prominent. There is,
however, a very remarkable degree of
talent in the management of the style
adopted: and, if this design were carried
into effect, it would be an ornament to
your town.' In practice Godwin made
many alterations to the original design,
which included strengthening the brackets
supporting the roof of the Great Hall and
adding a balcony, and removing the
second floor windows to the back elevation and the dormers at the front.

Northampton Town Hall was Godwin's

first major work, begun when he was
28 years old. The style is 13th cen...
Gothic, the rich texture and sta...
pointing to his willingness to accep...
fashionable Continental model as su...
for an English town hall. In 1889-...
addition was made to the west in the...
of Godwin's work by Matthew Hol...
The painted decorations in the ...
Hall were contributed by Colin G...
1925.

Lit. *BN*, 8 November 1861, p. 893.
28 May 1864, p. 520. S. Muthesius
*High Victorian Movement in archite*
*1850-1870*, 1972, N. Pevsner, N...
*amptonshire*, 1961, p. 316.

*Ground Plan*
*V & A M E.581-1963*

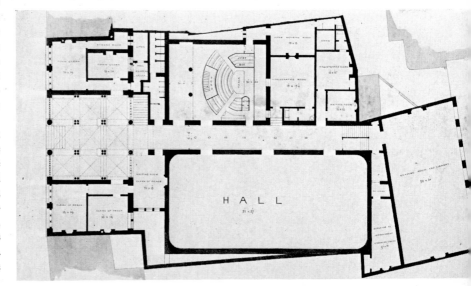

**85** Edward William Godwin
Congleton Town Hall
Congleton, Cheshire,
1864
*Signed on the back*
E. W. G. *Inscribed*
Congleton Town Hall
*Pen and ink, pencil,
water- and body-colour*
$20\frac{7}{8} \times 13\frac{3}{4}$ (53 × 33.5)
E.626-1963, given by
Mr Edward Godwin,
son of the artist
Victoria and Albert
Museum

Godwin was asked to design Congleton Town Hall on the strength of his design for Northampton Town Hall won in competition in 1861 (84). Confined to a long narrow irregularly shaped site with only 71 feet frontage, he achieved maximum breadth of effect by butting the building up to its neighbours. In spite of this expediency it has been remarked that 'the tower in the middle of the front demands more space left and right. Also five bays is not enough for so ambitious a design.' As completed, a clock tower, not shown in the drawing, was included, protruding from the top of the central tower. According to the *Builder*, this was so elevated 'that it may be seen from the market square as well as from the principal streets.' Godwin's plan included at the rear of the site a large assembly room sufficient to seat one thousand people, which, like the Court Room on the first floor, was lit from above. The main elevation was of local stone, the arches of the windows were filled in with small round glass panels made in Germany and the statues were representative of events in the history of the town.

Congleton Town Hall, like that of Northampton, with its central tower, high-pitched roof and dormers, and Gothic arcading derives from the precedent set by Scott for public buildings with his unexpected designs for Hamburg Town Hall of 1854, and the first project for the Government Offices of 1857. The machicolations on the tower, which are absent at Northampton and in Scott's projects, probably derive from Burges's work which Godwin much admired.

Lit. S. Muthesius, *The High Victorian Movement in architecture 1850-1870*, 1972, pp. 125-26. *Br*, 16 July 1864, pp. 528-30. N. Pevsner and E. Hubbard, *Cheshire*, 1972, p. 184.

**86** Cuthbert Brodrick
Oriental Baths, Cookridge Street, Leeds. 1866
*Pen and water-colour* 19 × 30¼ (48.5 × 84.4)
U 8/34
Lent by the Royal Institute of British Architects

It is perhaps not surprising that the essentially Romantic sense of monumentality evinced in the designs both for the Leeds Town Hall (83), and for the Grand Hotel, Scarborough (128) should have led Brodrick to interest himself in Eastern Styles. This interest was almost certainly given added impetus by his experiments in structural polychromy. The *Builder* had noted of his Leeds Corn Exchange in 1862 that 'Mr Brodrick has done good service by introducing the use of... moulded brickwork into his King Street warehouses. Thus, with red, blue and black brick, moulded brick string cou and mouldings, encaustic tiles and cotta, we have a stock of materials w no climate will touch or destroy; with them a field for design, both in f and colour that will give archi opportunities for exercising every art faculty they possess.' These were materials that appear in the Baths de and in another design done later in year for the Custom House at Bom 'in a mixture of Hindoo and Moh medan', but this was never built.

The Cookridge Street baths refaced in 1882 and demolished in

Illus. *Catalogue of the Drawings Colle of the RIBA*, vol. B, fig. 92. *Cou Life*, 1 June 1967, p. 1379, fig. 2.
Lit. *AR*, vol. lxxix, November 1936, 33-5. D. Linstrum, *Historic archite of Leeds*, 1969, p. 60. D. Linstrum *Journal of the Royal Society of* January 1971, pp. 84-5.

Alfred Waterhouse

The Town Hall, Manchester, Lancashire. 1868
*Pen and ink and water-colour* 31 × 25
(78.7 × 63.4)
D.1882-1908, given by Mr P. Waterhouse, FRIBA, for the Phené Spiers Collection of architectural drawings
Victoria and Albert Museum

An open competition for the new Town Hall was held in March 1867, and 136 designs received. George Godwin, the editor of the *Builder*, was asked to inspect them and he selected ten by eight architects, who were then invited to submit further designs by 14 February 1868. These were then submitted to T. L. Donaldson and G. E. Street, who placed Speakman and Charlesworth first for 'architectural excellence'; J. Oldrid Scott second; Thomas Worthington, third; and Waterhouse, fourth. Waterhouse, however, who had submitted nineteen drawings in the second competition, including seven perspectives, was placed first for 'arrangement of plan and construction' and for 'economy and likelihood of being executed for the stipulated sum [£250,000].' Furthermore, his design was said to be the best for 'natural light and ventilation', and he was declared the winner.

The Great Hall, with its early English Gothic detailing and hammer-beam roof, was decorated with wall paintings by Ford Madox Brown between 1876 and 1888. These depict various scenes from Manchester history including the Romans building their Manchester fort, the expulsion of the Danes from Manchester, the opening of the Bridgewater Canal, and Dalton collecting marsh gas. The *Builder* remarked that 'the public hall is placed in the centre of the building. It is approached by the public from Albert Square by the grand staircases through a large hall on the main floor, forming a sort of ante-room to it, and adding about one third more available standing space on the occasion of a crowded town's meeting. The hall is lit on either side by two-light windows. The roof, though of hammer-beam construction, has a ceiling of an average height of only 42 ft. (to render successful the acoustic properties of the room). In order to prevent outward thrust at so great a height from the ground the roof is tied across. The walls of the central hall will be of stone, the lower part panelled in oak, with seats in the window recesses. At the further extremity of the hall are two entrances, with retiring rooms attached, which communicate with the two secondary central staircases, and the Lloyd-Street and Princess-Street corridors. Above these retiring-rooms is a gallery for an organ and orchestra, or capable of seating sixty people.'

Lit. *Br*, 11 April 1868, pp. 259-61; 2 May 1868, p. 317. N. Pevsner, *South Lancashire*, 1969, pp. 281-82. F. Jenkins, 'The Making of a Municipal Palace—Manchester Town Hall', in *Country Life*, 16 February 1967, pp. 336-39.

**88** Edward William Godwin
Competition design for Baths and Wash-houses, Manchester,
Lancashire. 1877
*Inscribed* South West, North East. South East Elevation
*Pen and ink and pencil* $17\frac{3}{4} \times 29\frac{1}{8}$ (45 × 74)
RAN 7/F/1(2)
Lent by the Royal Institute of British Architects

The need for new public baths and wash-houses in Manchester
appears to have been first brought to attention by E. T. Bellhouse
in a paper on that subject read before the Manchester Statistical
Society in June 1877. His remarks, coupled with the success of
similar establishments recently erected in Liverpool, persuaded
the Council to advertise an open competition for new buildings in
July 1877, with premiums of £200, £100 and £50. The site, in
Ancoats, covered some 2,210 square feet and accommodation was
to be provided for 'first and second class swimming and private
baths, and women's private baths, together with a public steam

laundry and drying stoves, steam engines and boilers comp
with all the most recent improvements; and also a residenc
the Superintendent. In addition two public rooms each 72 f
36 ft. for ward meetings and election purposes, balls or con
with the necessary retiring rooms in connection with them.'
Council specifically stated that the designs should be 'in a
style of architecture and free from any elaborate ornam
Thirty-one sets of plans were received and Thomas Worthir
appointed to judge them. Early in November that bearing
motto 'Economy well considered' submitted by John Joh
was declared the winner, and Mangnall and Littlewood, a
Low the runners up. Godwin's design, although illustrate
the *British Architect*, was almost certainly among those by se
well-known London architects which were considered as
'drawn in compliance with the instructions, especially
architecture, and [were] therefore omitted from consideratio

Lit. *BN*, 28 September 1877; 12 October 1877, p. 356
16 November 1877, p. 496. *Br*, 24 November 1877, p.
*BA*, 4 June 1878.

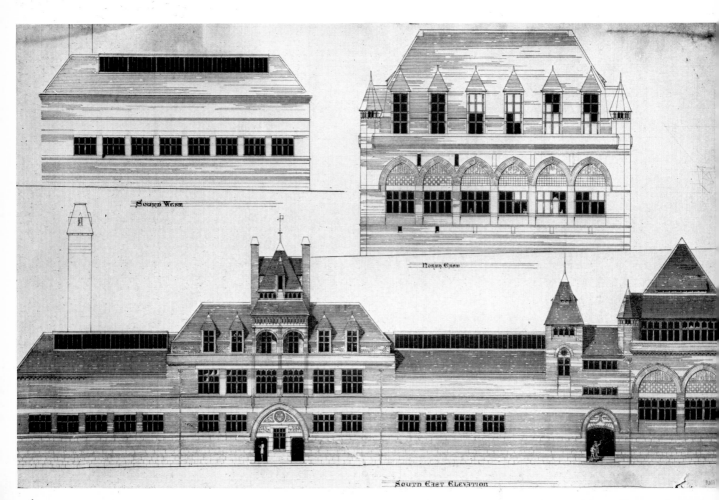

Edward Schroeder Prior
Swimming Baths, West Bay, Dorset, c. 1894
Inscribed Club. Promenade. Baths. West Bay, Cross Section,
Elevation to Esplanade, Elevation to Harbour Mouth
Pencil, pen and ink and water-colour 10 × 22¼ (25.3 × 56.5)
RAN 5/G/4/4
Lent by the Royal Institute of British Architects

One of four drawings, of which one is on paper watermarked 1894.

Prior's design incorporated (besides the swimming bath) a tea room, billiard room, shops, library, and smoking and reading rooms. The swimming pool itself could be separated by means of a floating partition into baths for men and women, or could be used as a single bath 65 feet long. The keeper's box provided accommodation for a look-out who was in charge of operating the swing bridge giving access to the baths from the tow path on the other side of the harbour.

Prior's simple design with its green roof of 'transparent felt' is reminiscent of the work of Voysey (35), and is typical of those designs of the 1890s and early 20th century which in their simple shapes and unornamented surfaces attempted to break away from earlier historicism.

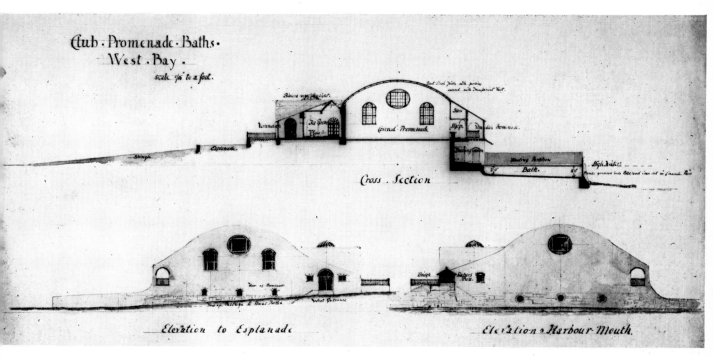

ations to the sea and harbour
A RAN 5.G.4

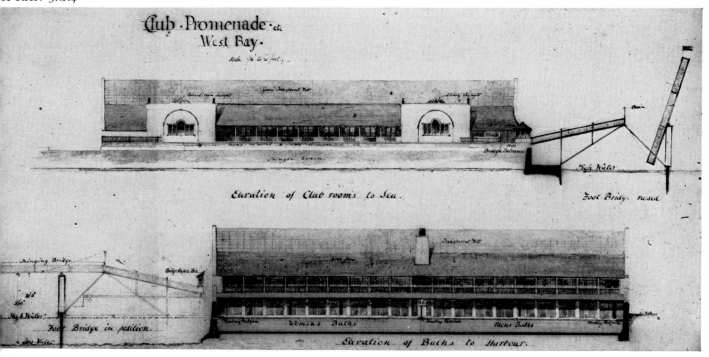

**90** Lieut.-Col. Haywood
Offices for the Commissioners of Sewers, Basinghall Street,
London, 1896
*Signed* D. J. Ross, Guildhall *and dated* 23rd October 1896.
*Inscribed* City Sewers New Offices. Modified Drawing No. 7,
Basinghall Street. Front Elevation
*Pen and ink and water-colour* $23\frac{1}{4} \times 36\frac{1}{2}$ (59 × 92.7)
Lent from the Corporation of London Records Office

Haywood's design provided for each department of the Commissioners having a floor to itself. The Chief Clerk and Medical
Officer were accommodated on the first; the Commissioners with
a large Court Room on the ground; the sanitary inspectors and
rate collectors on the second; and the street inspectors, gas
inspector and strong rooms in the half basement. The foundation
stone was laid on 22 January 1896 by the Chairman, Alderman
J. C. Bell, and the building work supervised by David James Ross,
engineer to the Commission. The contractors were Chessum &
Sons of Haggerston.

The *Building News* remarked that 'the buildings generally will
be of fire-proof construction, be heated throughout by hot water,
and lighted by electricity. A lift will be provided to the several
floors, and book lifts from the strong rooms in the basement to the
departments above. The principal entrance will be in Basinghall
Street, adjoining the City Library. The architectural decoration
of the buildings is designed to accord generally with the Guildhall
Library adjoining, but somewhat more Flemish in character.' The
most impressive room was undoubtedly the Court Room 46 feet
long by 41 feet wide 'handsomely fitted up with oak panelling'.

Lit. *BN*, 8 February 1895, p. 188.

# Catalogue

## 8 Town Planning

Thomas Allom
Design for the Thames Embankment, London. 1846
*Signed on the back and inscribed on a label* A design for improving the property on the banks of the Thames between London and Blackfriars Bridges, with a view to a line of communication from thence to the Houses of Parliament, thereby obtaining a healthy and agreeable promenade and carriage-way, relieving the overcrowded thoroughfares of the City, creating valuable frontage for shops and public buildings, giving additional convenience to the wharfingers and warehousemen, and retaining all the present communications with Thames Street. It is proposed to receive all the present sewers into a large one forming the foundations of the lower terrace
*Water-colour* 21 × 47½ (53.4 × 120.7)
P.7-1913, bequeathed by Mrs Amy Giovanna Storr, daughter of the artist
Victoria and Albert Museum

Allom made two designs for the improvement of the Thames Embankments, of which this was the first. (The second, shown at the Royal Academy in 1848, is also in the Museum, Department of Paintings, P.3-1913). Both received considerable praise in the contemporary press as paintings but were criticized as architectural designs. 'A very able drawing, but the architecture is rendered quite subordinate, being treated as little more than background to the splendid and animated river view, which, as pictured, would have been just as good had the present houses been represented. Perhaps it would be unfair to consider the buildings here put in as intended to do more than convey a general idea of the proposed line, for they are made up of just the same showy fronts as are now in vogue for new trading streets. Were the separate elevations drawn out as usual and left to speak for themselves as designs, some of them, we fancy, would cut a sorry figure.'

Many schemes were put forward for Thames Embankments during the early 19th century, some of which were considered by the Select Committee on Metropolis Improvements of 1838. The most famous of these are probably those of John Martin from 1833. The Victoria Embankment was eventually built between 1864 and 1870 to the designs of Sir Joseph Bazalgette.

Exhib. RA, 1846, no. 1319. Exposition Universelle, Paris, 1855, no. 1386. International Exhibition, London, 1862, British Section, Architecture, no. 1651 or 1652. International Fine Art Exhibition, Rome, 1911.
Lit. *Br*, 9 May 1846, p. 217. *CE&AJ*, 1846, p. 171.

**92** James Bunstone Bunning

Elevations of properties in Cannon Street, London, between Laurence Pountney Hill and Queen Street.

c. 1856

*Pen and ink and water-colour Folded*
$120\frac{1}{2} \times 21\frac{3}{4}$ (356.7 × 35.6)
Surveyors' City Land Plan 2343
Lent from the Corporation of London Records Office

The London (City) Improvement Act of 1847 provided for the widening of Cannon Street and of its extension by demolishing the properties bounded by Budge Row, Cloak Lane and Tower Royal, to Queen Street. A later Act of 1850 provided for the further extension called Cannon Street West, which meant that the new road, opened for traffic in 1854, carried straight through from the top of London Bridge to St Paul's Churchyard. Lease books in the Corporation of London Records Office indicate that the properties depicted in the drawing were erected between 1851 and 1855 by speculative builders particularly William Lawrence, William Lawrence the younger and James Clarke Lawrence. At least one block was designed by John Belcher. The stuccoed façades compare with numerous similar properties being erected elsewhere in London, and it is interesting to note how even in the short space of time between 1851 and 1855 the designs become noticeably richer to keep pace changing fashions.

Bunning's work in the city invo laying out several roads besides Car Street. In 1845 he designed a stree run from the west end of Cheapsid Carey Street; associated with Car Street was a new street from Earls S to the Mansion House (completed 18 He continued Victoria Street, Cler well, to Coppice Row (opened 18 widened Threadneedle Street (1846) continued Tudor Street to Whitefr Dock (1849). In 1848 he made a de for bridging the Holborn Valley and before his death he drew up plans f street from the Coal Exchange to Monument and a proposed widenin

*Plan. Corporation of London Records Office*
*Surveyors City Land Plan 2341*

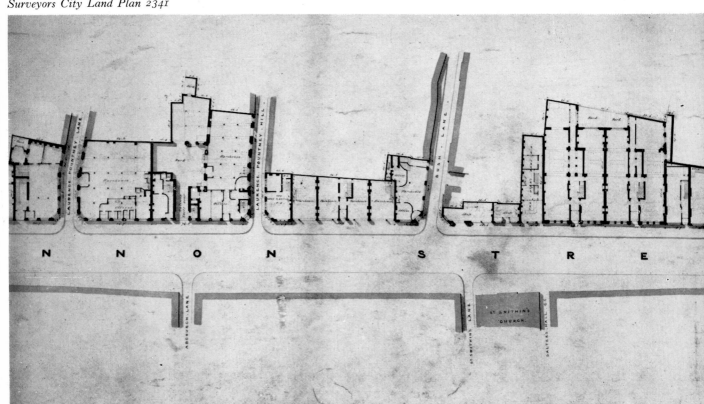

hames Street from Billingsgate to St
agnus's Church. Before his appoint-
ent as Clerk of the City's Works in 1843
had laid out many streets at New Cross,
cluding Hatcham and Albert Terraces,
r the Haberdashers' Company.

*Br*, 28 January 1854, p. 45; 7 November 1863, p. 782. *ILN*, 6 May 1854,
p. 418.

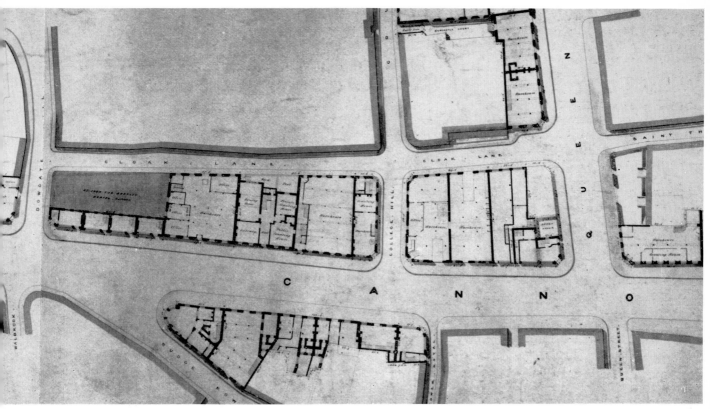

**93** Maurice Bingham Adams
Bedford Park, Chiswick
London c. 1877
*Inscribed* Bedford Park, Chiswick, A.D. 1896. Plan showing original area laid out in A.D. 1877, this being the initial projected scheme of the Garden Cities Movement of the 20th century. This map presented and made by Maurice B. Adams, FRIBA. *Other inscriptions record the names of residents and the architects of various buildings on the estate.*
*Water-colour* 18 × 18 (45.7 × 45.7)
Given by the artist
Lent by Hounslow Library Services, Chiswick Library

In the early 1870s Jonathan T. Carr, a cloth merchant with interests in both art and property speculation, purchased 45 acres of land near the new Turnham Green Station, and determined to lay out a housing estate on entirely new principles. He first employed E. W. Godwin as his architect, but few buildings from Godwin's designs were erected; they included 1 The Avenue, of 1876, the first house to be built on the new estate. Godwin's designs were heavily criticized in the contemporary press, and by 1877 Carr had turned to Norman Shaw, who in the next two years provided the designs for many houses, the first of which was a pair of semi-detached cottages at 19-22 The Avenue. By 1878 the *Building News* reported that a Mr. Wilson, who is known to have designed 7 Queen Anne's Gardens for the artist T. M. Rooke, and to have modified some of Godwin's designs, was also being employed. Maurice B. Adams, who as principal draughtsman and as Editor of the *Building News* was responsible for illustrating both Godwin's and

Shaw's designs, also proposed some architectural designs for Carr. The Art School, opened in 1881, parish hall, and Chapel of All Souls added in 1907 to the church, were amongst his works. The remaining houses were designed by E. J. May (1853-1941), and included the Bedford Park Club of 1878, the vicarage, and a terrace, 15-25 Queen Anne's Grove, of 1883. By July 1881 Carr was in financial difficulties and the Bedford Park Company was formed. The company evolved a scheme to develop

land to the west which fell through in 1886, when the company went into liquidation, and at this time many houses were erected by speculative builders, the most notable of which was 14 South Parade, designed by Voysey in 1891.

Norman Shaw's work included an inn, stores (130) and a church, and it is consequently not surprising that contemporary writers referred to the area as a 'townlet' or 'village'. The concept of a self-contained, residential unit with its own

religious and social activ[...] and an emphasis on [...] places planted with t[...] which this definition imp[...] appears to have been ful[...] for the first time in a s[...] scheme at Bedford Park, [...] is the reason why it is us[...] referred to as the first ga[...] suburb.

Illus. W. Creese, *Search [...] the environment*, 1970, p [...] fig. 33.
Lit. T. A. Greeves, 'Lond[...] first Garden Subu[...] *Country Life*, 7 and [...] December, 1967.

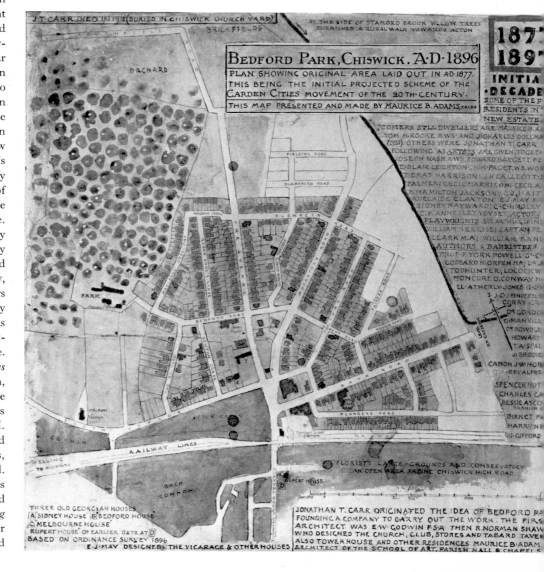

John Pollard Seddon
Housing scheme, Birchington, Kent.
c. 1880
*Inscribed in pencil* Birchington-on-Sea
*and in ink with the names of owners of
some properties*
*Pen and ink and water-colour* 24 × 32
(60.9 × 81.2)
D.1404-1896
Victoria and Albert Museum

Seddon appears to have been involved
with Birchington at least as early as 1870,
when John Taylor, who at one time
worked with him, was building his
pioneering bungalows there on what was
apparently Seddon's land. The *Building
News*, writing about two of Taylor's
bungalows in September of that year, also
noticed 'an estate of considerable extent
. . . laid out for building, under the
direction of Mr C. N. Beazley . . . a far
better character is observable in the few
houses already built than is usual among
the speculative erections of the district . . .
the forms of many of the villas are
pleasing.' By 1879 Taylor had erected
many more bungalows—from the Indian
word *Bangla*—and found no difficulty in
selling them complete with his patent
'chair furniture' to amongst others, D. G.
Rossetti (who is buried in the local
churchyard of All Saints) and Prof.
Erasmus Wilson. Taylor himself lived
in one at Westcliff. It is not clear how
Seddon's proposals related to these earlier
schemes nor how much of this plan was
built. A volume of drawings by Seddon
in the Museum contains many designs
for Birchington done over several years
and includes houses for members of his
family. It also contains a proposal for a
'bungalow terrace' which may have been
drawn up in collaboration with Taylor,
although the details are dissimilar from
Taylor's earlier work. Seddon's concept
of a partially self-contained community
with its own station and hotel in a 'garden'
setting is an obvious, and apparently
previously unknown, precursor of later
garden cities.

Lit. *BN*, 16 September 1870, p. 200;
6 February 1874, p. 157; 16 August
1874, p. 166; 28 March 1879, p. 343.
A. D. King, unpublished thesis on the
bungalow.

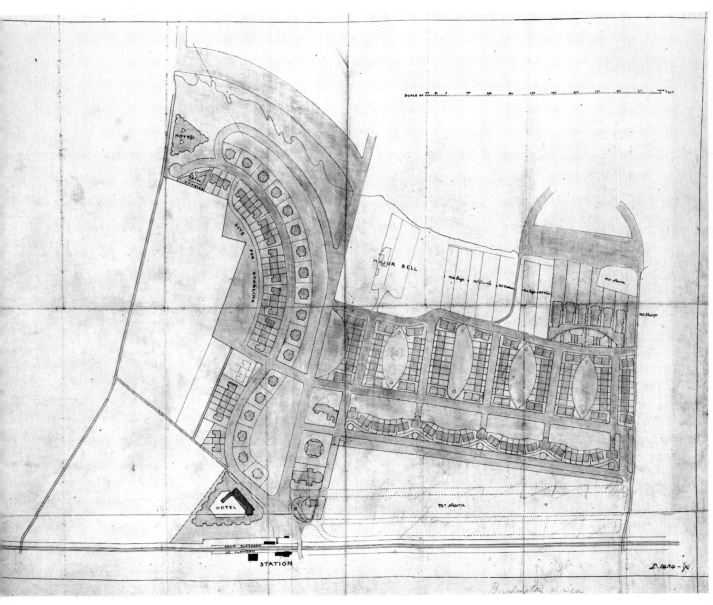

**95** Henry Francis Lockwood and Richard Mawson

Saltaire, Yorkshire. c. 1881

*Lettered*. Plan shewing the town and works of Saltaire, the property of Sir Titus Salt, Bart. Lockwood & Mawson, Architects, London and Bradford

*Lithograph* 21 × 12½ (53.4 × 31.7)

SAL 1881 MAW/2

Lent by Bradford City Libraries

In his book *Sir Titus Salt, his life and lessons*, 1877, Belgarnie notes that Salt, who had risen from a working class background to become Mayor of Bradford in 1848, intended to retire at 50 to assume the life of a country landowner, but that he decided instead to move his large manufactory for making worsted from alpaca, to a new site outside the town. This was picturesquely situated on the banks of the River Aire and was close to the existing Leeds and Liverpool Canal and the Railway. Salt believed that the troubles of the nation stemmed from a surfeit of 'drink and lust' and determined to attach to the factory a new town for his employees which would diminish both vices by helping to strengthen family ties. He declared that he had given instructions to Lockwood and Mawson, his architects, that 'nothing should be spared to render the dwellings a pattern to the country.'

Work on the factory, a large Italianate building designed by Sir William Fairbairn with additions by Lockwood and Mawson, commenced immediately and it was opened amidst great celebrations in 1853. The town was laid out on a grid-iron pattern with provision for churches, a hospital, almshouses, schools, a club, an Institute, and 600-700 houses. By 1854 150 houses were ready, but work slowed until a new lease of life in 1866. When Salt died, ten years later, over 800 houses had been completed. The scheme was probably influenced by the similar but much smaller one undertaken by Col.

Akroyd at Copley in the previous (1849), which also involved rows back-to-back cottages. The usual san disadvantages of this plan were avo at Saltaire by building service la seven feet wide, between the backya Each house was provided with a par a kitchen and two or three bedro Lockwood and Mawson's most di guished building was the Congregati Church—Salt was a devout Con gationalist—opened opposite the fac in 1859, and it was there that Salt buried after his death in 1876.

Lockwood exhibited a model of Sal at the International Exhibition hel London in 1862 (Class xxxvii, B, 212

Illus. J. S. Curl, 'A Victorian m town', *Country Life*, 9 March 1 pp. 542-44.

Lit. N. Pevsner, *Yorkshire, the Riding*, 1959, pp. 427-28. J. Richards, 'Sir Titus Salt or The of Saltaire', *AR*, vol. lxxix, 1936, 213-18.

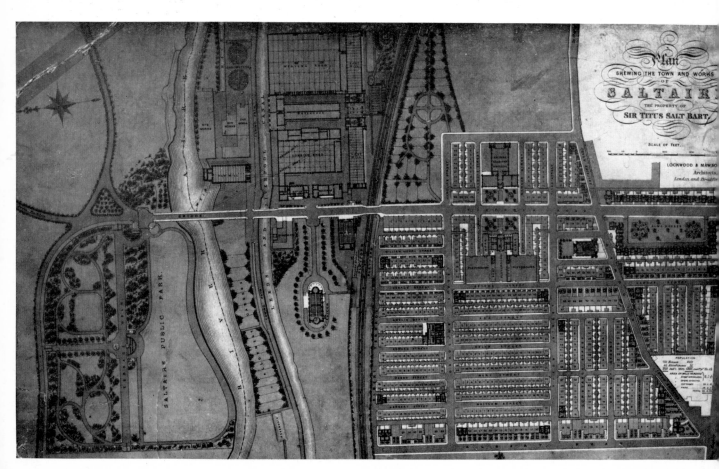

# Catalogue

## 9 Theatres, Music Halls, Clubs

Sir Charles Barry
Travellers' Club, Pall Mall, London. 1841. Garden elevation showing proposed smoking tower
*Pencil and brown wash* $20\frac{3}{4} \times 27\frac{3}{4}$ ($52.7 \times 71.4$)
Lent by the Royal Academy of Arts

The Travellers' Club was founded in 1819 'to form a point of re-union for gentlemen who had travelled abroad; and to afford them the opportunity of inviting as Honorary visitors, the principal members of all the foreign missions and travellers of distinction.' In March 1828 the club acquired the Pall Mall site, and in May held a limited competition for designs for a new building. Eight plans were received and on 20 August, after each architect had been interviewed, those submitted by Barry were chosen. Subsequently Barry altered the drawings to allow for a reduction in the size of the plot and these revised plans were eventually passed on 17 July 1829. Tenders were received from several firms and that of H. Lee and Sons for £19,688 selected. This was above the

£19,000 limit set by the club and it was decided at a general meeting that the smoking tower, which had appeared in Barry's revised drawings as a small belvedere placed asymmetrically to the east, should be omitted. Building commenced almost immediately and the Club was ready for occupation by July 1832. The smoking tower as it appears in this design, Barry's Diploma drawing, was eventually added to the south front in 1842-43 and the room was used initially as a coffee room.

The Travellers' Club is the first of Sir Charles Barry's masterpieces and the inspiration for numerous later buildings in the Italian Palazzo style. In his Royal Institution at Manchester of 1824-45 and his earlier churches at Liverpool and Brighton, Barry had shown that he was quite capable of handling the more fashionable Graeco-Roman Classical and Gothic styles. The Travellers' represents his desire to escape from those traditions to something that was richer and where more attempt was made to emphasize the solidity and form of the building.

Lit. L.C.C. *Survey of London*, vol. xxx, Parish of St James, Westminster, Part I, South of Piccadilly, 1960, p. 399 & pl. 85B.

**97** Henry Flower
Gresham Club, King William Street, London. c. 1843
*Water-colour* 18⅛ × 27 (46 × 68.5)
W 3/7
Lent by the Royal Institute of British Architects

The building as executed differs radically from the elevations and plan in this early design. The main entrance was moved to the back of the building, a second storey inserted, and bay windows added in place of the balcony on the King William Street façade. Various ornamental details were removed, including the pilasters with their coupled columns and rusticated bases and the crowning parapet. The foundation stone was laid by the Lord Mayor on 8 February 1844 and the builder, Thomas Cubitt, undertook to complete the building by October of the same year. The *Civil Engineer and Architects' Journal* were highly critical of the detail, noting that 'a due proportion of ornament gives pleasure to the spectator, but the thing overdone turns the composition into ridicule, and, as in the Gresham Club, places it on a level with the tasty exhibition of the compo shops in the Paddington and Commercial Road. . . . It is to be hoped that if *clubs* shall continue to be trumps, those architects who hold the honours in their hands will in future play the game according to Hoyle, and not lead the knave to be taken by their competitor's queen.'

Illus. *Catalogue of the Drawings Collection of the RIBA*, vol. C-F, 1972, fig. 93.
Lit. *Br*, 9 March 1844, pp. 114-15. *CE&AJ*, March 1844, p. 98.

George Tattersall
Army and Navy Club, Pall Mall, London, 1847
*Signed* Geo. Tattersall. *and dated* 1847. *Inscribed* Army and
Navy Club
*Pencil, water- and body-colour* $26\frac{1}{2} \times 36\frac{1}{4}$ (67.5 × 92)
56.10 given by Miss G. Williams
Lent by the London Museum

In 1837 Sir Edward Barnes and some other officers recently
returned from service abroad found the waiting list for member-
ship of the Junior United Service Club so long that they proposed
to establish a new club for Army Officers. The Duke of Wellington
proposed that the club should be open to officers of the Navy and
Marines also, and in 1838 the Army and Navy Club opened in
premises at 18 St James's Square, recently vacated by the Oxford
and Cambridge University Club. In 1846 the Club purchased a
site on the corner of George Street and Pall Mall for the erection
of more permanent headquarters and in January 1847 the *Builder*
announced that they intended holding an open competition for the
new building, and that prizes of £200 and £100 would be offered
for the two best designs. The Club failed to act on suggestions
that they should employ a professional architect to advise on the
selection of the designs and in April a ballot of the entire club
nominated Tattersall for the First Premium and F. Fowler and
Fiske for the Second. The *Builder* criticized Tattersall's plan as
leaving too little space for the purposes of the Club. This fault

was accepted by the members, who at a meeting on 11 May 1847
decided to enlarge the site by the purchase of an adjoining
property and to hold a further competition limited to the six
designs which had received the largest number of votes in the
ballot. The six architects in the second competition included
(besides Tattersall, and Fowler and Fiske) C. O. Parnell and
A. Smith, H. B. Richardson, A. Salvin (who was invited after
G. S. Clarke withdrew because of an accident), and Sydney
Smirke. The Committee selected Parnell and Smith's design;
building began in 1848 and was completed in 1851.

Parnell and Smith submitted the same plans in both competitions. Their Venetian façade was much less orthodox than
Tattersall's Classical design and compared favourably with
Sydney Smirke's Venetian Carlton Club, then almost completed,
on the opposite side of Pall Mall. While the *Builder* objected to
Tattersall's interior plan, the elevation they felt had 'some
excellent features'. More recently the richness of the design with
its bas-reliefs and sculptural groups, the one surmounting the
pedestal over the main entrance apparently symbolizing Britannia
and Neptune, has been described as 'brash' and 'pompous'.

Exhib. RA. 1848, no. 1094 or 1229.
Illus. L.C.C. *Survey of London*, vol. xxx, Parish of St James
    Westminster, Part I, South of Piccadilly, 1960, pl. 116.
Lit. L.C.C. *Survey of London*, vol. xxix, Parish of St James
    Westminster, Part I, South of Piccadilly, 1960, pp. 180-81.
    *Br*, 8 May 1847, pp. 213-15.

**99** Charles John Phipps
The Savoy Theatre, Victoria Embankment, London. 1881
*Pencil and water-colour Sight size*
16 × 23¾ (40.5 × 60.3)
Enthoven Collection, given by the executors of the estate of Harry R. Beard
Victoria and Albert Museum

The *Building News* reported in April that the Savoy Theatre was 'now b erected', and it was eventually opene 10 October 1881 with a presentatio 'Patience or Bunthorne's Bride' an thetic opera' by W. S. Gilbert and Ar Sullivan, under the management Richard D'Oyley Carte. This partner had been founded at the Royalty Th in Dean Street, Soho, where Gilbert Sullivan assisted D'Oyley Carte wi one act cantata 'Trial by Jury'. By it had led to the formation of the Con Opera Company, which put on its work at the Opéra Comique in that During the run of *H.M.S. Pinafore* ii following year, Carte became sole l and manager of the theatre, and, v his lease was about to expire, he dec to build a new theatre, the Savoy, pecially suited to the requirements o modern school of theatre-goers. T innovations, he later claimed, invo the first use of electric lighting in a p building and the inauguration of queuing system for pit and gallery. interiors of previous theatres were ge ally, Carte stated, 'conceived with litt any, artistic purpose, and gene executed with little completeness, an a more or less garish manner.' The S interiors were decorated 'with del plaster modelling designed in the ma of the Italian Renaissance. The colour tones are white, pale yellow gold. The stalls are covered with plush—while the curtains of the b are of yellowish silk, brocaded wi pattern of decorative flowers in br colours.' This, Carte felt sure, 'wi appreciated by all persons of taste.' decorations were carried out by Colli & Lock, and the contractors for building were Patman & Fotherinha

Extensive redecorations and re were carried out by A. Bloom Jackson in 1903. In 1929 the three auditorium capable of seating 1 persons was completely rebuilt by F A. Tugwell to accommodate only tiers, and decorations were carried ou Basil Ionides.

Lit. R. Mander and J. Mitchenson,
  *Theatres of London*, 1961, pp. 174
  *BN*, 1 April 1881, p. 360 (ill
  *Illustrated Sporting and Dramatic N*
  29 October 1881, p. 161 (illus.). D'O
  Carte's original prospectus in
  Enthoven Collection.

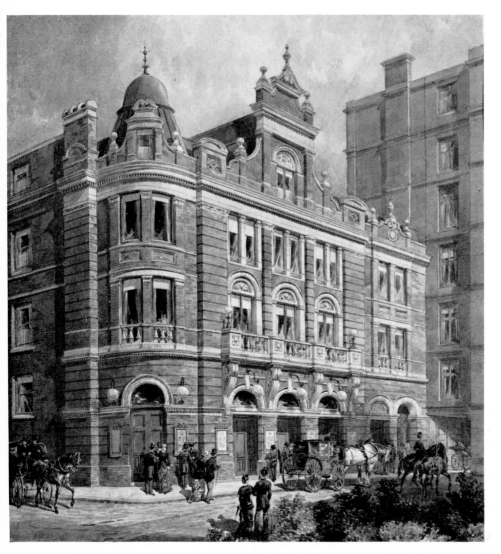

John Dibblee Crace
Auditorium ceiling, Royal Standard
Music Hall, Victoria Street, London.
1898
*Stamped* John G. Crace & Son,
Wigmore Street, W. *Inscribed in ink*.
This is one of the drawings referred
to in Contract dated August 4th,
1898. Brown & Barraude (?) *and in
pencil* Standard Music Hall
*Pencil and water-colour* $9\frac{3}{4} \times 19\frac{5}{8}$
$(24.7 \times 49.8)$
E.1839-1912, given by the artist
Victoria and Albert Museum

The Royal Standard Music Hall was
opened on 26 December 1863 after its
forerunner, the Royal Standard Hotel,
later unofficially known as Moy's Music
Hall, in Stockdale Terrace, was demolished
to make way for Victoria Street. On 9 July
1911 the *Builder* reported that a company
had been formed to acquire the Royal
Standard Music Hall and an adjoining
site in Allington Street for a new Hall, the
Victoria Palace, which was designed by
Frank Matcham and opened on 7 November 1911.

Crace's decoration, deriving mainly
from Renaissance prototypes, was of the
sort advocated by D'Oyley Carte for the
Savoy interiors (99). It appears to have
been commissioned by Samuel Dickie,
who took over the management of the
Royal Standard in 1897.

Lit. *Br.* 9 July 1911, p. 51. D. Howard,
  *London theatres and music halls*, 1970,
  no. 834, pp. 249-50.

# Catalogue

## 10 Railway Buildings, Carriages

101 Philip Hardwick
The Propylaeum. 1837
*Pencil and water-colour* 29 ×
(73.6 × 111.2)
Diploma Work, 1841
Lent by the Royal Academy of
London

Exhib. RA, 1837, no. 1106. RA, B
Architecture, 1937, no. 1465. RA,
First Hundred Years of the
Academy, 1951, no. 662. RA, B
tenary Exhibition, 1968, no. 255.
Neo-Classical Exhibition, 1972,
1155.

Lit. G. D. M. Block 'London's C
Rail Terminus', *Country Life*,
pp. 554-56, 1453. A. and P. Smit
*The Euston Arch*, 1968.

102 Philip Charles Hardwick
Great Booking Hall, 1849
*Water-colour* 28½ × 24 (72.5 ×
Given by Mrs Lysons, 1923
Lent by the Royal Institut
British Architects

Exhib. RA, 1849 (1108). RA, B
Architecture, 1937, no. 1482. RA,
First Hundred Years of the
Academy, 1951, no. 707.

Lit. L.L.C., *Survey of London*, vol.
1949, pp. 108-09, 112-13. N. Ta
*Monuments of commerce*, 1968, pp
17 & pl. 10.

# Euston Station, London, 1837-1849

Various proposals were made for building a railway line from London to link up with the existing lines in the North of England from 1826, but it was not until an Act of Parliament, which became law on 6 May 1833, that the London to Birmingham Railway Company came officially into being. The Company established its first London terminus at Chalk Farm in the same year, but in August 1834 Robert Stephenson, the engineer, suggested that it should be moved to Euston, and an extension of the original Act was granted on 3 July 1835 making this legally possible. Stephenson drew up plans for the station with the assistance of Charles (later Sir Charles) Fox, who designed the platform sheds, and Philip Hardwick, who was commissioned in July 1836 to design the Propylaeum or Arch. The first section of the new line to Boxmoor was opened on 20 July 1837 and the whole line from Euston to Birmingham on 17 September 1838. The total cost of the works was in excess of £5½ million. Of this sum the Propylaeum, with its 44 foot high columns and flanking lodges constructed from 80,000 cubic feet of Yorkshire stone, accounted for £35,000. Hardwick's model was the restoration of a gateway at Athens published in Stuart and Revett's *Antiquities of Athens* and called by them the entrance to an agora.

The *Civil Engineer and Architects' Journal* noted in June 1838 that workmen had completed the removal of the immense scaffolding surrounding the arch, and that the iron entrance gates made by J. J. Bramah, to Hardwick's designs (not depicted in the drawing), would be added in the next week.

In 1846 the Company amalgamated with the Grand Junction and Manchester and Birmingham Railways to form the London and North Western Railway and almost immediately new works were put in hand to provide more accommodation for increasing numbers of passengers. These included a great hall, meeting room, board room, general offices and new booking offices, and Philip Charles Hardwick, who took over his father's practice at about that time was chosen as architect. The Great Hall, completed in 1849 at a cost of £122,562, was the outstanding feature of this new scheme. The huge coffered ceiling, 128 by 61 feet and clerestory with Ionic order, frescoes (not carried out) and balcony were apparently inspired by Peruzzi's Palazzo Massimi in Rome. Iron formed the structural part of the roof, and plaster and scagliola painted in imitation of grey and red granite, the enrichments. The consoles, relief panels symbolizing London, Liverpool, Manchester, Birmingham, Carlisle, Chester, Lancaster and Northampton, and the sculptural group over the entrance to the General Meeting Room at the head of the central staircase, depicting Britannia accompanied by a lion, a ship, the Arts and Sciences, and Mercury, were by John Thomas. The large statue of Robert Stephenson at the foot of the stairs was by E. H. Baily. At one time it was intended to position a large refreshment counter in the centre of the Hall and departure boards on the piers between the arches on the ground floor. The building was ventilated by a system of hot water pipes and coils in the roof which extended from the heating system.

The Hardwick's grandiose Arch and Great Hall, both of which were demolished in 1961-62 after considerable public protest, reflect the desire of the railway company not only to make known the pride they felt in their achievement in building the railway, but also to make clear to mounting numbers of critics that not all protagonists of the Industrial Revolution were devoid of informed aesthetic opinions. This did not impress the *Civil Engineer and Architects' Journal*, however, which remarked of the Great Hall that it was 'marked by oversights and defects in its design that might easily have been corrected or avoided. In our opinion the ceiling is too much decorated, so much so as to cause the lower part of the apartment to appear bare and unfinished, while the long curved brackets or trusses which support it are out of keeping with the order below, and take off considerably from its importance, more especially as the columns themselves are shorter than they needed or ought to have been; for, strange to say, the pedestals on which they are raised are made higher than the railing between them, which produces a very awkward and disagreeable effect.'

Lit. G.L.C., *Survey of London*, vol. xxi, 1949, pp. 109-11. N. Pevsner, *London, except the Cities of London and Westminster*, 1952, pp. 366-67.

**103** George Townsend Andrews
Engine House, York Station, Y...
1840
*Signed* G. T. Andrews, Archi...
York *and dated* 1840. *Inscribed* (...
North of England Railway. Plan...
elevation of the Engine Hous...
York
*Pen and ink and wash* $16\frac{1}{4}$ ×
(41.2 × 26.7)
8936.13
Victoria and Albert Museum

The Great North of England Ra...
Company was formed in Darlingt...
build a line from Newcastle to...
joining the York and North Mi...
Railway Company's line outside the...
walls. In 1846 the Great North of En...
was absorbed by the Newcastle...
Darlington Junction Railway Com...
and later still became part of the N...
Eastern Railway. In 1838 the Great N...
of England agreed to pay £5,000 t...
York and North Midland for a...
interest in the site in York whic...
latter had acquired for a station. And...
was selected as architect and with...
York and North Midland's eng...
Thomas Cabrey drew up plans...
booking hall, refreshment room...
engine shed which were approve...
1840. A later agreement between...
companies provided that the st...
would be used for passenger traffic...
and that the Great North of En...
would build a goods depot outsid...
city. The latter was designed by And...
as was the enlargement of the N...
Postern Gate in the City wall g...
access to it. Later he designed fo...
company other depots at Alne and Th...
and supervised the erection of statio...
Raskelf and Sessay, which he may...
have designed. York station, to whic...
engine house was attached, with its...
iron and glass shed, and hotel, the...
station to have a hotel, is justifiabl...
best known of Andrews' many ra...
buildings. Unlike the more utilit...
engine house, the station of grey...
and stone dressings with Tuscan c...
nades, was inspired by Classical m...

Lit. N. Pevsner, *Yorkshire: York an...
*East Riding*, 1972, pp. 139-40...
Parris, 'British Transport hist...
records and their value to the a...
tectural historian', *Architectural H...
vol. ii, 1959, pp. 56-61. *Victoria C...
History, City of York*, 1961, pp. 47...
C. L. V. Meeks, *The railway statio...
architectural history*, 1957, p. 33.

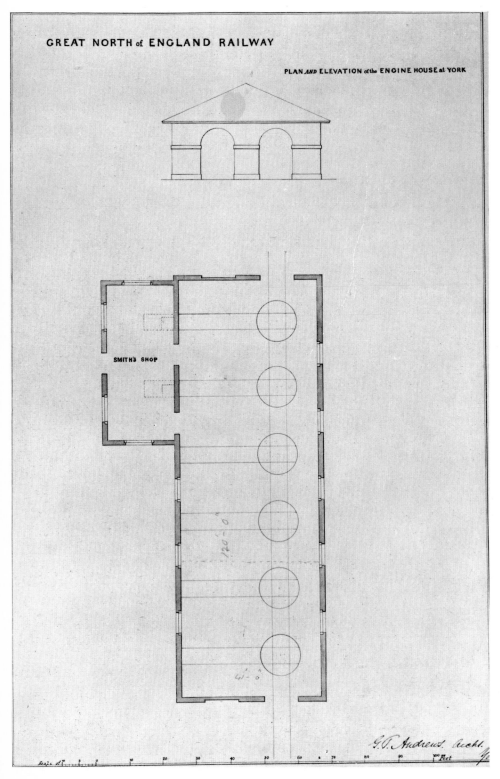

GREAT NORTH of ENGLAND RAILWAY

PLAN *AND* ELEVATION of the ENGINE HOUSE at YORK

SMITH'S SHOP

*G. T. Andrews. Archt.*

David Mocatta
Horley Railway Station, Horley, Surrey. c. 1840
*Inscribed in pencil* Horley Station, Next Railway
*Paper watermarked* 1839
*Pen and ink and water-colour* $12\frac{7}{8} \times 19\frac{1}{2}$ (32.9 $\times$ 49.6)
V 9/3/2
Lent by the Royal Institute of British Architects

Horley Station was one of numerous works which Mocatta designed for the London Brighton and South Coast Railway, drawings for many of which are in the Royal Institute of British Architects. Work on construction of the railway began in 1838 after considerable debate about the route for the new line and after several companies had placed plans before Parliament. In December 1838 the *Civil Engineer and Architects' Journal* reported that works on the new line were progressing well and with great rapidity. By April 1841 many of the stations and two of the tunnels, those at Balcombe and Merstham were completed, and work on the tunnel at Clayton almost completed. On 5 July sections of the line from Croydon Junction to Haywards Heath and from Clayton tunnel to Brighton were opened. In September Brighton station was said to be completed externally and the whole line was opened soon after.

Lit. *CE&AJ*, December 1838, p. 415; April 1841, p. 139;
  September 1841, p. 327. N. Taylor, *Monuments of commerce*,
  1968, pp. 24-5.

**105** Frederick Crace
Ceiling decoration, Refreshment
Room, Swindon Station, Swindon,
Wiltshire. 1842
*Signed* F & I Crace, Desr. *and dated*
1842
*Water-colour* 14 × 20⅜ (35.5 × 51.7)
E.1827-1912, given by Mr J. D.
Crace
Victoria and Albert Museum

As the London and Birmingham Railway
had provided a stopping place at Wolver-
ton where passengers could rest and eat,
so the Great Western Railway provided
a similar service at Swindon, where all
trains stopped for ten minutes. The town
was not only conveniently situated some
70 miles from London and 40 from Bristol,
but was also the meeting place of the
Great Western, and Cheltenham and
Great Western Railways. The line was
routed a mile or so to the North of the
town, and the station, with large loco-
motive repair and workshops, which were
associated with it, formed the nucleus of
a northernward extension of building
now called New Swindon. The passenger
station was situated to the east of the
depot and consisted of two blocks, each
170 by 37 feet, placed on either side of the
main line. Each block was composed of
three floors, a basement equipped with
kitchens, a principal floor in which the
refreshment rooms were situated surrounded by a broad platform, and a top
floor with bedrooms. Bourne described
the decorations of the walls and ceilings
of the refreshment rooms as 'Arabesque—
the columns are painted after a r[...]
invention to resemble inlaid woods;
room is divided into two parts by col[...]
and an oval counter, at which the ref[...]
ments are sold; and which separate[...]
first class passengers at one end fro[...]
second at the other.' Catering wa[...]
vided at first by the proprietor o[...]
Queen's Hotel in Cheltenham. The
buildings were connected by a co[...]
gallery forming a bridge across the tr[...]

Crace's decorations are similar to [...]
he provided in the same year for [...]
mouth Castle and appear to deri[...]
much from Renaissance sources as [...]
earlier illuminated manuscripts.

Lit. J. C. Bourne, *History and descr*[...]
*of the Great Western Railway,*
N. Pevsner, *Wiltshire,* 1963, p. 4[...]

CRACE, DesT 1842

George Townsend Andrews
The railway station, Scarborough,
Yorkshire. 1844
*Signed* G T Andrews Archt. York
*and dated* 1844. *Inscribed* York and
Scarbro Railway, Station at Scarboro
*Pen and ink and water-colour* $13\frac{7}{8}$ ×
$20\frac{1}{2}$ (35.3 × 62)
8936.14
Victoria and Albert Museum

Like the station which Andrews built at
Hull two years later, Scarborough is a long
symmetrical composition with a central
projection with coupled columns forming
an open colonnade. The *Builder* reported
on 22 March 1845, that 'at Scarborough
a large number of workmen are being
employed in digging and laying the
foundations of the building of the railway
station, which agreeable to the contract,
is to be completed by the 25th of next
month.' Work progressed satisfactorily
and on 19 July they were able to announce
that 'the York and Scarborough Railway
was opened on the 7th inst.' Andrews'
plan provided for a large refreshment
room not shown in the elevation and a site
for an inn. Here he follows the precedent
he set at York station, designed in 1840,
which was the first to include a hotel as
part of the general scheme, although the
latter was not built until 1853. In London
the first combined hotel and station was
that of Hardwick and Brunel at Paddington (from 1851).

Scarborough station was enlarged in
1882, when a large Baroque central tower
was added.

Lit. *Br*, 22 March 1854, p. 161; 19 July
1854, p. 346.

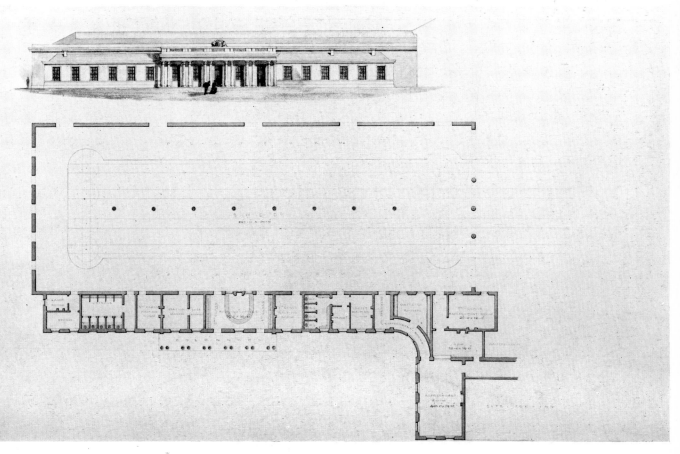

**107** Alfred Stevens
Railway Carriage, 1848
*Pen and ink and water-colour on
tracing paper* 7¾ × 18½ (19.8 × 47)
418-1895 A.M.
Victoria and Albert Museum

Stannus records that the carriage was
executed in 1848 for King Frederick VII
of Denmark, whose arms it bears. The
commission he thought probably came
through the sculptor Thorwaldsen, with
whom the King, while Crown Prince,
had been on friendly terms. Stevens had
met Thorwaldsen in Rome in 1841 and
was apparently much attached to him,
since he was the only man from whom
Stevens received any tuition. Thorwaldsen's departure from Rome in 1842 was
the reason for Stevens leaving too. When
the carriage had been completed the King
was apparently so pleased with it that he
invited Stevens to go to Denmark, but
Stevens disliked foreign travel and declined. He was at the time of this design
working for Collmann and Davis, of
Portman Square.

Lit. H. Stannus, *Alfred Stevens and his
work*, 1891, p. 9.

**108** Alfred Stevens
Scheme for the decoration of a Royal
reception or waiting room designed
by Matthew Digby Wyatt, Padding-
ton Station, London. c. 1852.
*Signed on the back* Alfred Stevens
*Pen and ink and water-colour Sight
measure* $14\frac{7}{8} \times 9\frac{3}{4}$ (37.7 × 24.7)
E.996-1914
Victoria and Albert Museum

Paddington station was designed by I. K.
Brunel in 1851 to replace the existing,
much smaller station of 1838 as the main
London terminus of the Great Western
Railway. Brunel employed Matthew Digby
Wyatt as his assistant, writing in January
'I am going to design in a great hurry and
I believe to build a station after my own
fancy with *engineering* roofs . . . it is a
branch of architecture of which I am
fond . . . and of *course* believe myself fully
competent for . . . but for detail of ornamentation neither have the time or
knowledge and with all my confidence in
my own ability I have never any objection
to advice and affection even in the department which I keep to myself namely the
general design. I want to show the public
also that colours ought to be used.' Wyatt
in turn appears to have turned both to
Owen Jones and to Alfred Stevens for
further advice particularly on the form of
the coloured and painted decorations.
Some had apparently been carried out by
April 1852, when the Chairman of the
company and several members of the
Board visited the station. They dis-
approved of what they saw and the
Secretary was instructed to write to
Brunel ordering modifications to the
design. 'The Directors . . . beg you will
not introduce any ornamental or coloured
tiles but will have the ordinary stucco . . .
under the roofs of the sheds. There is
very decided objection on their part to
any sort of decorative ornament to the
passenger platforms or offices which they
wish to be as plain and inexpensive
looking as possible.' Consequently neither
Stevens's nor Jones's suggestions appear
ever to have been carried out.

Three letters in the Library of the
Museum from Stevens to Wyatt refer to
Stevens's payment for making the design.
A variant design is recorded as having
belonged to Mr R. Phené Spiers in 1914.

In one of the letters Stevens wrote that
of the two designs he preferred the blue
one. 'My price for painting the figures as
arranged in this drawing would be about
£15 for each of the eight sides . . . Some
of the figures would, as you will see by
referring to the scale, be as large as life.'
A little later, he asks Wyatt for £10 in
payment for a drawing, 'since it seems
unlikely that the scheme for decorating
the Queen's waiting-room at Paddington
Station will ever be carried out . . .'

Lit. H. Parris, 'British Transport Historical Records and their value to the
architectural historian', *Architectural
History*, vol. ii, 1959, pp. 54-5.

**109** George Douglas
Station, Ellesmere Port, Cheshire.
1862
*Signed* Geo. Douglas, Engineer.
Lockwood & Farrimond, Builders
*and dated* 15 Sep. 1862. *Lettered*
Birkenhead Railway. Hooton and
Helsby. Ellesmere Port and Whitby
Station. Elevation to rails. *Inscribed*
Approved by Joint Committee Aug.
8 1862
*Pen and ink and water-colour* $24\frac{1}{4}$ ×
18 (75·7 × 45·7)
RAIL 35/36 no. 1
Lent from the Public Record Office

In the late 18th century it was intended
to develop Ellesmere as a watering place,
but after the opening of the Ellesmere
Canal from Chester in 1795, the
erection there of some warehouses by
Telford in 1830, and the building of the
Birmingham and Liverpool Junction
Canal in 1835, Ellesmere became established as an important port. William
Cubitt built the sea lock and a new dock
in 1839-40, the railway was built during
the 1860s and the Manchester Ship
Canal followed in 1891 with the result
that Ellesmere Port is now a centre for
heavy industry.

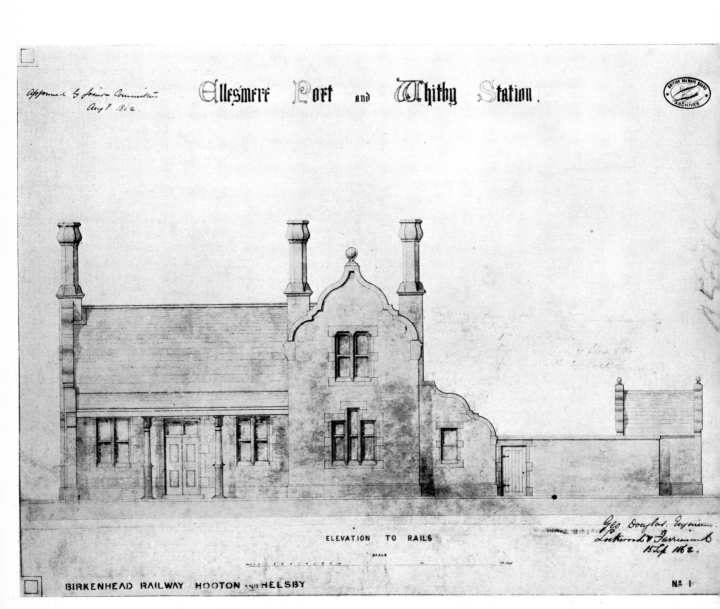

Ellesmere Port and Whitby Station.

ELEVATION TO RAILS

BIRKENHEAD RAILWAY HOOTON AND HELSBY

Sir Matthew Digby Wyatt

Offices and refreshments rooms, Temple Meads Station, Bristol. c. 1870

*Lettered* Drawin[g]. *Inscribed in pencil* contract. *Stamped* To be returned to chief engineer's plan office G.W.R. Paddington

*Pen and ink and water-colour* 18½ × 23¾ (45.5 × 60.2)

Lent by British Railways Western Region

The proposal to build the Great Western Railway from Bristol to London received the Royal Assent on 31 August 1835. Contemporary with this proposal was a plan to extend a railway west from Bristol, which resulted in the passing of the Bristol and Exeter Railway Act in 1836. Both lines were to be constructed with broad gauge track. The station of the Great Western Railway, which opened on 30 June 1841 and that of the Bristol and Exeter Railway, which opened its first section of line in the same month, were, the *British Association Handbook* later noted, 'planned by an unpractical and short-sighted engineer, Mr. Brunel, at right angles with each other'. The two lines were connected outside the stations by a curve. The Great Western Railway Station—Brunel's famous Temple Meads with its Tudor façade of Bath stone and shed with a cantilevered roof of 72 feet span—and the much cruder Bristol & Exeter Railway station were soon found to be inadequate to cope with mounting numbers of passengers. In 1865 the two companies, with the Midland Railway Company, who were using Great Western Railway facilities, agreed to co-operate on a large-scale extension and the Bristol Joint Station Act was passed to facilitate this. The works involved the construction of a new terminus in place of that previously occupied by the Bristol and Exeter Station, and the construction of these offices, refreshments rooms and clock tower in the angle between Brunel's Temple Meads and the new station. The works, carried out under the architectural supervision of Sir Matthew Digby Wyatt, were begun in March 1871 and completed by January 1878 after the downside track had opened on 6 July 1874.

The roof of the clock tower was destroyed during the blitz.

Lit. R. A. Buchanan and N. Cossons, *The industrial archaeology of the Bristol Region*, 1969.

**III** M. W. H.

Offices, Waterloo Station, London. 1877
*Signed* MWH *and dated* 21.6.77. *Lettered on the mount*
L&SWR. Design for new offices at Waterloo Station *and
on the back* The Hon. R. H. Dutton, Chairman, June 1877.
Wyndham S. Portal Esq., Deputy Chairman. William
Jacomb MICE, Chief Resident Engineer
*Water-colour* 9¾ × 22¼ (24.7 × 56.5)
RAN 10/A/7
Lent by the Royal Institute of British Architects

The *Builder* noticed in January 1877 that the works at Waterloo
had 'been going on for two years' and that they were 'on a scale
of great magnitude, involving the purchase from time to time of
extensive blocks of property. A considerable portion of this
enlargement has already been completed, but other works of a
costly character yet remain to be carried out before the intended
enlargement is finally finished.' In April of the following year
they noticed that 'for the purpose of providing additional and
separate space for the local traffic on the main line to Wimble[...]
Epsom, Leatherhead and Hampton Court, so as to set fre[...]
room on the old station for the main line through traffi[...]
extensive widening of the terminus is being affected on the S[...]
East side. The whole of the extension is constructed on a via[...]
and thus formed will provide a very large space, havi[...]
double frontage approached by two lines of rails. An exte[...]
range of offices is also being constructed next to the old sta[...]
forming an arcade over the footpath leading from the Wat[...]
Road to the main-line departure side.' The works were ca[...]
out under the direction of Archibald Scott, the general man[...]
from designs drawn up by William Jacomb, the chief res[...]
engineer, and were executed by Perry & Company, builde[...]
Bow. It was expected that the works would be complete[...]
July, but trains did not in fact use the new line until Dece[...]
at which time the cost was said to be £120,000.

Lit. *Br*, 20 January 1877, p. 66; 27 April, 1878, p. 437[...]
December, 1878, p. 685.

Frederick William Stevens
The Bombay, Baroda and Central India Railway Administrative Offices, later the Victoria Railway Terminus, Bombay. 1878
*Signed by the artist Axel Herman Haig A H H and dated 1878*
*Water-colour over preliminary pencil* 36 × 82 (91.5 × 157.5)
WD 2443 Revised Foster Catalogue No. 628. Presented by the London Office of the Great Indian Peninsula Railway Company
Lent from the India Office Library and Records

Exhib. RA, 1880, no. 1181.
Lit. M. Archer, *British drawings in the India Office Library*, vol. ii, 1969, p. 437. *BN*, 30 April 1880, p. 507; 20 March 1896, p. 419. *A*, 29 May 1880, p. 366.

Stevens designed the station, described as being 'the largest building of its time to be erected in Asia' some time before 1878, but construction did not begin until April 1894 and was completed in 1896. Difficulty was experienced in making the foundations, since the station was situated close to the sea; in parts they were 24 feet deep. In execution many alterations were made to the design and the building was reduced in size. The *Architect* remarked that it was 'a vast pile of modern buildings, with certain Gothic features freely added, but yet not Gothic'. The *Times of India* noted that Stevens carried out in his designs 'with conspicuous success that blending of Venetian Gothic with Indian Saracenic by which he created a style of architecture so excellently suited to the climate and environment of Bombay.'

Surprisingly few commentators noticed Haig's drawing at the Royal Academy in 1880, probably because it was overshadowed by his other entry, a spectacular view of the Library in William Burges's Tower House in Melbury Road, London.

When Stevens died in Bombay in 1900, the *Times of India* remarked 'The City of Bombay has lost in Mr. Stevens a man who did infinitely more for its embellishment than any other of our generation . . . Endowed with creative genius of a very high order, gifted to originate with boldness and distinction, he yet, by a somewhat rare combination of qualities, loved almost equally the details of his art.'

# Catalogue

## 11 Exhibition Buildings

*Catalogue 116*
*The Crystal Palace at*
*Sydenham*

Sir Joseph Paxton

**113** Blotting paper sketch. 1850
*Inscribed with names and numbers. A
telegram dated* 15th July, 1850 *and
inscribed* from Mr Rickman to Mrs
Paxton Chatsworth. 'I have a [...]
sage from London to say that [...]
Paxton's plan has been approve[d]
the Royal Commission', *has [...]
pasted to the bottom*
*Pen and ink* $15\frac{3}{8} \times 11$ (39.2 $\times$
Lent by Mr E. Ridgeway Paxt[...]
Victoria and Albert Museum

Exhib. Sir Joseph Paxton,
Council, 1965, no. 85.
Illus. G. F. Chadwick, *The wor[...]
Sir Joseph Paxton*, 1961, ch. 5,
p. 92. H. R. Hitchcock, *[...]
Victorian architecture in Br[...]
1954, pl. xvi, 4. P. Ferriday, *[...]
torian architecture*, 1963, p. [...]
pl. lii.

**114** Perspective sketch of first de[...]
1850
*Inscribed* J. Paxton, Archt. Cl[...]
worth (?) Villas (?) *and dated* [...]
*Lettered* Original Sketch of the G[...]
Exhibition Building as submitte[d]
the Royal Commissioners.
*Pencil and water-colour* $15\frac{1}{8} \times$
(38.5 $\times$ 54)
D.29-1905, given by E. M. Wre[...]
Esq. FRCS
Victoria and Albert Museum

Exhib. New Gallery, 1891-92, no. [...]
Sir Joseph Paxton, Arts Cou[...]
1965, no. 86.
Illus. *ILN*, 6 July, 1850, p. 18. C[...]
Gibbs-Smith, *The Great Exhib[...]
Victorian and Albert Museum, [...]
fig. 3, p. 43. H. R. Hitchcock, *[...]
Victorian architecture in Br[...]
1954, pl. xvi, 2.

**115** Owen Jones
Scheme for the internal decora[...]
1850
*Lettered on the mount* Design [...]
Owen Jones (b. 1809 d. 1874) for [...]
decoration of the Great Exhib[...]
building of 1851 submitted to [...]
Majesty's Commissioners, Dec[...]
ber 5th 1850. Painted by Wil[...]
Simpson (b. 1823 d. 1899).
*Pen and ink and water-colour* S[...]
size 28 $\times$ 39 (71 $\times$ 99)
546-1897
Victoria and Albert Museum

Lit. M. Darby and D. Van Zanten 'C[...]
Jones' Iron and Glass Buildings o[...]
1850s', *Architectura*, forthcoming i[...]

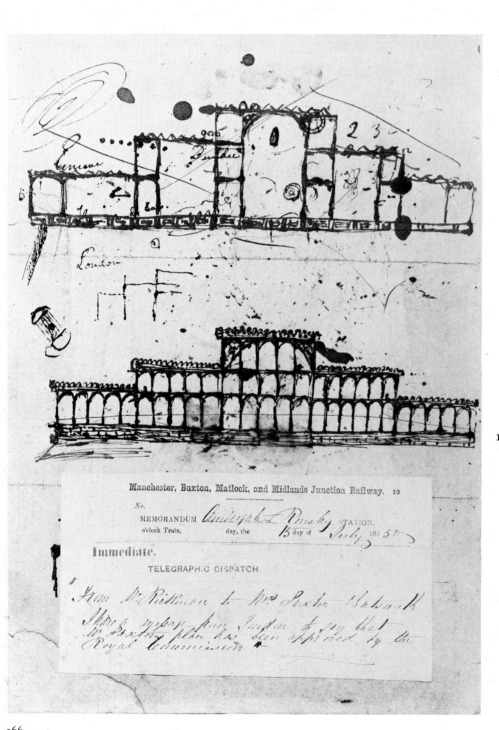

## Great Exhibition Building, Hyde Park, London 1850-52

On 13 March 1850, after considerable debate about a site for the Great Exhibition Building, an open competition for plans was announced, less than one month being allowed for the preparation and submission of designs. By April 245 designs had been received. Two, by Richard Turner of Dublin and Hector Horeau of Paris, both iron and glass buildings, received special mention but all were eventually rejected in favour of a design prepared at the direction of the Committee responsible for the building. This was drawn up under the supervision of Owen Jones, I. Brunel and M. Digby Wyatt and was published in the *Illustrated London News* on 22 June 1850. It did not appear to be any more satisfactory than the competition designs in so far as it would have been expensive to erect, and was incapable of being built quickly. Rumours of these proceedings had reached Paxton, who when visiting John Ellis MP at the house of Commons later recorded that 'I told him I had a notion in my head, and that I would ascertain whether it was too late to send in a design'. Ellis took him to see Lord Granville at the Board of Trade, but he was out and they spoke instead to Henry Cole, who assured them that a new design would be considered, later noting in his diary 'Mr. Paxton called to propose his flat roof of glass.' On Monday 10 June Paxton visited North Wales to view the floating into position of the third section of Robert Stephenson's Menai Bridge. He returned to Derby the next day and it was at a railway meeting there that he did the famous blotting paper sketch. He returned to Chatsworth in the evening and with assistance from W. H. Barlow spent the next eight days preparing plans. By the 21st he was in London where he again saw Cole who noted 'Mr. Paxton Duke of Devon[shire's] gardner came with his plans which he said would cost only £80,000 for the hire.' On the 22nd Lord Granville saw the designs and on the 23rd Paxton had a long interview with the Prince Consort. In spite of this the Exhibition Commissioners were unable to make a decision and Paxton, impatient, decided to go over their heads by appealing to the public. He arranged for the perspective drawing to be published and used for an engraving which appeared

in the *Illustrated London News* on 6 July 1850. His strategy was successful and on 26 July, after some alterations had been made to the design and tenders obtained from Fox & Henderson, the contractors, the Commissioners officially accepted Paxton's proposals. These later alterations included the addition of a barrel-vaulted transept, suggested by Paxton, to accommodate some trees on the site. On 1 August Charles Fox began a series of 18 hour days lasting for seven weeks while he prepared the working drawings and on 1 May 1851 the exhibition was opened to the public. The erection of the building, which covered some 18 acres in less than nine months, is an achievement that is now difficult to comprehend. After the exhibition had closed the building was dismantled and later re-erected with many alterations under Paxton's supervision at Sydenham, where it survived until destroyed by fire in 1936.

The *Builder*, upset that an architect had failed to win the original competition, referred to Paxton in its obituary of him as an 'art architect', stressing that he had not discharged the functions of an architect in the exhibition building. Furthermore Matthew Digby Wyatt in a paper read before the Institution of Civil Engineers entitled 'On the Construction of the Building in the Exhibition of the Works of Industry of all Nations' on 14 January 1851, gave surprisingly little credit to Paxton. While Charles Barry, Charles Fox, Owen Jones and others made alterations and additions to his design, this does not obscure the fact that the original conception was undeniably Paxton's. The relationship between the exhibition building and the lily house which he had built at Chatsworth to house the Duke's *Victoria regia* water lily (1849-50), or the earlier Capesthorne conservatory (before 1843) leaves no doubt about Paxton's authorship.

When Owen Jones was asked to decorate the 1851 Exhibition building he wrote to some twenty architects and decorators soliciting their suggestions as to how it should be painted. When no two agreed, he invented a system of his own which he demonstrated to the Royal Commission on 5 December, 1850 by painting two bays of the partially completed structure in different manners; one with plain red columns, the other with stripes of the primary colours red, yellow and blue. The latter, which was ordered in modified form, was based on Jones' belief that during all great periods of art

only the primary colours were whereas during decadent period secondaries and tertiaries preva *The Times* (6 December 1850) mented 'What the appearance of interior may be, with the colours the Commission have selected, it i easy to say but, at least, their sele is an improvement upon the desig Owen Jones.' What the *Builder* du 'The Great Paint Question' was p and a flood of letters to various jou sought to assist Jones, sugges ranging from Frederick Sang's tha glass be coloured and the metal painted a bronze green, to that of Artist' that the ironwork be painte superimposed glazes to achieve a vi grey similar to that in Titian's paint Jones eventually defended his view convincingly in a lecture before Institute of British Architects o December 1850, that the Commis reversed their original decision accepted his first scheme without mo cation. On 21 January 1851 Henry noted in his diary 'Albert visited— the colouring of the transept.' I accounts grew more enthusiastic as work progressed and on opening day effect of space and colour was relate several commentators to that in Tur paintings.

The large appliqué hangings were mentioned by Jones in his lecture. ' were probably conceived as a si and inexpensive method of achie internally the effect of a barrel vau the nave, which Charles Barry, a mer of the building committee, had sugge would improve the appearance Paxton's design.

**116** Sir Matthew Digby Wyatt
The English Mediaeval Court,
Crystal Palace, Sydenham. 1852-53
*Pen and ink and water-colour*
$21\frac{1}{2} \times 38\frac{1}{4}$ (54.5 × 97.1)
E.555-1911, given by Mr T. H.
Wyatt
Victoria and Albert Museum

When the Crystal Palace was moved
from Hyde Park to Sydenham in 1852
Wyatt was employed under Sir Joseph
Paxton as architect responsible for the
erection of Courts representing the
architecture, sculpture and ornament of
Pompeii, Italy, and Byzantium and of
the Mediaeval period. The Mediaeval
Court, situated in the South East of the
Nave, was divided into three sections
illustrating German, French and Italian,
and English examples, of these the latter
formed the central and largest section.
The drawing, of the façade towards the
nave, illustrates in the centre a doorway
copied from one in the West front of
Tintern Abbey flanked by statues on the
right from the West front of Wells
Cathedral and on the left from Westminster Abbey. The remainder of the
façade, and the cloister immediately
inside the entrance, were copied from
Guisborough Abbey. The brightly
coloured painted, mosaic and tile decorations, a feature of all the courts, Wyatt
justified in a chapter entitled 'The
Polychromatic Decoration' of *A Handbook to the Mediaeval Courts*, 1854,
written by himself and J. B. Waring.
Objections to the colouring of the Greek
Court, which was designed by Wyatt's
friend Owen Jones, led to the latter's
publication of *An apology for the colouring of the Greek Court*, 1854. The Court
was constructed by Mr Cundy of
Pimlico on a framework erected by
Fox, Henderson & Co. Much of the
detail was prepared from casts made
from the originals and painted by Mr
Bulmer superintended by R. P. Pullan.
Charles Fowler acted as principal super-
tendent and Robert Dudley as principal draughtsman.

Exhib. Exposition Universelle, Paris,
1855.
Lit. M. Digby Wyatt and J. B. Waring,
*A handbook for the Mediaeval Courts*,
1854.

**117** Owen Jones
Design for an exhibition building,
St Cloud, Paris. c. 1860.
*Signed* OJ
*Water-colour* $14\frac{3}{4} \times 28\frac{3}{8}$ (37.5 × 72.2)
D.946-1886
Victoria and Albert Museum

The documentation of the various projects to erect exhibition buildings at St Cloud is sparse and difficult to follow. A volume of drawings and photographs by Jones in the Department of Prints and Drawings (E.9-37—1937) establishes that he drew up proposals for three quite separate buildings there in 1860. One scheme, based on his abortive design for a crystal palace on Muswell Hill of the previous year, is titled 'Palais de Cristal de Saint Cloud, Exposition Permanent de l'Industrie Française, Jardin d'Hiver et Parc de Plaisance.' The second design, of a single long nave with three attached rotundas, is obviously the prototype for Paxton's later drawing for a palace on the same site now at Yale; and the third design, illustrated here, is possibly derived from Jones's project submitted in competition for the Manchester Art Treasures Exhibition building of 1857 but not carried out. It seems likely that Jones and Paxton were members together of a company, possibly partly financed by Baron Rothschild, for whom Paxton had built Ferrières between 1854 and 1859, formed to build the Palace at Saint Cloud, and that some time during 1862 the company was dissolved and Jones dropped out of the project. Certainly a new company was in the offing on 14 November 1862, when George wrote to Paxton, 'V. de Thury and a long talk with Mr Jackson this mor —he agrees with us that there mus two companies one for the Palace the other for the Boulevards' (Pa papers, Chatsworth). That nothing of these projects is probably accou for by the fact that a French comp had begun erection of the Universal Permanent Exhibition building desig by Lehmann and Peignet which op nearby at Auteuil in 1863 and w would certainly have provided siderable competition.

Lit. M. Darby and D. Van Za 'Owen Jones' Iron and Glass B ings of the 1850's, *Architectura*, f coming issue.

John Gregory Crace
Decorative scheme for the 1862
Exhibition building, London. 1862
*Signed* J G Crace Desr. *and dated*
1862. *Inscribed* Decoration of glass
domes
*Water-colour* 25⅜ × 20 (65.5 × 51.1)
E.1833-1912, given by Mr J. D.
Crace
Victoria and Albert Museum

On 22 October 1861 Henry Cole noted
in his diary 'with Hudson to Ex[hibition]
building & told I had recommended him
to advise on the colouring—Kelk called
—said Fairbairn wished that Crace
should be employed'. On both 20 and
22 December he noted that Hudson's
colouring was unsatisfactory and on the
31st sought the advice of Lord Granville,
who pressed him to continue with
experiments suggested by Fowke. On
New Year's Day Fowke was 'in difficulties about colouring' and he and Cole
spent the next three days trying various
schemes unsuccessfully. By the middle
of the month Crace was involved, and
finally on the 23rd he was given
'authority from the Royal Commissioners to assume the decoration of
the building with the entire responsibility of the results—the work must be
completed by March'.

In a lecture to the Society of Arts on
19 April Crace explained that 'when I
first saw this interior my heart quailed—
My principal difficulty in carrying out
the decoration of the domes was, that I
could see nothing of them. The scaffold
formed a series of solid stages or floors,
through which it was impossible to view
anything, and I confess I never could
mount a ladder above 100 feet—At last
Mr Ashton contrived to get for me an
open square box into which I got, and
was drawn up by means of his beautiful
little engine, very pleasantly to the top;
and yet when I got there the ceiling
almost touched my head, so that I had
no opportunity of judging beforehand of
the effect of distance and light upon my
colouring—The knowledge that the
scaffold would be taken down before I
could possibly judge of the effect, and
that when once down I could never hope
to touch my decoration again, caused me
many an anxious thought.'

Crace's scheme, like that of Jones for
the 1851 building, relied on balanced
primaries producing a vibrant grey when
seen from a distance, and on making
evident the structure which Crace considered, in spite of many opinions to the
contrary, to be 'very ingenious'. Unlike

Jones, he used large quantities of
ornamental decoration, employing more
than 100 stencillers, of which 'scarcely
half a dozen had ever done it before'. The
walls of the domes he explained presented special problems: 'it was necessary to consider the probable effect of
the great mass of light above. On the
one hand it was desirable to sustain it
with sufficient strength of colour, on the
other it would be dangerous to make it
too heavy.' The result breaks up the
wall surface into so many elements that
it destroys the architectural unity and
consequently appears to defeat Crace's
aim.

Lit. *BN*, 11 April 1862, p. 259. Diaries
of Sir Henry Cole, 1861 and 1862,
Victoria and Albert Museum Library.

# Catalogue

## 12 Bridges, Lighthouses

James Meadows Rendel and Sir Matthew Digby Wyatt
Bridge over the river Son, near Patna (Bihar), India. c. 1855
*Inscribed on the mount* Soane Bridge. Length 4536. Number
of spans 28 of 150 feet each
*Water-colour* 27¾ × 50½ (70.4 × 128.4)
Given by the London Office of the East India Railway
Company
Lent from the India Office Library and Records

After the death of Rendel on 21 November 1856, Wyatt
succeeded to his position as official architect to the East India
Company. The *British Cyclopaedia* records that previously he
had 'co-operated with the late Mr Rendel in the design of several
great bridges, viz the Soane, Keul and the Hullohur'.

The Calcutta, Delhi and Lahore, or East Indian Railway, was
officially inaugurated on 3 February 1855, when the first part
of the line, begun in 1851, was opened by the Governor-General
of India. The *Illustrated London News* described the construction

as 'one of the most gigantic works ever undertaken by man—
a line of railway, which, with 1,350 miles of unbroken length,
will bridge the sacred Ganges, the Soane, the Jumna, and the
Sutlej; traverse the most fertile tracts of India; connect its most
populous and ancient cities with the ocean; open out the
inexhaustible wealth and resources of remote, and at present,
for commercial purposes, inaccessible districts; ameliorate the
condition, weaken the prejudices, and enlarge the minds of
millions of the human race; consolidate our power in the East;
and finally leave an imperishable monument to the end of time,
of the energy and beneficent dominion of the adventurous
Saxon.' The Soane bridge was apparently sufficiently finished at
this time to take single line traffic but it was not opened for double
line until 1870, since much of the earlier work was destroyed
during the Mutiny of 1857, and had to be rebuilt.

Lit. M. Archer, *British drawings in the India Office Library*, 1969,
vol. 11, p. 370.

## Tower Bridge, London, 1876-89

**120** Sidengham Duer
Proposed high level bridge across the Thames at the Tower, London. 1876
*Signed* Sidengham Duer, 6, Westminster Chambers, Victoria Street, *and dated* 30 September, 1876.
*Lettered* High Level Bridge with Hydraulic Lift Approaches. Transverse section on XY. Elevation. Plan
*Pen and ink and water-colour* $27\frac{1}{4} \times 41$ (69.2 × 104)
Surveyors' Bridges Plans 281
Lent from the Corporation of London Records Office

Exhib. To God and the Bridge, Guildhall Art Gallery, 1972, Catalogue no. 147
Lit. *Br.* 30 December, 1876, p. 1255

In 1871 the Tower subway, an iron tube 7 feet in diameter from great Tower Hill to Pickle Herring Stairs was opened for pedestrians at a toll of $\frac{1}{2}$d. for each passage. The popularity of the tunnel (a million people used it each year) and the difficulty of widening London Bridge, drew attention to the need for a new bridge over the Thames, and from that date until Tower Bridge was begun in 1886 numerous proposals were put forward. The erection of a bridge over that part of the river raised several problems not met in earlier Thames bridges, the greatest being that it had to allow for the passage of tall ships beneath. This either meant a moving bridge, or one in which the roadway was elevated, and if the latter, some means had to be found of raising the traffic to the required height.

As early as November 1872 a Bill was put before Parliament seeking authority to build a 'tower bridge' across the river between Little Tower Hill on the north bank, and Horsleydown Lane Stairs on the south—the site of the eventual bridge—but nothing came of these proposals. The designer was R. M. Ordish, who proposed two spans over the river and four tunnels beneath. The

cost estimated at £373,000 was to recouped by charging tolls. In May 1 the Bridge House Committee were c sidering the plans of a Mr Perrett a bridge involving three arches 90 above the high water mark and lo approaches, and in March of the follo ing year, Frederick Burnett laid pl before the Society of Arts for a sin duplex bridge. In December 1876, Bridge House Committee conside these proposals and others submit by Mr Keith, Mr Guthrie, Mr (la Sir George) Bruce, Mr Waller and Duer. Keith proposed a subwa Guthrie, a framed staging running rails set into the river bed; Bruc platform rolling between six fixed pie Waller, a steam ferry; and Duer, Perrett, a high level bridge with a pai hydraulic lifts at each end. All w rejected. The *Builder* remarked Duer, who included a model of hydraulic lifts with his drawings, 'p poses to carry 250 vehicles in ea direction over in an hour, besides passengers. The cost of the bridge hydraulic apparatus is estimated £136,500 and working expenses £1,872 . . . There is no doubt tha the case of a swing bridge, or a bridg

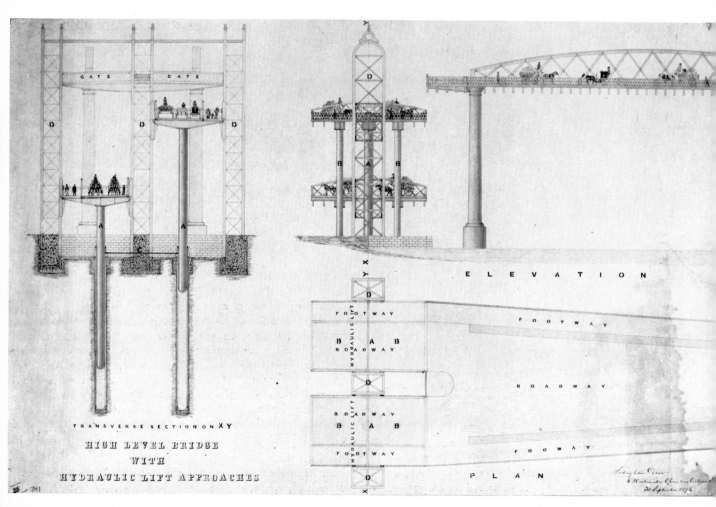

TRANSVERSE SECTION ON XY

HIGH LEVEL BRIDGE WITH HYDRAULIC LIFT APPROACHES

ELEVATION

PLAN

anyway worked by machinery, the cost of the approaches would be comparatively small, but it will require very much to induce the carriers and travelling public to entrust themselves to Hydraulic lifts, instead of making use of their own and their horses feet'.

In March 1878 Sir Joseph Bazalgette, as engineer to the Metropolitan Board of Works, drew up plans for several different fixed bridges based on the same elevated approaches, and in 1879 the Board applied to Parliament to build one of these, a single span steel bridge 850 feet long. The wharfingers, however, complained that the clearance of 60 feet was insufficient and the project was abandoned. Meanwhile, the Corporation had obtained plans of their own through their engineer Horace Jones. He proposed a bascule bridge which the Special Bridge and Subway Committee recommended unsuccessfully to the Common Council in October, 1878. The Council's main objections were that the form of the superstructure did not allow the bascules to open fully and that passing ships were consequently confined to too narrow a passage.

In 1879 an elegant medium level single span cantilevered bridge was proposed by J. Sedley, and in 1883 a private company put before Parliament proposals for a tunnel served by 'Large and numerous hydraulic lifts'. The latter was opposed by the Metropolitan Board of Works, who suggested a tunnel of their own in 1884 with mile-long entrance ramps. These schemes were rejected, but did inspire the Government to appoint a committee to examine the whole problem, and after much deliberation they reported in favour of a low level bridge with minimum problems of approach ramping, and a central opening span, and asked the Corporation to undertake the work. The Corporation arranged for a deputation from the Bridge House Committee to study opening bridges on the Continent, at Newcastle-upon-Tyne, and other places, and after careful consideration they recommended that Horace Jones's original idea for a bascule bridge be adopted. At the same time they appointed Sir John Wolfe Barry as engineer and Jones as architect, the immediate result of which was that Barry suggested replacing Jones' arched span with a straight span connected high enough up the towers to allow the bascules to open fully. This higher span was also to serve as a pedestrian bridge when the bascules were open. Detailed drawings of this scheme were eventually approved by Parliament in 1885, and after further alterations to the design, including the addition of entrances, work began on 21 June 1886 and Tower Bridge was finally opened amid great festivities on 30 June 1894.

Sir Horace Jones originally conceived the bascules opening like castle drawbridges with chains, but this idea was abandoned by Barry, who put aside architectural problems until the basic mechanism had been worked out and the foundations laid. The Gothic detail which clads the iron structure is consequently probably not so much the work of Jones, who died in 1887, as that of Barry himself. The style was to a certain extent dictated by the Government, who, in allowing a small encroachment to the Tower ditch, required that the design should accord with the architecture of the Tower. Their other condition, that the bridge might be armed with cannon, was later abandoned.

Lit. *Br*, 30 December 1876, p. 1255, etc. T. Crosby, *The Necessary Monument*, 1970.

**121** Sir Horace Jones
Proposed bascule bridge across the Thames at the Tower, London. 1878
*Signed* By Horace Jones, F.R.I.B.A. *and dated* 1878. *Inscribed* Design for a 'Bascule' Bridge Across the River Thames.
*Pen and sepia wash* 12 × 28½ (30.5 × 72.1)
V13/84 (2)
Lent by the Royal Institute of British Architects

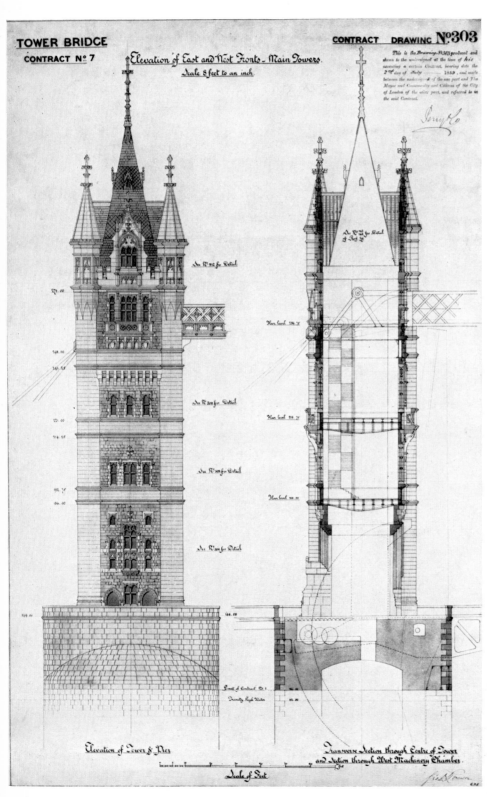

**122** George D. Stevenson
Contract drawing. 1889
*Signed* Geo. D. Stevenson. *Lette*
Tower Bridge Contract No. 7. C
tract drawing No. 303. *Inscr*
Elevation of East and West Front
Main Towers Scale 8 feet to an ir
This is the drawing No. 303 p
duced and shown to the undersig
at the time of his executing a cer
Contract, bearing date the 2nd
of July, 1889, and made between
undersigned of the one part and
Mayor and Commonalty and C
zens of the City of London of
other part, and referred to in
said Contract. *Signed* Perry & Co
*Pen and ink and water-colour* 37½
25 (95 × 63.4)
Comptrollers' Bridge House P
2A (303)
Lent from the Corporation of L
don Records Office

**123** Sir James Nicholas Douglass
Scale model of the present Eddystone lighthouse tower at low tide. 1882
*Inscribed* Model of the Douglass Tower of the Eddystone Lighthouse executed from the rock of the foundation and presented by John Goad of the firm of J. & E. Goad, Plymouth (Phoenix Steam Marble Works), to H.R.H. the Duke of Edinburgh, in commemoration of the opening ceremony 18th May, 1882
*Granite with brass lantern and fittings and a wooden base.*
*Height* 50 (128). *Base* 24½ × 24½ (62 × 62)
1886. L1.
Lent from the Royal Scottish Museum by courtesy of the Corporation of Trinity House

The present lighthouse is the fourth erected at Eddystone. The first, designed by Winstanley at the end of the 17th century, was destroyed during a storm on 26 November 1703, and the second, erected by Rudeyard in 1709, was destroyed by fire. These structures were made of wood, but between 1755-1759 a third lighthouse made of stone was erected by Smeaton. Doubts about the safety of this lighthouse were expressed at various times during the 19th century, particularly after gales and high seas made repairs necessary in 1839 and 1865. In March 1878 Douglass, who had been Engineer in Chief to the Corporation of Trinity House since 1862, reported on the practicability of removing the Eddystone rocks as an alternative to building a new lighthouse. He estimated that some 2 million tons of rocks were involved and that the cost of removing them would be £500,000. This proposal was rejected and in July 1878 the Corporation announced that they would build a new lighthouse to Douglass's designs. The three previous lighthouses had been built on the same site, but Douglass chose a new site on the south reef some 100 feet from Smeaton's tower, a position which he considered would be more sheltered. Work began on the rock on 17 July 1878, and it was proposed that the Duke of Edinburgh should lay the foundation stone on 21 June of the following year. Bad weather prevented this, however, and the stone was eventually laid on 19 August. By June 1880 work was reported to be proceeding very rapidly and the cyclindrical base, 44 feet in diameter, was said to be almost completed. Work on the tower continued throughout 1881 and the building was eventually commissioned on 18 May 1882.

Douglass's design was in principle similar to that of Smeaton, and his tower the same concave elliptic frustrum in shape. It was, however, much larger: the tower was 142 feet high and 35 feet wide at the base. The whole work was carried out in interlocking pieces of granite from the De Lank Quarries at Bodmin with the use of some stone from Aberdeen, the total weight of granite used was said to be 5,150 tons. Each piece was cut exactly to shape on the mainland before being sent to the site. The lantern was made by Messrs Chance of Birmingham, the same firm that supplied the glass for the 1851 exhibition building, and was said at the time to be the largest ever made. The fog bells weighed two tons each. Accommodation for the lighthouse keeper was provided on nine floors in the centre of the tower.

Smeaton's earlier lighthouse was re-erected at the southern end of Plymouth Hoe in 1882 after public protest by, amongst others, Sir John Lubbock, when it was proposed to demolish it. The base is still visible at Eddystone at low tide.

Lit. *Br*, 23 March 1878, p. 309; etc.

## 13 Hotels, Inns, Boarding Houses

**124** Philip Charles Hardwick
The Coffee Room, Great Western Hotel, Paddington,
London. 1850-52
*Sepia, pen and water colour* 18 × 26¾ (45.7 × 68)
Lent by the Royal Institute of British Architects

The Great Western Hotel was the largest and most sumptuous
hotel in England of its time. As one of the first buildings erected
in this country during the 19th century in a French Second
Empire style it set the pattern for many later examples such as
the Grosvenor Hotel by J. T. Knowles, begun in 1860, and the
Grand Hotel at Scarborough by Cuthbert Brodrick, begun in
1863 (128). The exterior, of stucco to blend with the surrounding
terraces, included a sculptural group in the central pediment
by John Thomas illustrating the theme of 'Peace and Plenty,
Science and Industry', and giant caryatids by the same sculptor
supporting the balconies. The interior, solid and fireproof,
originally contained 112 bedrooms and 15 sitting rooms, some
forming suites with dressing rooms, reached from galleries

extending the length of each floor. The coffee room, and rea[d]
smoking and billiard rooms, which adjoined it on the ground f[loor]
no doubt fulfilled the aim of the proprietors, which was [to]
provide the public with every luxury at moderate cost, an[d]
produce a substantial building as comfortably arrange[d as]
possible, with due regard to a handsome exterior, with[out]
exceeding the limits of strict economy'. One suite of room[s on]
the ground floor was used as a club, which was felt to be n[ot]
needed in that part of London.

The hotel, which was almost completed during 1852, rema[ined]
empty for one year before being taken over by a com[pany]
formed within the Great Western Railway Company itself [and]
opened by the Prince of Wales on 9 June 1854.

Exhib. RA, 1852, no. 1197.
Illus. N. Taylor, *Monuments of commerce*, 1968, pl. 32, p. 5[0]
Lit. *CE&AJ*, June 1851, p. 355. *ILN*, 18 December 1[852]
     pp. 537-38. H. R. Hitchcock, *Early Victorian architectur[e in]
     Britain*, 1954, pp. 211-14.

John Pollard Seddon
The Dunraven Arms Hotel, later the Southerndown Hotel
and now the Welsh Sunshine Home for Blind Babies,
Southerndown, near Bridgend, Glamorganshire. 1852-53
*Pen and ink and water-colour* $16\frac{1}{4} \times 23\frac{3}{4}$ (41.2 × 55.4)
873-1896
Victoria and Albert Museum

Five tenders were received for the new hotel in the summer of
1852 and that of J. Brown of Stoke's Croft, Bristol, for £1,339
accepted. By January 1853 the *Builder* reported that the work
was nearly completed, noticing that the hotel was built 'to
supply the want of proper accommodation which has long been
felt by visitors who during the summer months have been in the
habit of frequenting this watering place of South Wales'. They
further noticed that 'the projecting wall at the farther end of the
raised terrace is for the purpose of protecting the front somewhat
from the wind, which is violent at some seasons. The whole
structure is a quadrangle on plan, of which the side not seen in
the drawings is two storeys in height, and the hotel is arranged so
that the portion to be let privately is separate from that wherein
its ordinary business is carried on.'

The hotel, one of Seddon's first works, was built for a relative,
and it was apparently during its construction that Seddon first
met John Prichard, with whom he later went into partnership.
It was built from local limestone, and some Bath stone. The
name Dunraven Arms, which was soon dropped, was inspired by
Dunraven Castle, the home of the Dowager Countess of Dunraven, on the opposite side of the valley. An addition to the hotel
to the left of the main façade was made probably in the early
20th century.

Illus. *Br*, 15 January 1853, p. 37.

**126** Owen Jones
St Pancras Station and Hotel, London, 1865. Competition
design
*Pen and ink and water-colour. Sight size* 20 × 37 (51 × 95)
Lent from the collection of the late Sir Arthur Elton

Exhib. Architectural Exhibition 1866, no. 127. International
   Exhibition, London, 1874, Works of the Late Owen Jones,
   no. 146.
Illus. F. D. Klingender, *Art and the Industrial Revolution*,
   rev. ed. by Sir Arthur Elton, 1968, p. 104.
Lit. *Br*, 5 May 1866, p. 318.

In May 1865 the Midland Railway Company, which had been
founded in 1844, decided to hold a limited competition for the
design of station buildings and a hotel to front the train shed and
platforms designed by W. H. Barlow and F. Ordish which were
already under construction. The successful competitor was to
carry out his plans for the usual rate of commission, and three
prizes of £200, £100 and £50 offered for the runners-up. The
competition designs were submitted in the autumn and put on
exhibition in the Shareholders' Room at Derby in December.
Early in the New Year the Directors announced that Scott's
designs had been selected, followed by those of G. S. Clarke,
E. M. Barry and T. C. Sorby.

   Scott's designs exceeded the requirements laid down in the
instructions most noticeably in the addition of two extra storeys
of bedrooms, and his estimate of £316,000 was more than
£50,000 higher than the next most expensive design. His
drawings were thus more spectacular than those of the other
competitors, and it is not difficult to see why they attracted the
Midland Board, who were no doubt conscious of the desirability
of obtaining so eminent an architect. Scott later recorded that he
had prepared the designs in a small hotel at Hayling in September

and October 1865, and that, although he had at first rejecte[d]
offer to enter the competition, he was glad to be able to [build]
a large Gothic building in London, since Lord Palmerston [had]
insisted on his altering his Gothic designs for Whitehall. [After]
he had agreed to omit two floors of station offices and o[ne of]
the hotel, Scott's plans were accepted in April 1866, but it [was]
not until many other economies had been made that work fi[rst]
started in March 1868. After further partially successful atte[mpts]
by the Directors to obtain other reductions in cost the G[rand]
Midland Hotel eventually opened on 5 May 1873. Int[ernal]
fittings and other building work continued until February [1876]
when the Chairman announced that the total expenditure o[n the]
hotel was £438,000. Since the station proper had cost more [than]
this, the whole works involved a sum in the region of one m[illion]
pounds.

   The *Builder* reported in 1866 that Scott had simply re-use[d his]
rejected designs for the Government offices at the station[. But]
as comparison with that design (9) makes clear, this was not [so.]
The former was to be built with Portland stone, wherea[s the]
latter was constructed from the patent bricks made by Ed[ward]
Gripper of Nottingham. As Pevsner has remarked 'all that is [true]
is that he [Scott] had made a thorough study of French [and]
Italian Gothic details for that building [the Foreign Office] [and]
put them to good purpose now'.

   Jones's drawing appears to be the only competition entry fo[r the]
Hotel, apart from those of Scott, which has survived. It was [one]
of three which he showed at the Architectural Exhibitio[n of]
1866 when the *Builder* commented 'the designs . . . by Mr O[wen]
Jones [are] full of colour, the façades being relieved by [red]
granite columns and ornamentation, and the roofs tinted gr[een;]
[he] boldly grapples with the engineer's design, and assu[ming]
for the nonce to be *Ingegnere-architetto*, he brings the [great]
span of the roof to the front, and, placing it between [two]
towers, makes it (through a more ornamental manner) lik[e the]
terminus at Kings Cross, and the Strasbourg Railway in Par[is.']

once the prominent and leading feature of the frontage. He also, unlike his competitors, keeps up the distinctive character of the monster hotel by the side of it, joining the hotel and terminus by a wing of lower proportions.' Several of the other competitors concentrated on hiding Barlow's shed, believing that the naked product of engineering skill could never be classed as architecture. Jones on the other hand makes it at once the most prominent and important part of his design, to the extent that the hotel, which was after all the subject of the competition, assumes, in this view at least, a secondary importance. Much of the detailing of the latter appears to have been influenced not just by the fashionable French paradigm set by Hardwick with the Great Western Hotel of 1850 (124) but also by John Giles's Langham Hotel of 1863, for which Jones had designed the interior decorations. The significance of the place names which frame the end of the shed is not understood.

Lit. J. Simmons, *St Pancras Station*, 1968. N. Pevsner, *London: Except the Cities of London and Westminster*, 1952, pp. 368-69. Sir G. Gilbert Scott, *Personal and professional recollections*, 1879, pp. 271-72.

Sir George Gilbert Scott
Midland Grand Hotel, St Pancras Station, London. 1865-77
*Lettered* Midland Railway Terminus, St Pancras Station and Hotel *and numbered* 10
*Pen and ink and water-colour* $56\frac{1}{2} \times 29\frac{1}{8}$ (143.5 × 74.1)
Lent from the Public Record Office

**128** Cuthbert Brodrick
Grand Hotel, Scarborough. 1867
*Water-colour* 29¼ × 49 (74.2 × 119.3)
Given by Miss E. Harris, great-niece of the artist
Lent by Scarborough Public Libraries

Pevsner has said 'At the bottom end of the valley, past the Cliff Bridge high up, turn left and approach the wondrous Grand Hotel, a High Victorian gesture of assertion and confidence, of denial of frivolity and insistence on substance than which none more telling can be found in the land.' The Cliff Hotel Company was formed in 1862 to build a new hotel in Scarborough on the pattern of those recently erected in America; that is, with suites of large public rooms combined with bed-rooms and private sitting rooms; Hardwick's Great Western Hotel was similarly inspired. Work commenced in the following year and by 1865 the shell had been completed up to the main cornice. At this time the original company collapsed and

work stopped. A new company was formed in September, building began again in the following January, and was completed in 1867. The general contractor was Archibald Neill of Bradford, and John Robinson acted as Clerk of Works for the company. The interior arrangements included a vast central hall, a dining room for 300 people and coffee and drawing rooms, each 110 × 80 feet fitted into the centre of a wedge-shaped site. The drawing room was decorated in white and gold with gilded furniture upholstered in amber silk and lighted by four bronze gas statues each bearing a cluster of twenty lights with crystal pendants. The kitchens and offices were situated in the basement, and each of the cupolas contained three bed rooms for employees.

Contemporary critics regarded the style as 'Italian' but much of the detailing, particularly the caryatids on the corner pavilions, the dormer windows and the swagged brackets supporting the main cornice, obviously reflected contemporary French fashions, particularly the recently completed new

Louvre. The *Building News* said o drawing 'Mr. Brodrick treats us t Palace of Aladdin of our youth, considerably increased since then. if we recollect aright had only one d now we have four roc's eggs and r each capped by its own parti incubator. Oh! that they would a dividend; great would be their and we might then forgive their wa beauty. The rest of the building ordinary hotel character, but cou changed; heretofore they have gene been red with white facings. This on a sort of bandsman's uniform of w faced with red.'

Exhib. RA, 1867, no. 913. 'Cut Brodrick Victorian Artist', borough Art Gallery, July 1967.
Lit. *Br*, 3 November, 1866, p. 813; 1 1867, p. 385. *BN*, 17 May 1867, p N. Pevsner, *Yorkshire, The Riding*, 1966, pp. 331, 32. 'Scarbor Grand', *AR*, vol. clxv, March 196 Linstrum 'Cuthbert Brodrick interpretation of a Victorian a tect', *Journal of the Royal Socie Arts*, January 1971, pp. 83-4.

William Eden Nesfield
The Rose and Crown Hotel, Saffron
Walden, Essex. 1872
*Signed* W. Eden Nesfield Archt. 30
Argyll Street, Regent St., London,
W. *and dated* July 1872. *Inscribed*
'Rose and Crown' Hotel, Saffron
Walden. This is one of the drawings
referred to in the contract dated
August 2, 1872. Signed F. J.
Whiffin for Geo. Whiffin. Witness
Francis Hames *and with notes.*
*Numbered* 11
*Pen and ink, pencil and water-colour*
19¼ × 29 (49 × 74.2)
D.1577-1907, given by Mr E. J. May,
FRIBA, for the Phené Spiers Col-
lection of architectural drawings
Victoria and Albert Museum

Brydon notices that Nesfield's 'new
Queen Anne front [is] quite in keeping
with the tradition of the old hostelry,
quiet and unostentatious'. So con-
vincing in fact that it has been thought
to be of c. 1700. An earlier drawing in
the Department of Prints and Drawings
(D.1576-1907) indicates that Nesfield
originally intended smaller second floor
windows and a more elaborate cornice.
It was also intended at that time to build
a glass roof between the offices and
coach house. The bank, which Nesfield
built in Saffron Walden to the left of
the hotel at the same time, was designed
more obviously in the contemporary
idiom with Neo-Tudor and Franco-
Flemish early 16th century details.

The hotel was apparently completed
by 1874. It was gutted by fire quite
recently.

Lit. N. Pevsner, *Essex*, 1954. J. M.
Brydon 'William Eden Nesfield, 1835-
1888', *AR*, vol. i, 1896-97, p. 287.

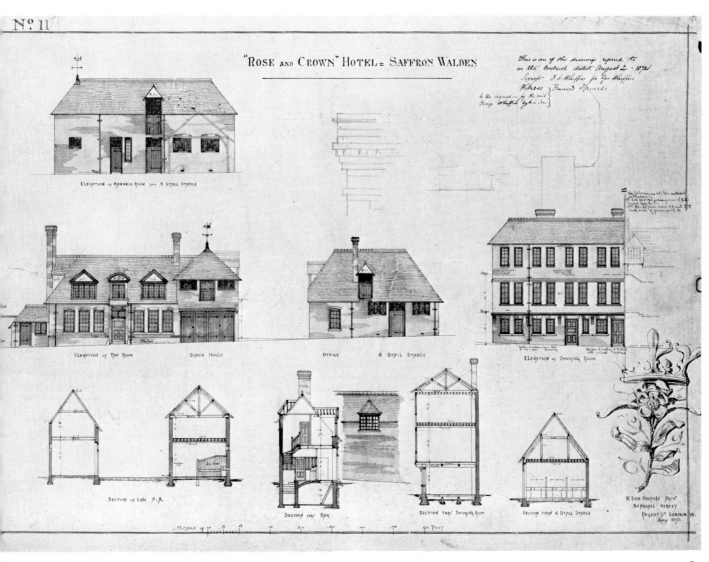

**130** Richard Norman Shaw

The hostelry and stores, Bath Road, Bedford Park, Chiswick. 1880

*Signed* R Norman Shaw RA Archt., 29 Bloomsbury Square *and dated* August 1880. *Inscribed* Bedford Park Estate: Turnham Green. Elevation of Stores and Inn. Elevation scale ¼ of an inch to a foot

*Pen and ink and water-colour* 19⅞ × 39 (50.7 × 99)

D.1722-1908, given by Mr Norman Shaw, RA, for the Phené Spiers collection of architectural drawings

Victoria and Albert Museum

The hostelry, or Tabard Inn as it became called, was decorated internally with tiles by William De Morgan and Walter Crane. Above the bars on the ground floor Shaw included a large hall with separate entrance, which was intended to supplement the drawing room of the Bedford Park Club as a meeting place for the various Bedford Park Societies. The stores, the *Building News* noted, 'will be conducted on the same principles as the "Civil Service" and other large co-operative establishments, so that the residents of the Bedford Park will have a series of shops all within one building, without leaving the boundary of the estate'. The block, which included a private house in the centre for the manager of the inn, was completed in 1880 on the opposite side of the road to the church.

Shaw's picturesque treatment of the façade, in three quite separate units, described as possessing 'a freshness of purpose and novelty of idea not found probably in any similar contemporary enterprise', did not relate to the interior plan since the inn premises extended in fact into the first of the 'private houses'. The fenestration of the inn was almost certainly the model for Voysey's 14 South Parade, Bedford Park, of 1891.

Illus. T. A. Greeves, 'London's first Garden Suburb', *Country Life*, 7 and 14 December 1967, pp. 1524-29, 1600-02.

Lit. *BN*, 2 January 1880, p. 10.

Bedford Park Estate: Turnham Green:
Elevation of Stores & Inn: Scale ¼ of an inch to a foot:

Elevation

R. Norman Shaw. RA Archt
29 Bloomsbury Sqe. Aug. 1880.

Sir Robert Rowand Anderson
Central Hotel, Gordon Street, Glasgow. 1884
*Signed* W. Ferguson *Delt, and inscribed* Central Station
Hotel View of Exterior
*Pen and ink* 23 × 31 (58.3 × 78.8)
Lent by British Transport Hotels Limited

The Hotel was apparently completed by May 1884, when the *Building News* noted that Anderson's drawing 'scarcely does justice to the executed building, in which there are some effective Renaissance features, especially the corner tower which is treated in a plain but dignified manner, relieved only by an arched window recess'. Gomme and Walker uphold this opinion, noting that 'the magnificent tower . . . seems to join the Scandinavian seventeenth and twentieth centuries together'. The *Builder*, however, was critical, noting that the drawing 'presents a singular combination of styles which give a result very difficult to name. Round arched window openings in the lower stages are filled in with a sort of Venetian tracery, while the upper storeys are unadulterated; Francois I, "Queen Anne" gables and dormers, and a nondescript tower complete the incongruous medley. The chimney stacks just peep over the roofs, and thus a chance of imparting some interest to an otherwise tame and spiritless sky-line is lost. The design is not up to the author's mark, and is in many ways weak and unsatisfactory.'

Anderson's Pollokshaws Burgh building of 1897 and Pearce Institute of 1903-05, both in Glasgow, like the Central Hotel, reveal the fastidious care he took over details. Gomme and Walker notice 'that the truly remarkable thing about the result [in the Hotel] is that Anderson is able to work such diverse elements together with no trace of architectural indigestion and get a Scots feeling into the building as a whole which, while it means that it strikes a somewhat foreign air in Glasgow, is proof total of his consummate mastery of style'.

Exhib. RA, 1884, no. 1313. Munich Salon, 1891. Chicago Exhibition, 1893.
Lit. *Br*, 17 May 1884, p. 693. *BN*, 9 May 1884, p. 703. A. Gomme and D. Walker, *Architecture of Glasgow*, 1968, pp. 197-98.

**132** Edward Schroeder Prior

Lodging houses and hotel, the 'Lost Sailor', West Bay
Dorset. c. 1885
*Signed* Edward S. Prior Archt. 17 Southampton Street,
Bloomsbury Square, London, W.C. *Inscribed* West Bay.
Plans of lodging house. Plan of hotel
*Pen and ink* 14 × 19 (35.7 × 48.2)
RAN 5/9/5/1
Lent by the Royal Institute of British Architects

Prior appears to have been involved between 1885 and 1905 with
a number of works at West Bay, including two terraces, a swimming bath (89) and a large house 'The Moorings', besides these
lodging houses and hotel. The latter closely resemble stylistically
drawings in the Royal Institute of British Architects for Quay

Terrace, and it is possible that these owe something, as Pev[sner]
has pointed out, to the vernacular tradition of building in [the]
West Country. They also owe something in their plannin[g to]
Norman Shaw, in whose office Prior had worked, and [it is]
interesting to note that they are not dissimilar to the draw[ings]
Prior published a few years earlier in Shaw's volume of *Ske[tches]
for cottages and other buildings* designed to be constructed i[n the]
Patent Cement Slab System invented by W. J. Lascelles.

H. S. Goodhart Rendel, who included Prior as one o[f his]
'rogue' architects, noted that, although Prior was one of the y[oung]
men in Shaw's office, he showed in his work 'a brave [and]
constant egregiousness that makes it impossible to regard [him]
as a school man in any sense'.

Lit. J. Newman and N. Pevsner, *Dorset*, 1972, pp. 443-44[4]

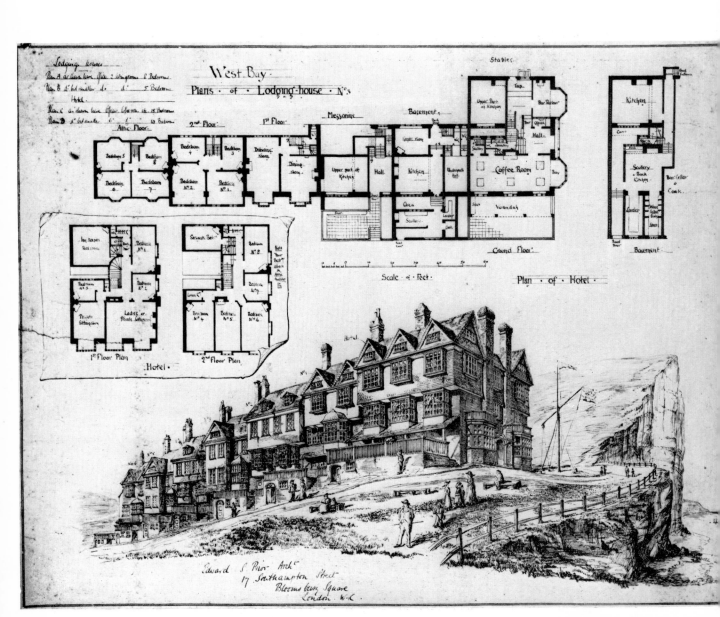

# Catalogue

## 14 Museums, Libraries, Art Galleries

*General view of the Kensington Gore estate*
*Courtesy, Aerofilms Ltd*

**133** Charles Robert Cockerell
Taylor and Randolph Building,
Oxford
*Pencil* $15\frac{3}{4} \times 38\frac{1}{2}$ (40 × 97.8)
E.2037-1909, given by Mr F. P. and
Mr L. P. Cockerell for the Phené
Spiers Collection of architectural
drawings
Victoria and Albert Museum

In 1788 died Sir Robert Taylor, a
highly successful sculptor turned architect, who had been Surveyor to the
Admiralty, Greenwich Hospital and the
Bank of England. Among his works of
sculpture are the monument to Captain
Cornewall, removed from the church
and now languishing in the cloisters of
Westminster, and the pediment of the
Mansion House. He bequeathed his
large fortune of £180,000 to his son
Michael Angelo Taylor for life, and then
to the University of Oxford to found an
institute for the study of modern
languages.

The University advertised in 1840 for
designs for a building to be used for
that purpose, as well as to house paintings and the Arundel marbles, for which
other bequests, such as that from Dr
Randolph, had been made.

Thirty-four designs were sent in, and
the University chose those submitted
by Cockerell. The construction work
was entrusted to the firm of Baker,
it was begun in April 1841. The buil[d]
was completed in 1845. The site sele[cted]
was in Beaumont Street, in which is [the]
main front, with a narrower façad[e on]
St Giles. The central portico [in]
Beaumont Street is surmounted [by a]
statue of Apollo, which, with the o[ther]
sculpture, was carved by W. G. Nic[holl]
who must have pleased Cockerell, fo[r he]
was later chosen by that archite[ct to]
carve the pediment of St George's [Hall,]
Liverpool.

The classical order selected [by]
Cockerell for the Oxford buildin[g is]
taken from the Temple of A[pollo]
Epicurius, at Bassae, near Phigalia.

Sir James Pennethorne
The Public Record Office, Chancery
Lane, London. 1850
*Signed* James Pennethorne *and dated*
10 May 1850. *Lettered* Proposed
General Record Repository. North
Elevation
*Pen and ink and wash* 22 × 30¼
(56 × 77)
MPD.177(T.1/5565B)
Lent from the Public Record Office

Until the middle of the 19th century, the custody of national records was somewhat disorganized, precarious and haphazard; the records themselves were dispersed in the White Tower and Wakefield Tower of the Tower of London; the Rolls House; in the Carlton House stables; the Chapter House of Westminster Abbey; and divers other places. Plans were drawn up in 1832 for a unified repository, and some years later Sir Charles Barry also designed such a building. However, it fell to Pennethorne to provide a Record Office on the Rolls estate in Chancery Lane. This had to be fire-proof, and to provide sufficient space to house all the records then in the custody of the Master of the Rolls, as well as make reasonable

provision for additional material for the following fifty years at least. The chief fire officer for London, Braidwood, was consulted, as well as Sir W. Hooker, of Kew, who was asked about ventilation and humidity problems.

Pennethorne provided his building with floors of wrought iron girders and brick arches. The 'sashes and door-frames will be of metal; the doors of slate; the roof iron. The brick walls inside will be coloured without plaster. The hall, which is entered from the south side of the building, will be lined with Portland stone, and have a panelled ceiling formed of zinc, and emblazoned. Externally the walls are of Kentish rag stone, with dressings of Anston stone. It is late Gothic in style, with something of a German character, and promises to be very successful in effect. The peculiarities of the elevation result from the construction and provisions of the building . . . Two windows are provided for each room, and as the rooms are fifteen feet high, divided by a gallery, it follows that the windows must be unusually lofty to light both floors, and to throw the light 25 feet down the passages between the records; these circumstances make the front a mass of

windows, precluding any plain surfaces . . . Again, the weight to be carried, and the consequent necessity for stiffening the front wall, weakened as it would be by many and lofty windows, has induced the adoption of deep buttresses. The clock tower . . . which is over the entrance on the [south] side, is novel in design. It is not included in the present estimates.' Trust the Office of Works not to be extravagant; this extra feature was not built.

When the Public Record Office was planned it was intended that the north side should be the main elevation on a new road between Chancery Lane and Fetter Lane. This, also, came to nought. An addition to the building along Chancery Lane was made between 1891 and 1896 by Sir John Taylor, chief architect to the Office of Works. Joseph Durham provided in 1866 statues of four Queens of England for the interior side of the entrance gateway. Sir Nikolaus Pevsner considers Penne-thorne's design 'remarkably functional'.

Lit. *Br*, 11 October 1851, pp. 635-36, plan p. 642, illus. p. 643. N. Pevsner *London, The cities of London and Westminster*, 1962, p. 297.

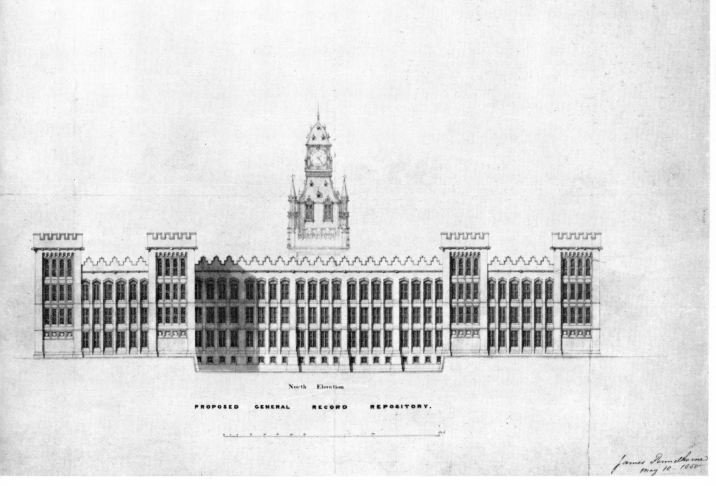

North Elevation

PROPOSED GENERAL RECORD REPOSITORY.

**135** Sydney Smirke and Alfred Stevens
Model for the proposed Reading Room of the British
Museum. c. 1853
*Wood and cardboard and plaster* 27 × 42 (58.5 × 106.7)
349-1890
Victoria and Albert Museum

Shortly after the completion of the British Museum by Sir Robert Smirke, it was realized that the space available for new books for the library would not house more than some 20,000 volumes, a smaller number than was then being acquired during one year. A new storage room was built which, for a few years, relieved the pressure, but eventually the Trustees had to construct yet another room. Even this was not sufficient and it was not long before Antonio Panizzi, the Librarian, was asking for still more space, and he suggested that the Museum should buy additional ground in Russell Square. This proposal was, however, abandoned because of the high costs involved.

In 1852 Panizzi put forward another plan, this time to put up a building in the Museum's inner quadrangle, which would comprise a reading room, with other rooms round it. His project found favour as, being within the Museum, no exterior architectural façades would be needed, and no new land would have to be bought.

By 1854 the new Library had been planned by Sydney Smirke, and a contract agreed with Messrs Baker & Fielder, who would erect the building for about £100,000.

'The Reading Room is circular, 140 feet in diameter, 106 feet high, lighted by twenty windows at the springing of the dome, with a glazed aperture in the crown which is 40 feet in diamet[er] The new room contains 1,250,000 cubic feet of space; its . surrounding libraries 750,000 cubic feet. The building is c[on]structed principally of iron, with brick arches between the m[ain] ribs, supported by twenty iron piers . . . Upwards of 2,0[00] tons of iron have been used in the construction. The weight [of] the materials used in the dome is about 4,000 tons. The ent[ire] dome was roofed in and the copper covering laid in Septem[ber] 1855.' The Reading Room was opened for public inspection [on] 8 May 1857 for one week, after which it went into regular u[se.]

The internal arrangements were for a raised central platfo[rm] for the Superintendent, encircled by two concentric ranges [of] catalogue cases, with readers's tables radiating from these.

Panizzi asked Alfred Stevens to design the painted and scu[lp]tural interior decoration, but this was never carried out. E[ven] if it had been begun, one doubts whether Alfred Stevens wo[uld] have done very much, for in 1857 he had started on his c[on]troversial monument to the Duke of Wellington in St Pa[ul's] Cathedral, which he had not finished when he died in 1875. [The] panels in the dome were coloured pale blue instead, with [the] remainder in white and gold. Plain glass was put into [the] windows, which were found later to be distracting. 'Art sho[uld] have been called in to decorate. The omission, however, is [not] the fault of the designer, as much as the consideration [of] £. s. d.; and the length of time which it would have taken [to] complete the work.'

Illus. *Br*, 24 March 1855, p. 139.
Lit. *Br*, 24 March 1855, p. 133; plan, p. 138; 25 April 1857, p. 2[

John Burley Waring

**National Institute of Art and Science adapted for the site of Burlington House, Piccadilly. 1859**

*Signed on the back* I. B. Waring. *Two addresses*, 22 Edward Street, Portman Square, *and* 2, Kidlington Place, Ampthill Square, London, *have been crossed out. Inscribed*. A design for the south front of a National Institute of Art and Science adapted for the site of Burlington House, Piccadilly, by J. B. Waring F.R.I.B.A. The glass dome and central group form part of the proposed galleries of the Royal Academy

*Pen and ink and water-colour* $23\frac{5}{8} \times 36\frac{7}{8}$ (60.3 × 94)

829.3, bequeathed by Mr J. B. Waring

Victoria and Albert Museum

In his autobiography, *My artistic life* (1873), Waring recorded making this design early in 1859 after returning from a tour of the Continent. 'In this I carried out my ideas of the style I would use, combining construction in stone, terra cotta, iron and glass. It was exhibited at the Royal Academy, and favourably noticed by the papers, but not noticed at all by the authorities, who had appropriation of that site.'

In point of fact not all contemporary criticisms were favourable. The *Civil Engineer and Architects' Journal* remarked 'It presents a curious admixture of the details of all styles of architecture, for it is amusing to observe how Gothic buttresses are interchanged with rusticated Italian piers, and how Classic, Saracenic, and Byzantine features are amalgamated. Carving and sculpture are freely introduced in various places with success,

but though novelty and ingenuity are manifested throughout, we cannot imagine that in execution such a building would have a satisfactory appearance. It must be evident that incongruities, such as could be readily pointed out in Mr. Waring's scheme, are by no means admissible.' The *Building News* objected to the lack of a plan noting that the façade was 'in extent very far from sufficient to fill up the available frontage towards Piccadilly'.

Waring expresses throughout his autobiography and in several books a belief that modern architecture should not imitate past styles, but that it should evolve a 'new style' of its own. Unlike Owen Jones, William Vose Pickett, and others who aspired to the same ambition through a knowledge of the principles applicable in earlier styles, Waring's design is no more than a re-grouping of existing elements. His lithographed *Designs for civic architecture*, published in 1850, was, he said, an attempt to form 'a style of my own', and it, like the design for a group of shops (55), was infinitely more successful, because it was less obviously eclectic.

Exhib. RA, 1859, no. 1070. International Exhibition, London, 1862, British Section, Architecture, no. 1512. Paris 1867, Class IV, 52, no. 79.

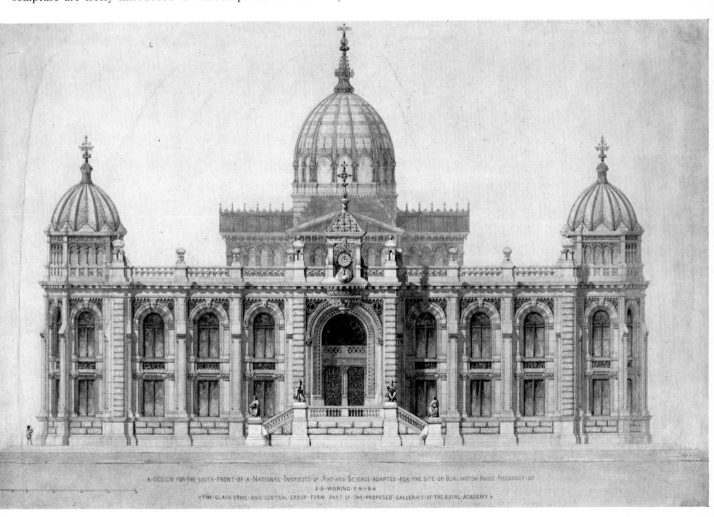

A·DESIGN·FOR·THE·SOUTH·FRONT·OF·A·NATIONAL·INSTITUTE·OF·ART·AND·SCIENCE·ADAPTED·FOR·THE·SITE·OF·BURLINGTON·HOUSE·PICCADILLY·BY J·B·WARING·F·R·I·B·A
·THE·GLASS·DOME·AND·CENTRAL·GROUP·FORM·PART·OF·THE·PROPOSED·GALLERIES·OF·THE·ROYAL·ACADEMY·

**137** George Edmund Street
Design for the National Gallery,
Trafalgar Square, south elevation.
1867
*Lettered with artist's name etc., and
scale*
*Pen and ink* 25 × 39¾ (63.5 × 101)
Lent by the Department of the
Environment
Victoria and Albert Museum

'The style in which [Mr Street] has worked out the problem to be solved will, of course, be called in general terms Gothic, but then it is Mr. Street's Gothic, and that, too, after visiting Spain, and this we submit makes all the difference. For it would be monstrous to accept this design as any, even the faintest, index of what really might be done by our Gothic school of architects, and because of the hasty conclusions people are apt to draw from one man's work in a given style, especially when that man happens to be a well-known one, we cannot but be sorry that Mr. Street should have been tempted to send this design out of his office. The composition is slight and not even picturesque. The front shows a long uninteresting straight building of two storeys, divided on each side into five arched compartments, with a single doorway in the centre, supported on each side by circular, dome-covered turrets, and crowned by a circular dome-covered tower. The whole design is singularly devoid of anything like dignity' (*BN*, 11 January 1867, p. 17). The *Builder* (26 January 1867, p. 57) considered the design 'anything but satisfactory'.

During the middle years of the 1 century, a certain indecision envelo the National Gallery building in Tra gar Square. There was a strong body opinion that the paintings should moved elsewhere. The attempt to a suitable location occupied a consid able amount of time, and was the sub of protracted debate and enquiry. So thought that the air of Kensing would be pure enough to protect pictures, and advocated a site on Prince Consort's Kensington G estate; others thought that somewh in Hyde Park or Kensington Gard would be more suitable. There was e a proposal to demolish Kensing Palace, while jealous eyes turned also to the land occupied by St Jam Palace.

However, by the late 1860s, Government had reached the decis that the Gallery should remain wher was, but that something ought to done with Wilkins's building. T courses of action, therefore, were op to demolish and rebuild entirely an or to enlarge and retain the origi building (Francis Fowke had produ designs to this end in 1858). T Trafalgar Square façade of this is lo

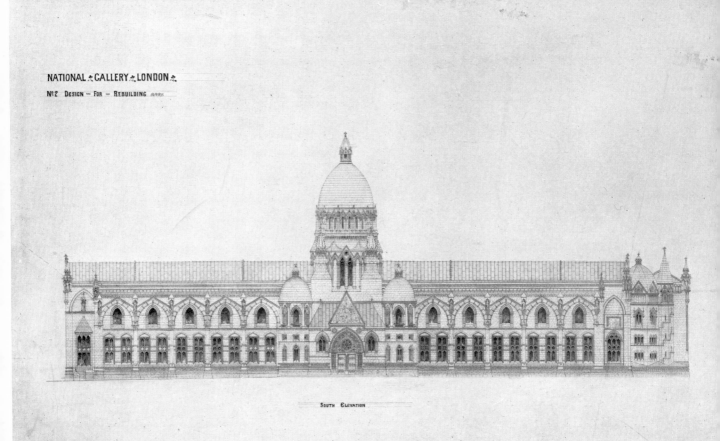

with a central portico adapted from that from Carlton House, a weak dome, and flanking 'pepper-pots'. It was a thin building, though, only one gallery in depth, a portion of which was occupied by the Royal Academy. The Government proposed to make available ground to the rear, on the western portion of which was a barracks.

In spite of already having held relatively disastrous competitions—the Government Offices, the Wellington Monument, the Natural History Museum, for instance—the Government embarked on yet another, but limited this time to invited architects. One of these was Gilbert Scott, but he refused to participate, 'wisely', in the view of the *Builder*. Scott may have been warned, it was thought, of the foregone conclusion that a classical building would be chosen and thus 'not care to become the St. Paul of modern architects, to be subjected to any more perils or stripes than he has already received anent the Foreign Office'.

In January 1867 designs showing either the rebuilding or enlargement were exhibited, the work of Owen Jones, Cuthbert Brodrick, G. E. Street, F. P. Cockerell, James Murray, E. M. Barry, F. C. Penrose, Somers Clarke, Matthew Digby Wyatt, and Banks & Barry. Only two designs were in the Gothic style, and the author of one of these (Somers Clarke) 'was so doubtful . . . that he has followed it up by a design founded upon the Venetian Classic Renaissance . . .'

The *Building News* dismissed Owen Jones's 'South Kensington type' building, and stated that Cuthbert Brodrick was 'great in pillars. There are some thirty-six Corinthian shafts in the front elevation alone and when we have said this, we have said nearly all that can be said of the design.' The same journal preferred, it said, not to discuss the design by Penrose, and took a poor view of most of the others as well—it congratulated Murray on his design 'if pillars and porticoes be the sort of thing desired in a country where driving rains and fogs, frosts and snow, and slush, are but too common'. It was evident that E. M. Barry had, with his huge dome, like that he had displayed in the Law Courts competition, gone all out to win, but his interior perspectives were criticized as misleading and distorted.

In its issue of 16 February the *Builder* gave publicity to a rumour which had begun to circulate that the First Commissioner intended to abandon these designs, and 'throw all the competitors overboard wholesale'. Once again the Government and the Office of Works found themselves in the centre of an architectural storm. The competing architects, having seen the report in the *Builder*, the same day sent a joint letter to Lord John Manners, stating that if this report were true it would constitute a 'breach of faith with us, and would confer a lasting injury upon every one of the competitors'. Lord John's predecessor in office, William Cowper, also wrote to him explaining that it was the duty of the judges to 'declare the winner of the race even though they may form a low opinion of the running'. Manners, however, took the view that at no time had the architects been told that one of them would be selected and that, consequently, he was prepared neither to modify nor to qualify his decision.

Once again, the competitors banded together, and M. D. Wyatt, as their representative, told Manners that if they had not all been under the impression that one of them 'would be . . . selected for employment, not one of us would have thought of wasting his time upon the competition'.

Nothing happened for more than a year, until E. M. Barry was suddenly given the commission. In thanking the First Commissioner Barry expressed his pleasure that, after the adverse report of the judges, it had been decided that his designs 'exhibited the greatest amount of architectural merit'. This was not at all the case, replied the Office of Works, consideration had been given to all the circumstances relating not only to the National Gallery competition, but that for the Law Courts as well. Barry was a little surprised to learn of this, but flattered himself, that though Street had been given the Law Courts (though he had not won the competition), Barry had been the only competitor 'who was distinguished by the favourable mention of the judges in both cases'. There remained with him, however, the nagging suspicion that he had been appointed to design the lesser building and had therefore been denied 'lasting fame . . . by having my name connected with the largest and most important building of the age'.

The Royal Academy moved into its new premises in Burlington House during 1869. Barry was not, in the end, able to demolish the Wilkins building, but had to content himself with adding galleries at the back. In 1887 Sir John Taylor, of the Office of Works, reconstructed the vestibule and entrance hall.

# South Kensington

Although the Prince Consort and the 1851 Exhibition Commissioners had acquired the Kensington Gore estate early in the 1850s, it proved difficult to find a use for the land, apart from a small off-shoot to the east, on which was built the South Kensington Museum. The main site was bounded by Kensington Gore to the north, Cromwell Road to the south, with Queen's Gate and Exhibition Road on either side, for which Prince Albert had originally asked Professor Gottfried Semper to design buildings for a museum and other cultural purposes.

A drawn-out argument over whether the National Gallery should be moved to Kensington successfully stopped any immediate development of the land. Eventually the Commissioners, fed up with Government hesitation, leased a large area to the Horticultural Society, which created a garden encompassed within arcades designed by Sydney Smirke and Captain Fowke, RE. To the north, on the highest ground, was a large conservatory, also by Fowke. This was demolished in about 1889 (at which time it was the southern entrance to the Albert Hall) following disagreement between the Commissioners and the Horticultural Society. The Gardens were opened in 1861 by the Prince Consort a few months before his death.

Along the southern fringe, on Cromwell Road, Francis Fowke also designed the building for the 1861 Exhibition (this was later postponed until 1862). Both Fowke and Henry Cole hoped that this building would remain as one of the permanent structures of South Kensington, but this was not to be, as the Government did not approve of the suggestion. Instead, the Exhibition was demolished, and the materials re-used for the Alexandra Palace in north London. The Government agreed, however, to buy the Kensington land, and decided to erect a museum for the Natural History Collections of the British Museum, as well as for the material belonging to the Commissioners of Patents. In January 1864, therefore, the First Commissioner of Works announced a competition for the building. He was rather coy, though, at the time, about the use to which the building would be put, stating that he would first be content to get a building, and then give further consideration to its purpose.

There were thirty entrants in the competition; their designs were judged by Lord Elcho, William Tite, James Pennethorne, James Fergusson, and David Roberts, the painter. To the horror and indignation of the architectural profession, the winner was announced as Captain Fowke, the Royal

Engineer officer attached to the Department of Science and Art. On the other hand, Henry Cole and the South Kensington set were overjoyed, as it was their strongly held opinion that Royal Engineers could be relied upon to put up better and cheaper buildings than professional architects. Among the unsuccessful competitors was Alexander 'Greek' Thomson, of Glasgow, who had entered under the pseudonym of 'Athenian'.

Francis Fowke died suddenly in December 1865 before there had been any action on his designs, and early in 1866 the First Commissioner asked Alfred Waterhouse to take them over. Not unnaturally, Waterhouse found that Fowke's proposals did not fit in with the requirements of the Natural History Museum, so he produced a design of his own. Work on this building started in 1873, the builders being George Baker & Son, who undertook to complete the building within three and a half years. According to the *Builder*, Waterhouse intended to envelop both his interior and exterior in terracotta, but for reasons of economy this form of decoration was eventually confined to the main façades. On the minor northern towers, for instance, terracotta was used only on the upper parts which would be seen above the main building.

The Natural History Museum was not complete by 1878, when Parliament was asked for an additional £80,000 for it. This brought the total of money voted up to that time to £395,000, even though the original estimate had been for only £300,000, and which was to have included everything, except for the display cases. The South Kensington Museum authorities (Cole had retired by now) were furious at this apparently lavish spending by the Government, as they had been suffering for some years under a strict economy campaign by the Treasury, in spite of much support for expansion to their own buildings. The Natural History Museum was not opened until 1881.

Henry Cole had, in the meantime, however, achieved a notable triumph up the hill on Kensington Gore, alongside Fowke's huge conservatory. Since the 1850s it had been his ambition to build at Kensington a large hall of Arts and Science. An early scheme to attach this to the 1862 Exhibition had been rejected as too expensive. A fresh impetus was given after the death of Prince Albert when his memorial was to include such a hall, but once again the project was abandoned through lack of money. Cole, however, was not the sort of man to be deterred by such setbacks. He asked Fowke to produce designs for a hall in 1864, and a model made by the Royal Engineers was shown to Albert Edward, Prince of Wales at Osborne, on 30 January 1865. Fowke's death later that year was yet another, but only temporary,

blow to Cole's ambition. He found ano[ther] Royal Engineer, Lieut.-Colonel Henry Sc[ott] who agreed to continue the developmen[t of] Fowke's design based on the model.

Cole was wedded to the form of a Ro[man] amphitheatre, but his original hopes fo[r a] building which would seat 15,000 gradu[ally] became scaled down to a more realistic [one] which would accommodate some 6[,000] people.

Finance was a problem, as no governm[ent] funds were forthcoming for the hall, and [the] 1851 Commissioners were, moreover, stra[nge]ly reluctant to put up large sums of money [for] the scheme, now that Cole had lost [the] Prince Consort's backing. Cole then had [an] inspiration—why not sell the seats? P[ros]pectuses were sent out to likely peo[ple] inviting them to buy on very long lea[ses] boxes for £1,000, less grand boxes for £[?] and single seats for £100. Slowly the mo[ney] began to come in; Queen Victoria bought [two] boxes, the Prince of Wales another, and [the] Duke of Edinburgh and the Duke [of] Cambridge each subscribed £500 and ag[reed] to share a third box; Gladstone refused. [The] 1851 Commissioners generously agreed [to] hand over to the Hall's organizers a plo[t of] land on a lease of £1 for 999 years.

Henry Scott had considerably modi[fied] Fowke's design when, by 1 May 1867, all [was] ready for Queen Victoria to lay the founda[tion] stone. Apart from being told to keep [the] amphitheatre form, other conditions given [to] Scott were that the exterior had to be of [red] brick with terracotta decoration, and that [the] building was not to cost more than £175,0[00]. He was assisted by a committee, among [the] members of which were William T[ite,] Matthew Digby Wyatt, James Fergus[son] and Richard Redgrave, which was, said S[cott] in a lecture to the RIBA, 'an advantage s[uch] as no architect ever yet enjoyed, or proba[bly] would care to enjoy'.

Scott had a problem with the roof, wh[ich] had to be unsupported, so he designed a [very] shallow dome of iron girders and glass. [It] was doomed, gloated his critics; once [the] scaffolding was removed, down it wo[uld] crash. Scott was extremely confident, tho[ugh] and consequently proud that, when the fi[nal] central support was removed, the struct[ure] settled by less than half an inch.

The terracotta decoration was designed [by] two men from the South Kensington M[u]seum, James Gamble and Reuben Town[send] and modelled by students of the School [of] Art, and made by Messrs Gibbs & Can[ning] of Tamworth. Running round the upper p[art] of the exterior is a mosaic frieze which [had] been suggested by Henry Cole; this [was] designed by Pickersgill, Stacy Marks, Yean[es,] Poynter, Armitage, Armstead and Hors[ley.] Their sketches were taken to one of

seum's photographers, Sergeant Spack-
, who projected them by magic-lantern
to large sheets of paper, and traced the
ines himself to the full size required.
se outlines were then handed over to the
th Kensington Museum Ladies' Mosaic
ss, among the members of which were the
girls, who produced the ceramic mosaic,
ch was then finished off by Minton,
lins & Co.

ueen Victoria opened the Royal Albert
of Arts and Science, as she named it, on
March 1871. At first it was not a financial
ess; its echo was greatly criticized, and it
thought to be too far from London,
cially as the new underground railway
not prove capable of absorbing the many
sands of people who surged upon South
sington station late at night.

he Royal Albert Hall was intended to be
crowning feature of the Kensington Gore
te, standing as it did on the highest ground
gside the conservatory. Below it to the
h were the spacious gardens of the
ticultural Society. Prince Albert had
ed that these would be enclosed by various
dings devoted to art and science, but only
, the eastern and western galleries, were
ted in connection with the International
ibition of 1871.

he disintegration of the Kensington
te began in 1886. On the 13th of
tember, the Prince of Wales wrote to the
d Mayor of London suggesting that an
itute should be founded to commemorate
en Victoria's Golden Jubilee, which
ht represent 'Arts, Manufactures and
mmerce of the Queen's Colonial and
ian Empires'. Other suggestions were put
ward, one of them being that a Victoria
pel should be built on to Westminster
bey as an Imperial Valhalla. Eventually,
ause of the very high cost of land in
tral London, the choice of a site fell upon
nsington. The agreement with the Horti-
ural Society was terminated and the
dens closed. The conservatory was sold
demolished, and Joseph Durham's
morial to the 1851 Exhibition was moved
thwards on to its present site, but it was,
he same time, deprived of its cascades of
er; one of the garden's band-stands found
way to Clapham Common in south
don. A large plot of land, virtually bisect-
the estate to the north of the just com-
ed Natural History Museum was selected
the Imperial Institute. It was a mistake,
aimed the Builder, 'to face the front of one
t building towards the back of another'.
was also an error to build laterally across
site and thus effectively to destroy the
th-south axis upon which the estate had
eloped.

t was not altogether clear at first what
purpose the new Institute was to serve, but
the requirements for the building included
a large reception hall, a library, conference
and committee rooms, and exhibition galleries
as well. A limited competition was held, the
architects who were invited to send in designs
being Aston Webb and Ingress Bell, T. E.
Collcutt, T. A. Jackson, A. W. Blomfield,
Rowand Anderson and T. N. Deane; public
interest in the designs when they were
exhibited was minimal. The successful
architect was Collcutt, and the building was
erected substantially to his submitted design.
The dominant feature of his Institute was a
central tower, nearly 300 feet high, surmounted by a copper cupola.

When Queen Victoria opened the Imperial
Institute, which by then had already cost
£280,000, on 10 May 1893, this tower was
incomplete, but it was announced that the
Prince of Wales had accepted the offer of an
Australian lady to provide and equip a peel
of bells. The *Builder* mused upon the alarm-
ing reports that the tower was subsiding, but
was able to reassure its readers 'that the
compression on the clay bed of this great
weight, now over 5,000 tons, is only half an
inch . . .'

Early in the present century the Institute
building was largely occupied by London
University, although there were extensive
exhibition galleries at the rear. At the
beginning of 1953 the Government asked
Imperial College to plan for an increase in its
student numbers. The College accordingly,
two years later, produced plans for new
buildings, which meant the demolition of the
Institute, the Royal School of Needlework,
and Waterhouse's City and Guilds College in
Exhibition Road, as well as some Norman
Shaw houses in Queen's Gate. Public reaction
was immediate and vehement, although it was
generally appreciated that the interior of
Collcutt's building was inconvenient and
could not be adapted. These proposals of
Imperial College had not really been made
public, but had been seen by only a relatively
small number. This prompted Goodhart-
Rendel to ask in *The Times* if it would be
possible to 'let us see what is offered in
exchange?'. When the exact plans were
revealed, it was apparent that they would have
to be considerably modified even to retain
only the tower, which Julian Huxley described
as an essential feature on the London sky-
line. Westminster City Council considered
that Collcutt's Institute possessed 'such
special architectural merit that every possible
effort should be made to preserve it'. In the
end, after consultation between the Royal
Fine Arts Commission, the Treasury,
Imperial College, and other interested bodies,
it was decided that the tower had to stay. The
scheme for Imperial College was then revised,
though unfortunately no attempt was made
to re-establish the north-south axis.

As a result of the demolition of such a
major building of the late 19th century,
people were alerted to the dangers of such
vandalism, often planned without publicity,
and this new awareness led to the foundation
of the Victorian Society shortly afterwards
in 1958.

**138** Alexander Thomson
Design for the Natural History
Museum, South Kensington. 1864
*Pen and ink and wash* 20¾ × 66¾
(52.5 × 178.5)
Lent from the Mitchell Library,
Glasgow

Of Thomson's design, the *Builder* noted,
'The . . . design marked "Athenian"
has great merit of grouping in the masses,
which include Doric temple-formed
structures raised aloft, each main portico
carried on a substructure having one
long opening filled in with dwarf shafts of
Indian character, and a larger opening
filled in with Telamones or elephants.
The portico is reached by side flights of
steps. To the main block of the temple-
formed structure, another block tran-
septwise is attached. The principal
portion of the building devoted to the
museums has for its external features,
plain openings between antae of pilasters
in the upper floor, and low windows,
with Greek doorways at certain dis-
tances, in the ground storey. A square
tower rusticated in horizontal lines, and
having marked *entasis*, and terminated
by a lantern and balcony, is placed at
the north-eastern corner of the ground.
There is fine effect in this design,
though it had no chance of selection

On the other hand, the *Building I*
thought that Thomson's proposal
'marred by the introduction of
ungainly-looking tower at one end o
perspective drawing, which dwarf
other features'.

Exhib. Royal Academy, The Ag
Neo-Classicism, 1972, no. 1368.
Illus. *AR*, vol. cxv, May 1954, p.
fig. 26.
Lit. *BN*, 22 April 1864, p. 298;
23 April 1864, pp. 289-91; 14
1864, p. 347. G. Law, 'Greek Th
son', *AR*, May 1954, pp. 307-16.

Alfred Waterhouse
Natural History Museum, South Kensington. 1876
*Signed and dated* 1876
*Pen and ink and water-colour* $16\frac{5}{8} \times 28\frac{1}{2}$ (42.5 × 72.5)
D.1859-1908, given by Mr P. Waterhouse, FRIBA, for the
Phené Spiers Collection of architectural drawings
Victoria and Albert Museum

Exhib. This may be no. 1004 in the Royal Academy Exhibition of
   1876.
   'A small coloured perspective adequately doing justice to this
   fine structure' (*BN*, 28 April 1876, p. 413. RA Bi-Centenary,
   1968-69, no. 285).
Illus. The same view, but with a different garden arrangement was
   illustrated *Br*, 4 January 1873, pp. 10-1.

**140** Francis Fowke
Design for the Conservatory in the Horticultural Society's
Gardens, South Kensington. c. 1861
*Water-colour and pencil* $7\frac{1}{4} \times 26\frac{3}{4}$ (18.2 × 67.9)
Lent by the Royal Institute of British Architects

Illus. *Catalogue of the Drawings Collection of the RIBA,*
vol. C-F, 1972, pl. 96.

Thomas Edward Collcutt
South elevation and section of the principal tower of the Imperial Institute, with plans at various levels.
1887
*Pen and ink and wash* 28½ × 21
(72.3 × 53.3)
W. 10/29.9
Lent by the Royal Institute of British Architects

Collcutt's design was generally pleasantly received by the critics, the *Building News* approving of his style, 'a phase of Renaissance in which English details have been combined with Flemish characteristics'. It was not really approving of the main tower; nor was the *Builder*. The whole design was considered graceful, but 'the tower we hardly think is so happy; it is rather too bare to assort well with the richness of the rest of the design, and seems at any rate, to demand a more richly-treated upper storey and lantern to be worthy of its position. Our conclusion as to the design generally, however, is that charming as it is in itself, it is not of the stately and monumental character which we should associate with a national building second only in importance to the Houses of Parliament, if second to that. This can, perhaps, hardly be charged, entirely at least, against the architect. The funds for a building such as the occasion demanded, have not been promised. Mr. Collcutt has evidently been influenced by considerations of economy; and we cannot say how far he might have risen to the occasion had he not had this stumbling-block of economy before his eyes.'

Lit. *Br*, 2 July 1887, p. 2. *BN*, 1 July 1887, p. 3.
Illus. *Catalogue of the Drawings Collection of the RIBA*, vol. C-F, 1972, pl. 34.

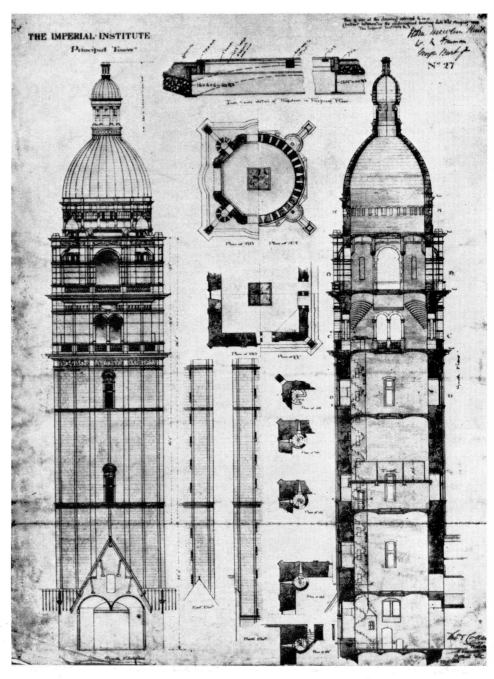

THE IMPERIAL INSTITUTE
Principal Tower

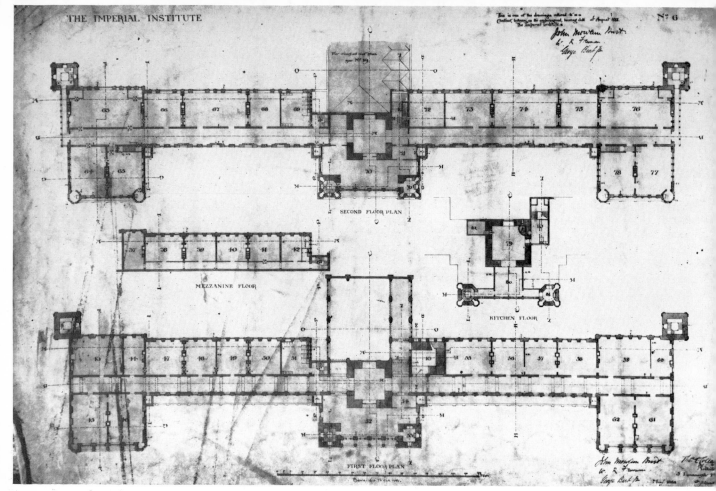

SECOND FLOOR PLAN

MEZZANINE FLOOR

KITCHEN FLOOR

FIRST FLOOR PLAN

Captain Francis Fowke
Model for the proposed Hall of Arts
and Science, South Kensington. 1864
*Cardboard, wood and glass* 22 × 28½
× 13 (55.8 × 72.3 × 33)
A.10-1973
Victoria and Albert Museum

This model was submitted by Sir
Henry Cole and Richard Redgrave,
to Queen Victoria at Osborne. It
relates chiefly to the proposed interior of the Hall. The model was
probably made in the museum by
Sappers.

Exhib. South Kensington Museum,
Museum of Construction no. 10Y.

*1. RIBA W.10/29.2*

*alogue 142*

**142A** Major-General Henry Young
Darracott Scott
Model showing an alternative treat-
ment for the exterior of the Royal
Albert Hall. 1868
*Plaster* 42 × 22¾ (106.6 × 57.6)
A.11-1973
Victoria and Albert Museum

General Scott, besides being the architect of the Albert Hall in its final form,
was also the Director of New Buildings
to the South Kensington Museum. In
1867 he prepared a statement on the
general method of designing the Museum's buildings which applies equally
to the Royal Albert Hall, on which he
also was working with Sir Henry Cole:
'. . . The nature of the accommodation required in the buildings, such as
the size of courts, corridors, lighting,
&c., are discussed between the General
Superintendent of the Museum [Henry
Cole] and the Director of the New
Buildings (an officer of the Royal
Engineers) [General Scott].

2. The Director of New Buildings
then prepares experimental plans and
sections, having regard, primarily, to the
above requirements, and, secondly, to
decorative construction subject to these
requirements. At this stage he consults
with the artists and modellers to be
subsequently employed on the architectural details. Several sketch plans are
generally prepared.

3. Block models are then made, but
without inserting architectural details.
Several models are generally made and
experiments tried and discussed with the
General Superintendent.

4. When the block model has been
settled the structural plans with sketches
are finally made, and the working drawings proceeded with.

5. To obtain the architectural and
decorative details structural plans with
sketches are sent to the studios of the
artists, who are both modellers and
painters.

6. The Director of New Buildings, in
concert with the artists, settles the
architectural details, which are generally

submitted to the Inspector-General for Art for suggestions, but the Director of New Buildings remains solely responsible. Many experiments by drawings and models are made.

7. Architectural models with details are prepared. Numerous experiments are made, frequent discussions are had with the Inspector-General for Art and others, and no trouble or cost are spared at this stage before the decision is finally made.

8. If necessary, an architectural drawing to the full size in perspective is made and put up and subjected to criticism.

9. Plans being finally settled, quantities are taken out by surveyors and a limited competition among contractors invited.

10. Models of the architectural detail are made in the artist's studio, superintended by the Director of New Buildings.

11. By taking all this trouble, and incurring the cost of such experiments, failures and alterations are very much avoided and final economy is ensured . . .' (*15th Report of the Department of Science and Art 1867*, 1868, p. 200.)

The Museum possesses other plaster models of the exterior of the Albert Hall, as well as photographs of at least one model prepared by General Scott.

The plaster models were exhibite the Museum of Construction at S Kensington (no. 11Y, Catalogue, 1 in which they were thus described 'These designs, founded on original proposition of the late Cap Francis Fowke, R.E. . . . were exec under the direction of Major-Ger Scott, R.E. . . .

No. 2 model represents the sec design. Exterior-1868.

No. 3 model represents the t design. Exterior-1868.

No. 4 model represents a portio the exterior of the Hall as executed

*Catalogue 142A*

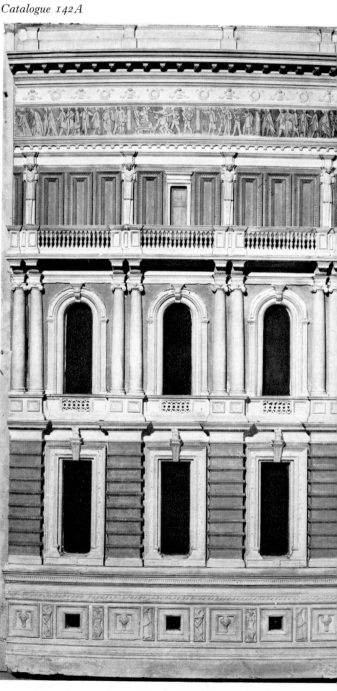

*Major-General Henry Scott, CB. Model of the proposed Albert Hall, made by Jackson & Sons, Rathbone Place, London, and exhibited at the Paris Exhibition of 1867.*

Francis Fowke
Design for the completion of the
South Kensington Museum. 1860
*Pencil* 7 × 49⅞ (18 × 127)
E.1024-1927
Victoria and Albert Museum

Owen Jones
Design for the decoration of the
oriental courts of the
South Kensington Museum. 1865
D.120-1905
Victoria and Albert Museum

The Victoria and Albert Museum
(then the South Kensington Museum)
opened during the summer of 1857 in an
iron building at Brompton. This, popu-
larly known as the 'Boilers', had been
erected by Prince Albert and the 1851
Commissioners. At the same time the
Department of Science and Art built
a small picture gallery, designed by
Captain Francis Fowke, RE, immediately to the north. Extending even
farther northwards, Fowke erected a
series of galleries for paintings from the
National Gallery.

A select Committee of the House of
Commons recommended in 1860 that
the various wooden shacks and dilapidated houses cluttering the site should

be swept away. Fowke had shown this
Committee a design which he had
prepared for a permanent museum, and
permission was granted for certain
portions of this building to be proceeded
with. A range on the western side was
finished by 1863, and formed part of a
projected inner courtyard; this housed
certain officials of the Museum. At the
same time a building was put up to the
north for the School of Art (now the
Royal College of Art), which was
finished by 1864. A start was then made
on the Lecture Theatre block, which by
early 1865 has 'been carried up to the
average height of thirty feet. The rate
of progress has been comparatively slow,
from the delay consequent on the careful
modelling and manufacture of the terra
cotta, which material is exclusively
employed in all the dressings and
ornamental details of the exterior. The
ornamental details of the terra cotta
have been designed by Mr. Godfrey
Sykes, and modelled under his immediate directions by his pupils, who were
students of the Schools of Art' (F.
Fowke, *12th Report of the Department of
Science and Art*, Appendix D, no. 13).

It had been Fowke's intention to use
Portland stone, but he and Henry Cole
had been so impressed by the terracotta
decorations of the Horticultural
Gardens, that they considered it the

'best material for architectural decoration
in large and smoky towns'.

Since Fowke had originally shown his
design to the 1860 Committee, he had
introduced a few slight changes, the
most noticeable being the pediment to
the lecture theatre. He died in December
1865, and his collaborator, Godfrey
Sykes, three months later. Fowke was
succeeded by another Royal Engineer
officer, Lt.-Col. Henry Scott, who completed this part of the Museum to
Fowke's design with no significant
alterations.

A feature of the Museum was its
highly decorated interior. Owen Jones
prepared schemes for the painting of
the walls and ceilings of the Indian and
Oriental Galleries. Of two of these
designs, which Jones exhibited at the
Architectural Exhibition in Conduit
Street in May 1865, the *Builder* stated
that although they were not so elaborate,
nor so splendid, as some of Jones's work,
they were perhaps more successful. 'It
was no easy task to devise a species of
"wall-veil" which should accommodate
itself to the ugly outline of a modern
segmental-headed window, and we think
Mr. Jones has done judiciously in tinting
his piers with flat colour and reserving
the richer portion of his design for the
spandrels.'

Other parts of the Museum were

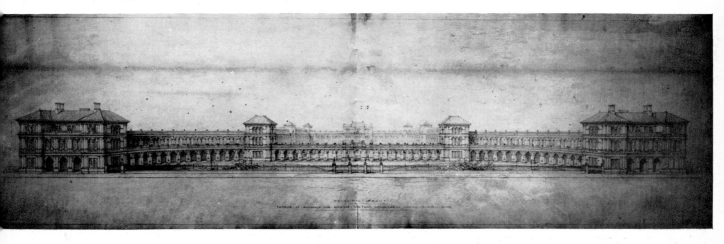

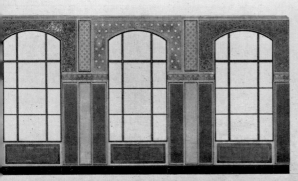
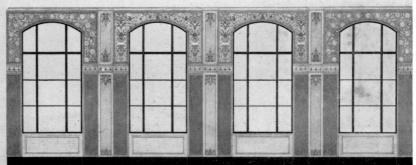

also decorated with mosaic or painting—Lord Leighton laboured for some years on two frescoes. Sir Edward Poynter, who had designed the painted tiles and glass in the Grill Room, put forward a scheme for the Lecture Theatre, which envisaged almost entirely covering the walls and ceiling with splendid pictures. The apse, for which Poynter produced the model in 1869, was to display a 'general scheme of Creation, the Sun, Moon, Day & Night, the Stars &c., beasts, rocks, rivers, plants, birds, rain, snow &c. &c. all done in the simplest decorative manner. Below, the picture will be divided into two parts; that to the left will treat with matters connected with Art & Poetry, that to the right with Science & Philosophy.'

In 1872 the figure of Michelangelo was made in mosaic for £150, but it was not a success. For a time, the scheme languished, but was resurrected some years later, and by 1877 was estimated to cost more than £6,000. Nothing was carried out, apart from the painting of the arch of the apse by students of the School of Art for £200, which included Poynter's payment for the design.

Except for the completion of the Library (1882), the Government allowed no further extension to the Museum until, as a result of mounting pressure, approval was given in 1890-91 for a competition to be held for a new building to cover all the open land flanking Cromwell and Exhibition Roads. Alfred Waterhouse advised the judges, and the successful architect was Aston Webb. The others invited to compete were T. E. Collcutt, Sir Thomas Deane, J. Macvicar Anderson (declined), John Belcher, William Emerson, Norman Shaw (declined), Bodley & Garner (declined), Mervyn Macartney and William Young.

Aston Webb did not have an easy time of it, however. Successive governments delayed the start; the dominant feature of the central tower was abandoned on grounds of economy, a useless open lantern eventually being substituted; indecision by the Government over a proposal that the College of Science should share the building, also added to Webb's design burden. Consequently it was not until 1899 that Queen Victoria laid the foundation stone, and gave the Museum its name on the same occasion. The new building was opened by Edward VII in 1909.

**145** Sir Edward Poynter
Model showing the proposed decoration of the semi-dome of the apse of the Lecture Theatre, Victoria and Albert Museum. 1869
*Wood, paper, cloth, painted* 50 × 48 × 33 (126.5 × 121.7 × 83.7)
A.12-1973
Victoria and Albert Museum

Sir Edward Poynter was sent to Venice by the Department of Science and Art to study the mosaics in St Mark's, preparatory to making a sketch for the design of the Lecture Theatre. On his return he made an oil-painting, 'using with it Parris's marble medium, which gives a "fresco"-like surface, upon a model made to scale'.

The *Architectural Review* described Poynter's Michelangelesque scheme in 1897:

'The figures around the base are (reading from the spectator's right) Herodotus, above whom is the Muse of History, Euclid, Archimedes, above whom are two figures with a drawing-board consulting together, who symbolize Geometry and Mechanics. Then comes Plato, with Philosophy deep in study above him. Next is Homer, above whom broods the Muse of Poetry. In the centre sits Michael Angelo, supported on the one side by Phidias, and on the other by Ictinus, the Architect of the Parthenon; above them is a fine group of three figures, symbolizing Painting, Sculpture, and Architecture, but which might be thought to be the Fates without any great effort of the Imagination. Then comes Beethoven, with the figure of Music above him. Then Shakespeare, accompanied by Tragedy and Comedy; then Galileo, attended by Astronomy; then Titian, robed as a Venetian

Senator; and finally, a figure of a ma[n] a religious habit reading a book, without a name, who has ano[ther] somewhat similar figure above him, [and] may, perhaps, symbolize Theology.

'The central niche is filled b[y a] symbolic tree, with a fountain at its b[ase;] a child climbs up to pick the fru[it,] perhaps from the tree of "knowled[ge." ] In the niche, to the spectator's left [is] Truth stands naked, but unasham[ed,] unveiling herself; a youth kneels [and] kisses the hem of her garment. [The] next niche holds a seated winged fig[ure] who bends forward to whisper sec[rets] into the ear of another kneeling yo[uth.] This should be Inspiration, Imaginat[ion.] On the other side is first a seated fig[ure] holding a mirror in one hand, w[hile] with the other she gives a burning la[mp] to a youth who, standing, holds it a[loft,] perhaps before starting on the rac[e in] which it will be passed, still flam[ing,] from hand to hand, till the imagina[tion] of the whole body of Artists shall [be] revivified by the united presence [of] Truth and Beauty; surely a symbol m[ost] suitable to a theatre where success[ful] students receive the prizes gained [by] their labours. Beyond is a seated fig[ure] teaching two children. Below, on [one] side, another group listens to a poe[t] who sings to the cithara. It is a g[reat] pity that so fine a scheme never [got] further than the sketch stage, bu[t in] England important works are o[nly] undertaken by the authorities with [so] much care and circumspection, and w[ith] so many tentatives that, as in this c[ase,] the original impulse lacks suffic[ient] vigour to provide for the comple[tion] of the work!'

Lit. F. Hamilton Jackson, 'The Wor[k of] Sir E. J. Poynter, P.R.A., Part III', [...] vol. i, 1897, pp. 127-28, illus. p.[...]

John Belcher
Design for the completion of the
South Kensington Museum. 1891
*Pen and ink and wash* $21\frac{1}{2}$ × 41
(54.7 × 103)
Drawn by W. B. McGuiness
Lent by the Royal Institute of
British Architects

Exhib. Possibly Chicago, 1893. RA,
   1894, no. 1637.
Illus. *BN*, 21 August 1891, pp. 258-59.
   *A*, 16 October 1891, p. 238.
Lit. *BN*, 7 August 1891, pp. 171-72.
   *Br*, 8 August 1891, pp. 96-7. *BA*,
   21 August 1891, p. 131. *A*, 21
   August 1891, pp. 106-07.

'Under the motto "Prince Albert," we
have a very poetically conceived group
of buildings reminding us of some
ancient palace. Cleverly drawn perspectives in Indian ink—one of the
exterior and the other of the staircase
hall—appear to conjure up in the mind
the ruins of some stately edifice in the
Venetian Lagoons; the dark and massive
features appear to rise out of a wet
shiny pavement or lake . . . These
drawings are certainly full of artistic
power, though sketchy. There is a
decidedly Spanish feeling in the design
for the main front. Its long, level line of
parapet is broken by two octagonal
cupolas and the quadrant recess of
centre, and by the square projecting
towers which terminate the wings of the
lower projecting gallery. This lower
storey, with its tall, stilted order on
pedestals, and the upper storey of Ionic
pilasters, resembles the façade of the
Palace at Granada; the orders have a
weak attenuated look, while the sculptured figures in relief between the lower
and entresol range of windows have no
structural base, and look out of scale'
(*BN*, 7 August 1891, p. 171).

# Catalogue

## 15 Memorials

*Catalogue 147*

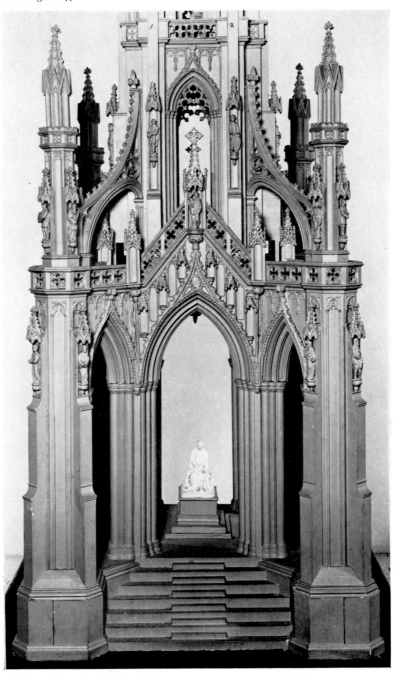

**147** George Meikle Kemp
Model for the memorial to Sir Walter Scott, Edinbur[
c. 1840
*Wood* 90 × 28 × 28 (228 × 71 × 71)
H.H. 394/04
Lent from the City Museums, Edinburgh

Three days after Sir Walter Scott had died on 21 Septem[
1832, thirty of his friends met in Edinburgh to appoint a co[
mittee to call a public meeting to consider the establishmen[
a national memorial to his memory. This meeting was held [
5 October in the Assembly Rooms, with the Lord Provost in [
chair. It was resolved to erect a public memorial on a s[
worthy of Scott's fame. Sir John Forbes, Bart, on behal[
various banks, offered to subscribe £500 to record th[
admiration of the fact that after his financial difficulties of 18[
Scott had agreed to 'dedicate his talents during the remainder[
his life to insure the full payments of his debts'.

At a subsequent meeting of subscribers held on 22 May 1[
it was reported that £5,752 14s had already been collec[
entirely from the City of Edinburgh with the exception of £[
from William IV and £250 from other sources. Eighteen mon[
later the amount had increased to £6,783 11s 8d. It was th[
decided that a sub-committee was to be instructed that no arc[
tectural monument was to be considered unless an integral p[
of it was a statue of Scott. Consequently, when the su[
committee advertised in March 1836, it was for a statue co[
bined with architecture, the cost of which was not to exce[
£5,000. The three designs considered the most suitable wo[
each be awarded £50. Fifty-four designs were received fr[
45 competitors, and were for 22 Gothic structures, 11 statu[
14 Grecian temples, 5 pillars, one obelisk, and a fountain.

At the end of 1836 the adjudicators decided to give first pl[
to a Gothic cross by Thomas Rickman, second place to anot[
cross by Charles Fowler and the sculptor R. W. Sievier, wh[
the third prize went to a local man, G. M. Kemp.

However, all was not yet plain sailing. The sub-commit[
spent a long time in consulting other architects and sculpto[
and it was not until March 1838, that the Committee was [
commended to adopt Kemp's design, which was then descri[
as 'an imposing structure, 135 feet in height, of beaut[
proportions, in strict conformity with the purity and style [
Melrose Abbey, from which it is, in all its details, derived. T[
statue according to this plan, will occupy a conspicuous positi[
at such a height from the eye of the spectator, that its excelle[
as a work of art, as well as its resemblance to the original may [
fully appreciated.' The statue of Scott was recommended to [
in marble, and its execution given to (Sir) John Steell. Havi[
obtained the support of the subscribers, Steell was commission[
to carve this figure in Italian marble, to be not less than 9 f[
high, for £2,000. The work was, says Rupert Gunnis in [
*Dictionary of British sculptures 1660-1851*, the first marble stat[
commissioned in Scotland, from a native artist.

The site for the memorial still had not been chosen, and, [
fact, the position in Prince's Street was not decided until 18[
the foundation stone was laid on 15 August of that year.

Besides the main statue of Scott, there are numerous nich[
in which were placed figures representing characters from Scot[
works, carved by such sculptors as Alexander Handiside Ritch[
Peter Slater and John Ritchie.

Exhib. The Scott Exhibition, Edinburgh, 1871, no. 25.

William Burges
Fountain for the City of
Gloucester c. 1856.
Four sheets joined with
alterations pasted on
*Pen and ink and water-
colour over preliminary
pencil* 21⅛ × 17¼ (53·5 ×
44·5)
E. 4667-1910 given by
Mr Sydney Vacher
Victoria and Albert
Museum

The fountain illustrates the story of Estrildis, and her daughter Sabrina after whom the River Severn, which flows through Gloucester, was named. The groups of sculpture at the base represent: 1. Estrildis brought captive to Locrin; 2. The marriage of Locrin and Guendolaena; 3. Locrin visiting Estrildis and Sabrina in an underground apartment. The group on the uppermost column represents Guendolaena ordering Estrildis and Sabrina to be thrown into the river. The animals, fish, etc., represent life abounding on the banks and in the river, and were thus described by the *Builder*. 'Uppermost of all is the otter holding a shield emblazoned with the arms of Gloucester; below are the frogs, firstly in their natural position, and secondly developed as gargoyles. Then come the fish; and lastly, intermingled with the foliage running around the lower basin, the lizards, the insects and the shells.' The background was described as 'an imaginary view of Gloucester at the beginning of the 13th century. On the right is an armourer's shop, on the left the pillory; behind is the town hall with a lofty belfry tower. An arched opening gives us a view of the town, while at the crown of the arch is hung a sabre taken from some Saracen by one of the Earls of Gloucester during a crusade.' Unlike many of his more finished drawings, this design exemplifies Burges's debt to the 13th century architect Villard de Honnecourt, whose vellum sketch book he had studied in Paris, and on which he based a similar volume of his own drawings.

Mr Sydney Vacher bought this drawing at the G. Aitchison sale, held by Messrs Puttick and Simpson, in November 1910.

Illus. A finished drawing showing the fountain *in situ* with an imaginary reconstruction of the medieval city in the background was illustrated in *Br*, 29 May 1858, p. 375 (reproduced in S. Muthesius, '*The High Victorian Movement in architecture*', 1972, pl. 119, p.158). An elevation drawn on vellum is reproduced as the frontispiece to *The architectural designs of William Burges A.R.A.*, ed. R. P. Pullan, London, 1883.

**149** Thomas Worthington
Memorial to the Prince Consort, Manchester. 1862-63
*Pen and ink* $9\frac{1}{2}$ × 22 (24.2 × 56)
Drawn by T. Raffles Davison
Lent by Thomas Worthington & Sons, Archite
Manchester

A committee formed by Manchester dignitaries to consider
town's memorial to the Prince Consort received various p
posals during 1862. These included a tower for the Cathed
an 'In Memorial' fund for the Infirmary, 'public baths an
Walhalla', model dwellings, a lending-library, a school of scier
a park, botanical gardens, and monuments in the style of
Scott Monument in Edinburgh. The Mayor had asked Matth
Noble to submit a design for a statue of the Prince, and t
design was considered by the committee during Septemb
when it was decided that as funds would not extend to m
than one form of memorial, this statue had best be combin
with a canopy. Several drawings of the Scott Monument ty
were examined, and the committee's choice fell on that wh
had been submitted by Thomas Worthington. He was at
same time appointed the architect to carry out the scheme.

Noble's statue, of Sicilian marble, portrayed the Prin
standing, wearing Garter robes. Worthington's design was
a Gothic canopy, 75 feet high, of white stone, 'open at the f
sides, the openings spanned by lofty Pointed arches, ea
surmounted by a high-pitched gablet, above which a tall spi
roof will rise . . . At the four angles will be square buttres
and pinnacles, or rich and elaborate design . . . The basement
the canopy will be divided into two stages, the upper of which v
be filled with a series of panels, five on each side, enriched w
armorial bearings. Each buttress will contain a shield emblazon
with the arms of the late Prince, surmounted by coronets.
the inner edge of the arches there will be an effective cuspi
the sloping edges of the archway will be enriched with cluste
spiral columns of Purbeck marble . . . On each of the piers
buttresses will stand a pinnacle, divided into two stage, t
lower stage to be decorated with spiral marble colum
terminated with gargoyles, and the upper stage of the pinnacles
be an open canopy, supported on similar spiral columns, and t
upper portion greatly enriched with tracery, foliated finials a
crocketing. Each of the four pinnacle canopies will contain
statuette . . . Each gablet will be terminated by a figure of
angel blowing a trumpet. The gablets are to be enriched w
arabesques in alto-relievo, and the centre is to be pierced w
a circular opening, filled with light tracery and two intersecti
equilateral triangles. The spiret roof is to be octagonal, a
terminated with a metal coronet. There is to be a grille around t
basement, divided into compartments filled with quatrefo
The building will stand elevated above the pavement on f
steps, each about 12 inches high. The cost is estimated at fr
£4,000 to £5,000.'

It was reported in the press that Matthew Noble submitt
the design to the Queen, who expressed her satisfaction with
saying that she thought 'nothing of the kind more beautiful
appropriate could be suggested'. She was also pleased to lea
that the architectural portion was by Thomas Worthington
whom the Prince had presented the Iris medal for architectu
design.

During October 1862, the Manchester Brickmakers' Protecti
Society told the Mayor that they would supply, without charg
all the bricks required for the foundations of the memorial as
'expression of sympathy towards our beloved Queen'. There w
at this time, however, a slight argument concerning the prec

site of the memorial. At first this had been intended to be near the Infirmary, but doubts had been expressed as to whether the Gothic monument might not be slightly discordant with the classical Infirmary. The Corporation offered, early in 1863, a plot of land in Bancroft Street, which was accepted by the committee, provided an open square was formed adjacent to land owned by the Corporation on which a new town hall might one day be built.

In order to have the heraldic details correct, Thomas Worthington made enquiries about the Prince Consort's armorial bearings. He received quite a lengthy letter, dated 15 July 1865, from Herman Sahl, German Librarian to the Queen (which is still in the possession of the firm). Sahl listed a number of crests of 'H.R. Highness's Saxon Dominions [which] may possibly offer a fair opportunity to fill up the many panels of the basement.' These were for the Dukedom of Saxony, the Margraviate of Meissen, the Landgraviate of Thüringen, the Palatinate of Saxony, the Dukedom of Cleve, and the Dukedom of Berg.

The monument was unveiled during 1867. Today it is in an appalling condition, and reported to be in danger of demolition.

Exhib. Thomas Worthington, Victorian Architect, Manchester College of Art and Design, May, 1973, no. 50.
Lit. *Br*, 24 September 1862. A slightly different, and earlier, view was reproduced in the *Br*, 8 November 1862, p. 803.

Sir George Gilbert Scott
Preliminary model for the national memorial in Kensington Gardens to the Prince Consort. c. 1863
*Plaster* 80 × 28 × 28 (203.2 × 71.2 × 71.2)
Bought from Sir Gilbert Scott
A.13-1973
Victoria and Albert Museum

A month after the unexpected death, on 14 December 1861, of Prince Albert, the Lord Mayor of London called a meeting at the Mansion House to consider 'the propriety of inviting contributions for the purpose of erecting a lasting memorial to his Royal Highness the Prince Consort, and to adopt such measures for carrying out the object as may then be decided'.

The site eventually chosen for a memorial was in Kensington Gardens, near the ground on which had been built the 1851 Exhibition. Gilbert Scott, James Pennethorne, T. L. Donaldson, P. C. Hardwick, Matthew Digby Wyatt and Charles and E. M. Barry were invited to submit designs. Those of Gilbert Scott for a Gothic tabernacle were accepted.

In November 1863 discussions were held with Scott to settle the exact design, and shortly afterwards the working drawings were prepared and a large model made, so that Queen Victoria was able the better to appreciate the effect of the memorial, and to consider its detail. The model was made by Farmer & Brindley of Westminster Bridge Road, the whole of the decorative sculpture being modelled by H. Armstead. It is entirely of plaster, coloured and polished to simulate the actual materials to be used, and was placed on a large pedestal in one of the rooms in Buckingham Palace, where it 'proved extremely valuable for reference during the discussions which took place at the early stages of the work, when it was feared that it would be necessary to make considerable modifications both in the sculpture and ornamental details'.

In 1867 Queen Victoria consented to the model being dis-

played in the Paris Exhibition of that year, and on its return it was sent to the Victoria and Albert Museum.

Sir Gilbert Scott later reflected that he 'ought to have exercised a stronger influence on the sculptors that I have done. My courage rather failed in claiming this, and I was content to express to them my general views both in writing and *viva voce* . . .

'The sculpture had been drawn out in a general way on the first elevations, partly by Mr. Clayton and partly by my eldest son. From these general ideas Mr. Armstead made small-size models for the architectural model, and imparted to the groups a highly artistic feeling.

'Without derogating from the merits of the sculpture as eventually carried out, it is but just to say that I doubt whether either the central figure or a single group, as executed, is superior to the miniature models furnished by Mr. Armstead. They remain to speak for themselves; while the two sides of the podium and the four bronzes, which he designed, give a fair idea of what his models would have proved if carried out to the real size.

'I mention this in justice both to him and to myself, as his small models were the carrying out of my original intention, and have in idea been the foundation of the actual result.'

Exhib. Paris, Universal Exhibition, 1867, Group I, Class no. 77 (174). South Kensington Museum, Museum of C struction, no. 41a.Y.

Lit. *The National Memorial to His Royal Highness The Pr Consort*, 1873. Sir G. G. Scott, *Personal and professio recollections* 1879, pp. 262-70. J. Physick, *Designs for Eng Sculpture 1680-1860*, Victoria and Albert Museum, 19 pp. 42-3, 190-97.

Sir Alfred Gilbert
Working model for the
Memorial Fountain to the
7th Earl of Shaftesbury
(d. 1885), Piccadilly
Circus, London
*Bronzed plaster on wood*
18½ (47) high
Lent by the Museum and
Art Gallery, Perth

Gilbert related that after
he had accepted the com-
mission, Sir Edgar Boehm
burst into his studio, 'and
I thought he meant to dance
round . . .: "At last—at
last!" he said, "We must
try to reverse that saying of
Marochetti's, 'For those
who worship Gibson any-
thing is good enough!'
. . ."' The model took
three months to complete.

The fountain, Gilbert's
best-known work, was un-
veiled by the Duke of
Devonshire on 29 June 1893.
It had a bust by Boehm
under a canopy, drinking
cups, and was surrounded
by a low parapet. During
the first night all the cups
were wrenched off, and
shortly afterwards Gilbert
removed the bust, canopy
and parapet. He was paid
£3,000 but the total cost
was about £7,000. That the
memorial is a fountain is not
apparent nowadays as the
jets of water are never turned
on. Gilbert chose an octagonal base as he thought that
this would best mask the
fact that the site was irregu-
lar. He was the first sculptor
to use aluminium for a
statue of this size.

At the time of the unveiling, the *Builder* thought it a
'far higher work of art than
most of our modern street
erections; in fact it stands
quite alone among recent
works of this kind in London', although the periodical
confessed to being disap-
pointed with it.

Lit. I. McAllister, *Alfred
Gilbert*, 1929, pp. 103-13.
E. M. Cox, *Commemor-
ative catalogue of models
and designs by the late Sir
Alfred Gilbert, R.A.*,
Victoria and Albert
Museum, 1936, no. 12,
pl. ix. A. Bury, *Shadow of
Eros*, 1952, pp. 44-5,
pl. x.

**152** Sir Francis Bernard Dicksee
'The House Builders'. 1880
Lent by the family of Sir Oliver
Welby, Bart.

The painting depicts Sir W. E. and the
Hon. Lady Welby-Gregory examining
the plans and model of Denton Manor,
which was built for them between 1879
and 1884 by A. W. Blomfield, and is now
demolished with the exception of the
stable block. The *Builder* remarked
about the painting 'A somewhat remarkable effort not so much in portrait
painting as in the art of making an
effective picture out of portraiture . . .
the head and figure of the gentleman
would pass as a very admirable portrait
*per se*; that of the lady is not quite so
successful.'

Exhib. RA, 1880, no. 40. Royal Jubilee
    Exhibition, Manchester, 1887.
Illus. M. Girouard, *The Victorian
    country house*, 1971, pl. 11.
Lit. *Art Journal*, 1880, p. 186. *Br*,
    8 May 1880, p. 561.

# Index of Lenders

*References are to catalogue numbers*

Her Majesty The Queen   17

Bearwood College   27
Bethlem Royal Hospital and the Maudsley
  Hospital, Board of Governors   75
Bradford City Libraries   95
Cardiff, Lord Mayor and Corporation   28
Edinburgh, City Museums   147
—Royal Scottish Museum   123
Edwards, Mr Derek   29
Elton, the late Sir Arthur   126
Elvetham Hall   24
Glasgow, Mitchell Library   138
Glasgow University, Mackintosh Collection   65
Hounslow Library Services, Chiswick Library
  93
Leeds City Art Galleries   83
Liverpool City Museums   81
London, British Railways Western Region   110
—British Transport Hotels Limited   131
—Corporation of London Records Office   50,
    52, 53, 53A, 70, 77, 78, 90, 92, 120, 122.
—Department of the Environment   8, 10, 137.
—India Office Library and Records   112, 119
—Kensington and Chelsea, Royal Borough of
    37
—London Museum   98
—Public Record Office   3, 4, 20, 67; 109, 127,
    134
—Royal Academy of Arts   9, 13, 58, 96, 101
—Royal Institute of British Architects, Drawings
    Collection   14, 15, 16, 22, 25, 38, 46, 51, 57,
    59, 61, 62, 64, 66, 68, 74, 76, 79, 86, 88, 89,
    97, 102, 104, 111, 121, 124, 132, 141, 146
—Sabin Galleries Limited   21
—Trinity House, Corporation of   123
—Westminster, Palace of   1, 2, 11, 12.
Osler, Mr P. A. G.   56
Paxton, Mr E. Ridgeway   113
Perth Museum and Art Galleries   151
Royal Commission on Historical Monuments
  (England)   82
Scarborough Public Libraries   128
Welby, The family of Sir Oliver   152
Worthington, Messrs Thomas and Sons   149

# Index of People

*References are to catalogue numbers*

Abraham, H. R.  14
Adames, A. J.  34
Adams, Maurice Bingham  93
Ainger, Alfred  42
Aitchison, George  46, 64
Akroyd, Col.  95
Albert, Prince  1-5, 17, 25, 83, 115, 146, 150
Alcer, Owen T.  22
Allom, Thomas  16, 91
Anderson, J. Macvicar  143-146
Anderson, Sir Robert Rowand  131, 138-142
Andrews, George Townsend  69, 103, 106
Arighi, Bianchi & Co  55
Armitage, E.  138-142
Armstead, H. H.  6-12, 138-142, 150
Ashbee, Charles Robert  48
Ashton, —  118
Atkinson, Robert & Partners  38
Auld, Spalding and  6-12
Ayrton, Acton Smee  1-5, 14

B., S.M.  67
Baily, E. H.  1-5, 101, 102
Baker, —  113-115
Baker, George & Son  138-142
Baker, Messrs  38
Baker & Fielder  135
Balfour, Major Kenneth  21
Banks, R. R.  20
Banks & Barry  37, 137
Barlow, W. H.  113-115, 127
Barnes, Sir Edward  98
Barry, Alfred  16
Barry, Sir Charles  1-12, 14, 16, 20, 38, 77, 83, 96, 113-115, 134, 150
Barry, E. M.  1-5, 6-12, 14, 127, 137, 150
Barry, Sir John Wolfe  120-122
Bate, George  117
Bazalgette, Sir J.  6-12, 91, 120-122
Beazley, C. N.  94
Belcher, John  143-146
Belgrave, Viscount  31
Bell, Ingress  6-12, 138-142
Bell, J.  1-5
Bell, Alderman J. C.  90
Bellamy, Thomas  6-12, 62
Bellhouse, E. T.  88
Benson, W., Archbishop of Canterbury  15
Benson, William  21
Bentley, John  33
Beresford-Hope, A.  14
Bessemer, —  52
Blachford, Lady Isabella  17
Blashfield, John M.  36, 37
Blomfield, Sir A. W.  14, 138-142
Blundell family  19
Bodley & Garner  143-146
Boehm, Sir Edgar  46, 151
Braidwood, J.  134
Bramah, J. J.  101, 102
Brandon, David  37, 82
Brandon, Raphael  14
Brighton, G. L.  10
Brindley, Dr  15
Brindley, Farmer &  150

Brodrick, Cuthbert  57, 83, 86, 128, 137
Brongniart, —  83
Brown, Capability  28, 29
Brown, Ford Madox  87
Brown, J.  125
Brown, Philip  21
Bruce, Sir G.  120-122
Brunel, I. K.  106, 108, 110, 113-115
Brydon, J. M.  6-12
Bulmer, —  116
Bunning, James B.  50, 52, 53, 70, 77, 78, 92
Burges, William  14, 28, 29, 85, 112, 148
Burke & Co.  46
Burn, William  31
Burne-Jones, Lady  23
Burnett, Frederick  120-122
Burton, Decimus  6-12
Bute, Marquess of  29
Butterfield, W.  23, 73
Buxton & Habershon  6-12

Cabrey, Thomas  103
Caldecott, Randolph  46
Calthorpe, Rt. Hon. Sir R.  24
Cambridge, Duke of  138-142
Canning, Gibbs &  138-142
Carew, J. E.  1-5
Carnarvon, 3rd Earl of  16
Carr, Jonathan T.  93
Chad, Sir Charles  21
Chance, Messrs  123
Charlesworth, Speakman &  87
Chawner, Thomas  37
Chessum & Sons  90
Christian, Ewan  6-12
Clarke, Lieut.-Gen. Sir A.  10
Clarke, G. S.  98, 127
Clarke, Somers  14, 15, 59, 137
Clayton,—  150
Clutton, H.  6-12
Cockburn, Sir Alexander  14
Cockerell, C. R.  49, 76, 79-81
Cockerell, F. P.  137
Cole, Sir Henry  113-115, 118, 137-146
Cole, Sir H, daughters of  138-142
Collcutt, T. E.  138-146
Collier, Sir R.  45
Collmann, L. W.  19, 40
Cope, C. W.  1-5
Cornewall, Capt.  133
Cowper, William  6-12, 14, 137
Crace, Frederick  105
Crace, J. D.  100
Crace, J. G.  41, 118
Crane, Walter  46, 130
Cressinet, —  6-12
Cresswell, H. B.  66
Cubitt, Thomas  17, 97
Cubitt, William  109
Cundy, S.  116
Cundy, Thomas Jnr  41

Darby, Mrs Rebecca  32
Davis, Edward  82
Deane, Sir Thomas  138-146
Deane, T. N.  6-12, 14
De Morgan, William  46, 130
De Thury, V.  117

Devonshire, Duke of  151
Dewer, Messrs  50
Dickie, Samuel  100
Dicksee, Sir F. B.  152
Donaldson, T. L.  87, 150
Douglas, George  109
Douglass, Sir J. N.  123
D'Oyly Carte, R.  99
Dudley, Robert  116
Duer, Sidengham  120
Dunraven, Dowager Countess of  125
Durand, J. L. N.  83
Durham, Joseph  134, 138-42
Dutton, Hon. R. H.  111
Dyce, William  1-5

Edinburgh, Duke of  6-12, 13, 123, 138-42
Edis, Col. R. W.  25
Egerton, Lord Francis  38
Elcho, Lord  6-12, 138-142
Ellis, John, MP  113-115
Elmes, Harvey Lonsdale  68, 76, 79-81
Emerson, William  143-146

Fairbairn, Sir W.  95, 118
Farmer & Brindley  150
Farrimond, Lockwood &  109
Fergusson, James  6, 7, 138-142
Ferrey, B.  6-12, 18
Fielder, Baker &  135
Fiske, Fowler &  98
Fitton, H.  67
Fletcher, Herbert  60
Flower, Henry  97
Foley, J. H.  1-5
Forbes, Sir John  147
Foulston, John  51
Fowke, Capt. F.  118, 140, 143-146
Fowler, Charles  116, 147
Fowler, Francis H.  6-12
Fowler, F. & Fiske  98
Fox, Sir Charles  101, 102, 113-115
Fox, Henderson & Co.  113-116
Franklin, —  79-81
Frederick VII, King of Denmark  107

Gamble, James  138-142
Ganoy, John  75
Garling, H. B.  6-12  14
Garner, Bodley &  143-146
Gates, Arthur  6-12
George, Sir Ernest  47
Gibbs & Canning  138-142
Gibson, John  1-5, 14, 151
Gilbert, Sir A.  151
Gilbert, W. S.  47, 99
Giles, John  127
Gill, Colin  84
Gladstone, W. R.  138-142
Glover & Salter  6-12
Goad, J. & E.  123
Godwin, Edward William  44, 63, 84, 85, 88, 93
Godwin, George  6-12
Goggs, Messrs  25
Goodhart-Rendel, H. S.  47, 132, 138-142
Götzenberger, J.  38

Granville, Lord  113-115, 118
Green, Edward  34
Gregory, J. C.  24
Gripper, Edward  127
Grüner, Ludwig  17
Guelfi, G. B.  15
Guthrie, —  120-122

Habershon, Buxton &  6-12
Haig, Axel Herman  112
Hall, Sir Benjamin  6-12
Hall & Powell  6-12
Hall & Sons  32
Harcourt, William  6-12
Hardwick, Philip  6-12, 101
Hardwick, P. C.  6-12, 14, 37, 106, 124, 150
Harland & Fisher  46
Harris, Thomas  24
Harvey, L.  15
Hathaway, Thomas  81
Haviland, John  77
Haywood, Lt.-Col.  90
Heaton, Butler & Bayne  31
Helliwell, —  66
Henning, John  70
Herbert, J. R.  1-5
Holding, Matthew  84
Hooker, Sir W.  134
Horeau, Hector  113-115
Horsley, J.  1-5, 138-142
Hudson, —  118
Humbert, Albert J.  25
Hunt, Sir Henry  6-12
Hunt, Verity &  6-12
Huxley, Sir Julian  138-14t

Ionides, Basil  99

Jackson, A. Bloomfield  99
Jackson, T. A.  138-142
Jacomb, William  111
Jay, John  52, 53
Johnson, John  88
Jones, Sir Horace  52, 121
Jones, Owen  36, 37, 56, 108, 1 118, 126, 137, 144
Jeckyll, Thomas  34
Jennings, Louis  15

Keith, —  120-122
Kelk, John  118
Kemp, George Meikle  147
Kendall, H. E.  37
Kennard, R. W.  53
Kent, William  1-5, 23
Keppie, John  65
Kerr, Robert  27
Kinnimont, J.  42
Kirk & Randall  45
Knowles, J. T.  37, 124

Lascelles, W. H.  132
Lawrence, James Clarke  92
Lawrence, William  92
Lawrence, William Jnr  92
Layard, Sir A. H.  14, 15
Lee, H. & Sons  96
Leeming, Messrs  6-12
Lehmann and Peignet  117

ghton, Lord  15, 143-146
naby, W. R.  23
dley, —  27
dsay, James  6-12
lewood, Mangnall and  88
kwood, H. F.  14, 95, 109
kwood & Farrimond  109
mbe, Edward  20
w, J.  88
bbock, Sir John  123

W.H.  111
bey Bros.  11, 12
cartney, Sir Mervyn  143-146
cdonald, George  42
cdowell, P.  1-5
ckintosh, Charles R.  65
clise, Daniel  1-5
cvicar Anderson, J.  6-12
ngnall and Littlewood  88
nners, Lord John  137
rochetti, C., Baron  151
rks, Stacy  138-142
rshall, W. C.  1-5
rtin, John  91
tcham, Frank  100
wson, Richard  95
xwell and Tuke  6-12
y, E. J.  93
lhado, —  50
ddleton, J. H.  42
ls, Henry Snr & Jnr  24
nton, Hollins & Co.  79-81, 138-
42
ford, A. B.  5-12
catta, David  104
lesworth, Sir W.  6-12
rris, William  23, 42, 43
rray, Andrew  78
rray, James  37, 137

ll, Archibald  129
sfield, W. A.  20
sfield, W. Eden  20, 26, 30, 33,
129
choll, W. G.  133
holls, Thomas  28, 29
htingale, B. S.  44
ble, Matthew  149

hardson, Sir W. Q.  42
ish, F.  128
ish, R. M.  120-122

mer, Sir R.  14
merston, Lord  6-12, 14, 128
izzi, Sir A.  135
er, Messrs  20
nell, C. O.  98
ton, Lady  113
ton, Sir J.  113-117
rson, J. L.  15
gnet, Lehmann &  117
nefather, A. R.  13
nethorne, Sir James  6-12, 37,
34, 138-142, 150
rose, F. C.  137
rett, —  120-122
ry & Co  111
rie Waugh, Col. W.  21
ffers, T.  6-12
lip, J. B.  1-5, 6-12
pps, Charles John  99
kersgill, F. R.  138-142
kington, Frederick  24
mbe, Rowland  61

Plunkett, David  15
Porden, William  31
Portal, Wyndham S.  111
Porter, Thomas  6-12
Portland, Duke of  67
Pownall, George  14
Poynter, Sir E.  6-12, 138-146
Prichard, John  71, 125
Prior, Edward S.  72, 89, 132
Pugin, A. W. N.  1-5, 18
Pugin, C. W.  18
Pugin, E. W.  18
Pullan, R. P.  116, 148

Quilter, Harry  44

Railton, W.  6-12
Randolph, Dr  133
Rawlinson, Sir Robert  79-81
Redesdale, Lord  6-12
Redgrave, Richard  142
Reid, Dr  1-5
Rendel, James Meadows  119
Richardson, H. B.  98
Rickman, Mrs  113
Rickman, Thomas  147
Ritchie, A. H.  147
Ritchie, J.  147
Roberts, David  138-142
Robinson, John  129
Robson, E. R.  42
Rooke, T. M.  93
Ross, D. J.  90
Rossetti, D. G.  94
Roumieu, Robert L.  22, 74
Rudeyard, J.  123
Rysbrack, J. M.  15

Sahl, Herman  149
Sang, Frederick  115
Salisbury, Marquess of  40
Salt, Sir Titus  95
Salter, Glover and  6-12
Salvin, A.  98
Samwell, William  31
Savill, Walter  58
Scott, Archibald  111
Scott, Sir George Gilbert  6-12,
14-16, 137, 138, 150
Scott, Maj-Gen. H. Y. D.  138-146
Scott, J. O.  87
Scott, Sir Walter  147
Seddon, John Pollard  15, 71, 94,
125
Sedley, J.  120-122
Semper, Gottfried  138-142
Shaftesbury, 7th Earl of  151
Shaw, John  14
Shaw, R. Norman  13, 32, 33, 42,
43, 58, 93, 130, 132, 138-146
Shields, Frederic  31
Siever, R. W.  147
Slater, P.  147
Smeaton, John  123
Smirke, Sir R.  1-5, 135
Smirke, Sydney  37, 75, 98, 135,
138-142
Smith, —  82
Smith, A.  98
Smith, C. H.  38
Smith, George & Co.  31
Smith, Prof. Robert  24
Soane, Sir John  1-5, 14, 54
Soden, Thomas  24
Sorby, T. C.  128
Spackman, Sergeant  138-142
Spalding & Auld  6-12

Speakman & Charlesworth  87
Spiers, Richard Phené  45, 108
Stannus, H.  107
Stark, Malcolm Jnr  6-12
Steell, Sir John  147
Stephenson, Robert  101-102, 113-
115
Stevens, Alfred  19, 107, 108, 135
Stevens, F. W.  112
Stevenson, George D.  122
Stevenson, John James  34, 42
Street & Son  20, 26
Street, A. E.  14
Street, G. E.  6-12, 14, 87, 137
Stirling-Maxwell, Sir W.  14
Sturt, Sir G. N.  21
Sturt, Humphrey  21
Sullivan, Arthur  99
Sykes, Godfrey  143-146

Tarver, E. J.  15
Tattersall, George  98
Taylor, John  94
Taylor, Sir John  137
Taylor, Michael Angelo  133
Taylor, Sir R.  133
Telford, T.  109
Temple, James  58
Teulon, Samuel S.  24
Theed, William  1-5
Thomas, John  1-5, 38, 101, 102,
124
Thomas, J. E.  1-5
Thomson, Alexander  138-142
Thynne, Lord John  15
Tite, William  6-12, 84, 138-142
Townroe, R.  138-142
Trego, William  50
Trevelyan, Sir Charles  6-12
Tugwell, Frank A.  99
Tuke, Maxwell &  6-12

Vacher, Sydney  148
Van Raalte, Charles  21
Verity & Hunt  6-12
Victoria, Queen  17, 83, 138-146,
149, 150
Voysey, C. F. A.  35, 93, 130
Vulliamy, G.  43

Wales, Prince of  25, 138-142
Walker, R.  52, 53
Waller, Mr  120-122
Walter, John MP  27
Waring, John Burley  55, 116, 136
Waterhouse, Alfred  14, 15, 31, 72,
87, 138-146
Watkin, John  84
Welby, Selina  18
Welby-Gregory, Sir W. E.  152
Wellington, Duke of  135
Wemyss, Mrs  E.  43
Westmacott, J. S.  1-5
Westmacott, R.  38
Westminster, Marquess of  41
Whistler, J. A. McN.  44
White, William  6-12
Wightwick, G.  51
William IV, King  147
Willson, J.  53
Wilson, Prof. E.  94
Wilson, H.  65
Wilson, Mr  93
Winstanley, Henry  123
Webb, Sir Aston  6-12, 138-146
Webb, Philip  18, 23, 42, 60
Woodhead, E. I.  10

Woodington, W. F.  1-5
Woodward, Messrs  46
Woodward, Deane &  6-12
Worthington, Thomas  87, 88, 149
Wyatt, Sir M. Digby  6-12, 108,
110, 113-116, 119, 137 138-142,
150
Wyatt, Thomas H.  6-12, 37, 74,
82

Yeames, W. F.  138-142
Young, William  6-12, 143-146

# Index of Places

*References are to catalogue numbers*

Adcote, Manor House  32
Alne  103
Auteuil, France  117

Bearwood  27
Bexley Heath, Red House  18, 23
Birchington-on-Sea  94
Birkenhead  109
Bodmin, De Lank Quarries  123
Bombay, India; Custom House  86
—Station  112
Brighton, Station  104
Bristol, Temple Meads Station  110
Broadlands  30
Broadleys  35
Brownsea Island, Castle  21
—Maryland  21
Bylaugh, cottages  20

Cambridge, Assize Courts  82
—Gonville and Caius College  72
Capesthorne,  Conservatory  113, 114
Cardiff, Castle  28, 29
—Castell Coch  28, 29
Chatsworth  113, 114
Cheltenham, Queen's Hotel  105
Chigwell  33
Clayton  104
Congleton, Town Hall  85
Croydon  104

Darlington  103
Dawpool  32
Denton Manor  152

Eaton Hall  31
Eddystone Lighthouse  123
Edinburgh, Scott Monument  147, 149
Ellesmere Port, Station  109
Elvetham Hall  24

Flete  32
Frogmore  37

Glasgow, Central Hotel  131
—Pearce Institute  131
—Pollokshaws Burgh  131
Gloucester  148
Guisborough, Abbey  116

Hamburg, Germany; Town Hall  85
Helsby, Cheshire  109
Highclere  16
Hooton, Cheshire  109
Horley, Station  104
Hull, Royal Institution  83
—Station  106

Ightham Mote  32

Ken Hill  34

Kew, Lodge  26

Lanteglos, Parsonage  18
Leeds, Corn Exchange  86
—King Street warehouses  86
—Oriental Baths  86
—Town Hall  83
Liverpool, Bank of England  49
—Everton; High School  68
—Kirkdale; Pauper Schools  68
—St George's Hall  71, 133
—West Derby; Deysbrook  19
Llandough, School  71
London, Albert Hall  138-142A
—Arlington Street  20, 40
—Army and Navy Club  98
—Basinghall Street, Offices for Commissioners of Sewers  90
—Bayswater; the Red House  42
—Billingsgate Market  52
—Bedford Park  93
——Inn and stores  130
——South Parade, 14, 130
—Bethlem Hospital  75
—Bridgwater House  38
—British Museum  135
—Budge Row  92
—Burlington House  136
—Cannon Street  92
—Carey Street  14
—Carlton House  137
——Stables  134
—Chelsea Embankment; Danvers Tower  48
——Magpie and Stump  48
——Old Swan House  33
——Studio and stables  134
—City and Guilds College  138-142
—Clapham Common  138-142
—Clapham Park  17
—Cloak Lane  92
—Coal Exchange  50
—Cromwell Road  143-146
—Danvers Tower  48
—Dover House, 8-13
—Eastcheap nos. 33-35  22
—Euston Station  101, 102
—Exhibition 1851  113-115
—Exhibition 1862  118
—Exhibition Road  143-146
—Government Offices  6-12
—Great Western Hotel  124
—Gresham Club  97
—Grosvenor Hotel  124
—Grosvenor House  41
—Harrington Gardens  47
—Haymarket, McLean's Fine Art Gallery  63
—Holloway Prison  77, 78
—Horticultural Society Gardens  138-146
—Houses of Parliament  1-5
—Imperial Institute  138-142, 141
—Junior United Services Club  98
—Kensington Gardens  150
—Kensington Palace Gardens, no. 8  36
—Kensington Palace Gardens, gates  37
—Langham Hotel  126
—Laurence Pountney Hill  92
—Leighton House  46
—Magpie and Stump House  48
—Marlborough House  8-13

—Melbury Road; Tower House  112
—Milner Square  22
—Moys Music Hall  100
—Muswell Hill  117
—National Gallery  14, 137-146
—Natural History Museum  138-142
—New Scotland Yard  13
—New Zealand Chambers  33
—Old Swan House  33
—Oxford and Cambridge Universities Club  98
—Paddington Station  106, 108
—Pentonville Prison  77
—Piccadilly Circus  151
—Prince Consort Memorial  150
—Public Record Office  134
—Queen Street  92
—Queen's Gate  138-142
—Regent's Park School  67
—Roger's Almshouses  78
—Rolls House  134
—Royal College of Art  143-146
—Royal Courts of Justice  14, 28, 29
—Royal Exchange Assurance Company  64
—Royal School of Needlework  138-142
—Royal Standard Music Hall  100
—Russell Square  135
—St James's Palace  137
—St James's Square, no. 18  98
—St Pancras Station Hotel  126, 127
—St Paul's Cathedral  135
—Savoy Theatre  99
—Shaftesbury Memorial Fountain  151
—South Kensington Museum  138-142, 146
—Strand,  14
—Sun Life Assurance Offices  49
—Sydenham; Crystal Palace  116
—Thames Embankment  91
—Threadneedle Street; Sun Life Offices  49
—Tite Street; White House  44
—Tower Bridge  120-122
—Tower of London  134
—Travellers' Club  96
—University of London  138-142
—Victoria and Albert Museum  138-142, 146
—Victoria Palace  100
—Waterloo Station  111
—Wellington Monument  137
—Westminster Abbey  15, 134, 138-142
—Whitehall; Banqueting House  10
Loughton Hall  33, 43

Manchester, Albert Memorial  149
—Art Treasures Exhibition  117
—Assize Courts  34
—Baths and Wash Houses  88
—Binyon and Fryer Warehouse  54
—Free Trade Hall  54
—Royal Institution  96
—Ship Canal  109
—Town Hall  87
Melrose Abbey  147
Menai Bridge  113, 114

Newcastle  103
Northampton, Town Hall  84,

Osborne, Isle of Wight  17
Oxford, Taylor and Rando Building  133

Paris, Ferrières  117
Patna, India  119

Rampsham, The Glebe  18
Ramsgate, The Grange  18
Raskelf, Station  103
Reading, Gaol  77
Rounton Grange  60

Saffron Walden, Bank  129
—'Rose and Crown' Hotel  129
Saint Cloud, France  117
Salisbury, St Marie's Grange  1
Saltaire  95
Sandringham House  25
Scarborough, Grand Hotel  124, —Station  106
Sessay, Station  103
Snettisham, Ken Hill  34
Southerndown, Hotel  125
Southwick Hall  32
Stone (Dartford), Stone Ho Hospital  78
Swindon, station  105

Taymouth Castle  105
Thirsk  103
Tintern Abbey  116
Trentham Park  16

Wells Cathedral  116
West Bay, Hotel  132
—Swimming Baths  89
Whitby, Station  109
Windermere, Broadleys  35
Wollaton Hall  16

York, North Postern Gate, 103
—Station  103, 106